NATURAL ENVIRONMENT RESEARCH COUNCIL

INSTITUTE OF GEOLOGICAL SCIENCES

MEMOIRS OF THE GEOLOGICAL SURVEY OF GREAT BRITAIN
ENGLAND AND WALES

Geology of the Country around Cockermouth and Caldbeck

(*Explanation of One-inch Geological Sheet 23, New Series*)

by

T. EASTWOOD, A.R.C.Sc., S. E. HOLLINGWORTH, M.A., D.Sc.,
W. C. C. ROSE, C.B.E., M.Sc. and F. M. TROTTER, D.Sc.

Petrography by
K. C. Dunham, S.D., D.Sc., F.R.S. and J. Phemister, D.Sc., F.R.S.E.

Palaeontology by
M. A. Calver, M.A., R. Crookall, D.Sc., W. H. C. Ramsbottom, M.A., Ph.D.
and Sir James Stubblefield, D.Sc., F.R.S.

LONDON
HER MAJESTY'S STATIONERY OFFICE
1968

DGV
ea
LGY c.4

ISBN 0 11 884156 4

PREFACE

THE DISTRICT described in this memoir is that covered by the Cockermouth (23) Sheet of the New Series One-inch Geological Survey Map of England and Wales. This sheet has replaced the Old Series One-inch Sheet 101 NE of which a hand-coloured geological edition appeared in 1890, without being accompanied by an explanatory memoir.

Small areas overlapping on to Sheet 23 from the Six-inch survey of Sheet 17 (Carlisle) and Sheet 22 (Maryport) were geologically resurveyed on the Six-inch scale during the period 1922 to 1926 under the superintendence of the late Dr. B. Smith; but the main part of the resurvey took place between 1928 and 1932, at first under the late Dr. B. Smith, but chiefly under the superintendence of Mr. T. Eastwood, who also carried out a considerable part of the survey.

The Six-inch maps of the Cumberland Coalfield which fall within Sheet 23 were published between 1931 and 1937; the remainder were made available for public reference in the Library of the Geological Survey and Museum, Exhibition Road, S.W.7 during the period 1938 to 1948. A One-inch geological Solid edition was published in 1959 and a Drift edition in 1960, both with National Grid lines.

Since the 1939–45 War all the four geological surveyors who undertook the main survey have resigned or retired. Their accounts have been revised by the late Dr. F. M. Trotter who has also edited the memoir, assisted by Miss E. M. Pyatt.

Final editing and press-marking was carried out under Dr. A. W. Woodland at the Leeds Office.

For chemical analyses of rocks we are indebted to Messrs. B. E. Dixon, C. O. Harvey, K. L. H. Murray, C. Park and W. F. Waters, all of the Government Chemist's Laboratory, during their attachment to the Geological Survey. We are also indebted to Mr. R. Garrett of the Royal School of Mines for permission to include his determinations of trace elements in a Geological Survey sample of the Carrock Fell Granophyre.

The petrographic description of the igneous rocks was commenced by Dr. J. Phemister and was completed by myself, when I succeeded him as Chief Petrographer.

The fossil material was collected mostly by Messrs. W. Dewar and S. W. Hester, M.B.E. The plants have been named by Dr. R. Crookall; the remainder of the fossils by Dr. C. J. (now Sir James) Stubblefield, mainly before 1939. Recently, Mr. M. A. Calver has revised some of the non-marine lamellibranch names, and Mr. M. Mitchell and Dr. W. H. C. Ramsbottom some of the other invertebrate fossils.

Thanks are given to the following for specialist assistance in naming fossils: Mr. W. S. Bisat, F.R.S. (goniatites); Professor O. M. B. Bulman, F.R.S., and the late Dr. Gertrude L. Elles (graptolites); the late Dr. Stanley Smith (corals); and the late Sir Arthur Trueman, F.R.S. (non-marine lamellibranchs).

Generous assistance on the sequence of the Carboniferous Limestone Series was given by Mr. Charles Edmonds.

For much help and information we are indebted to colliery managers and surveyors of the coal mines which were working during the resurvey. The collections of mining iv

records at the Lowther Estate Offices, Somerset House, Whitehaven, and at the Leconfield Estate Offices, Cockermouth Castle, were freely placed at our disposal and we record grateful thanks to the late Mr. Tom Durham of the first mentioned and the late Mr. Frank Ahier of the last mentioned Estate Offices.

K. C. DUNHAM
Director

Institute of Geological Sciences
Exhibition Road
South Kensington
London S W 7

20th August 1968

CONTENTS

LIST OF ILLUSTRATIONS
TEXT-FIGURES

PLATES
[In this edition the Plates are between pages 8 and 9]

EXPLANATION OF PLATES

PLATE I
On Elva Hill the quarry in the foreground is in diorite and that in the middle distance in diorite and grits of the Skiddaw Slates. The sky line is of high fells composed of Skiddaw Slates with the Skiddaw massif on the right.

PLATE II A
Quarry on Watch Hill showing columnar jointing in grits of the Skiddaw Slates.

          B
Folding of metamorphosed Skiddaw Slates. The Slates were folded, and subsequently metamorphosed by the Skiddaw Granite. Seen in River Caldew above Swineside.

PLATE III A
The beds of Skiddaw Slates are seen above the upper massive andesitic lava, and also beneath it immediately above the hammer head, in quarry at Whitefield Cottage, W. of Over Water and 700 yd W.N.W. of Whitefield House.

          B
The dyke cuts across a porphyritic lava of the Borrowdale Volcanic Series about ½ mile south-east of top of Eycott Hill.

PLATE IV A
A pale granophyre vein is seen locally widening to include angular fragments of the invaded rock, a pyroxene-rich basic gabbro, one mile west of Mosedale.

          B
The banding in the gabbro is caused by alternations of feldspathic and ferromagnesian rich bands, 1000 yd north-west of Mosedale.

PLATE V A
The view shows characteristic outcrops of massive limestone of the lower part of the Carboniferous Limestone Series one mile west of Sunderland.

        B
The rhythmic unit of massive sandstone posts at the base which are overlain by thin well bedded posts of limestone, in turn overlain by shales, best seen on the right, ¾ mile E. 30° N. of Uldale.

PLATE VI A
A typical view of false-bedded Penrith Sandstone, seen below High Head Castle, Highbridge.

         B
The quarry in St. Bees Sandstone on the left bank of Chalk Beck near Barnetrigg was worked for building stone. The regularly dipping beds are capped by Boulder Clay.

PLATE VII A
The view shows the semi-circular walls of Tarn Crags in Skiddaw Slates that form a northward facing corrie in the hollow of which lies Bowscale Tarn, dammed back by moraine.

          B
The glacially eroded step in the valley floor of Dash Beck is marked by Dash Waterfall which is flanked by glacially-plucked crags of Skiddaw Slates—Dead Crags on right and Nettle Crags on left.

LIST OF SIX-INCH MAPS

The following is a list of the Six-inch geological maps included wholly or in part in the One-inch map Sheet 23, with the initials of the surveyors and dates of survey. The names of the officers are as follows: E. E. L. Dixon; T. Eastwood; S. E. Hollingworth; J. Maden; W. C. C. Rose; L. H. Tonks; and F. M. Trotter. Those maps with an asterisk prefixed have been published. The remainder are available for public reference in manuscript form at the Library of the Institute of Geological Sciences, S.W.7.

CUMBERLAND

27 N.E.	Pelutho	L.H.T.	(1922)
27 S.E.	Edderside and Holme St. Cuthbert	L.H.T. & T.E.	(1922–6)
28 N.W.	Abbey Town	L.H.T.	(1922)
28 N.E.	Dundraw	L.H.T.	(1922)
28 S.W.	Bromfield	W.C.C.R.	(1931)
28 S.E.	Waverton	W.C.C.R.	(1931)
29 N.W.	Oulton and Wigton	J.M.	(1921)
29 N.E.	Crofton Hall and Thursby	S.E.H.	(1922)
29 S.W.	Red Dial	W.C.C.R.	(1930)
29 S.E.	Rosley	F.M.T.	(1929)
30 N.W.	Dalston	E.E.L.D.	(1922)
30 N.E.	Ratten Row	E.E.L.D.	(1922)
30 S.W.	Rose Castle	F.M.T.	(1930–1)
30 S.E.	Gatesgill	F.M.T.	(1931)
35 N.E.	Allonby and West Newton	T.E.	(1926–8)
*35 S.E.	Oughterside and Allerby	T.E.	(1926–8)
*36 N.W.	Aspatria and Brayton	T.E.	(1929)
*36 N.E.	Allhallows and Mealsgate	T.E.	(1929)
*36 S.W.	Aspatria and Bothel	T.E.	(1929–30)
36 S.E.	Torpenhow	T.E.	(1930)
37 N.W.	Bolton	T.E.	(1929)
37 N.E.	Broadmoor	F.M.T.	(1929–30)
37 S.W.	Ireby	F.M.T.	(1928–9)
37 S.E.	Caldbeck	F.M.T.	(1929–30)
38 N.W.	Welton and Sebergham	F.M.T.	(1930)
38 N.E.	High Bridge	F.M.T.	(1930–1)
38 S.W.	Hesket Newmarket	F.M.T.	(1930–1)
38 S.E.	Castle Sowerby	F.M.T.	(1930–1)
*45 N.E.	Tallentire and Gilcrux	T.E.	(1926–8)
45 S.E.	Dovenby and Bridekirk	T.E.	(1925–6)
46 N.W.	Wardhill and Sunderland	T.E.	(1928–30)
46 N.E.	Bewaldeth and Snettlegarth	T.E. & F.M.T.	(1928–31)
46 S.W.	Blindcrake and Isel	T.E.	(1931)
46 S.E.	Setmurthy and Bewaldeth	F.M.T. & W.C.C.R.	(1931–2)
47 N.W.	Uldale	F.M.T.	(1928)
47 N.E.	Fell Side	S.E.H.	(1928–9)
47 S.W.	Orthwaite	F.M.T.	(1931)
47 S.E.	Great Sca Fell and Coomb Height	S.E.H.	(1928–31)
48 N.W.	Haltcliff	S.E.H.	(1928–9)
48 N.E.	Howhill	S.E.H.	(1929–32)
48 S.W.	Carrock Fell and Mosedale	S.E.H.	(1929–31)
48 S.E.	Scale and Greystoke Park	S.E.H.	(1929–32)
54 N.E.	Cockermouth	T.E. & E.E.L.D.	(1922–6)
55 N.W.	Watchill and Embleton	T.E. & W.C.C.R.	(1931)

55 N.E.	Bassenthwaite Lake	..	..	F.M.T. & W.C.C.R.	(1932)
56 N.W.	Bassenthwaite Common	..	..	F.M.T.	(1931–2)
56 N.E.	Great Calva	..	..	S.E.H.	(1931–2)
57 N.W.	Mungrisdale	..	..	S.E.H.	(1930–2)
57 N.E.	Berrier and Murrah	..	..	S.E.H.	(1930–2)

The Cumberland County Six-inch Sheets of the Ordnance Survey have now been replaced by National Grid Sheets. In due course the geological Six-inch County Sheets will be re-constituted as National Grid Sheets.

Chapter I

INTRODUCTION

THE DISTRICT[1] DESCRIBED in this memoir, which includes the northern part of the Lake District and part of the West Cumberland Coalfield, is that covered by the Cockermouth (23) Sheet of the New Series One-inch Geological Survey Map (see Fig. 1). Its boundaries coincide with the Old Series Sheet 101 N.E. of which hand-coloured geological editions in 'solid' and 'drift' were published in 1890. No descriptive memoir accompanied the publication of Sheet 101 N.E., but an explanatory memoir 'The Northern Part of the English Lake District' accompanied the sheet to the south (Old Series Sheet 101 S.E.). The districts adjacent to Sheet 23 which have been resurveyed since 1920 are described in the following Geological Survey memoirs: 'Whitehaven and Workington' (Sheet 28), 1931; 'Maryport' (Sheet 22), 1930; 'Carlisle, Longtown and Silloth' (sheets 17, 11 and 16), 1926; 'Brampton' (Sheet 18), 1932.

PHYSICAL FEATURES

Topographically the district falls naturally into three areas: (a) an upland mountainous tract situated centrally in the southern part of the sheet, and consisting essentially of Ordovician rocks and igneous intrusions, from which the rivers flow to the west and to the north; (b) the foothills which extend in an arc around the mountainous tract except where they are breached by the valleys of the rivers, and which are mainly composed of Carboniferous rocks but include some Ordovician rocks in the west; and (c) a relatively low-lying tract north of the foothills, falling towards and forming part of the Carlisle Plain. In this last tract the underlying rocks consist of Coal Measures in the south and New Red Sandstone rocks in the extreme north of the Sheet.

The mountainous tract. The mountains form the northern part of the Lake District. They extend eastward and north-eastward from Bassenthwaite Lake to the broad north–south valley in which lie the villages of Mungrisdale and Mosedale. Although the actual summit of Skiddaw at 3053 ft above Ordnance Datum lies three furlongs beyond the southern margin on the Keswick (29) Sheet, the northern slopes of the mountain, known as Broad End and rising to over 2500 ft O.D., lie within Sheet 23. Other peaks extending above an upland surface at about 2000 ft O.D. include Great Calva, Bowscale Fell, Knott and High Pike. Much of the upland surface is covered by thin hill-peat. The high summits and the steep upper slopes of the valley sides are devoid of superficial deposits but screes have accumulated on many of the lower slopes.

The foothills. In the west the foothills extend eastward from the neighbourhood of Cockermouth to Setmurthy on the south side of the valley of the

---

[1]Throughout this memoir the word 'district' refers to the area represented on One-inch Sheet 23 (Cockermouth).

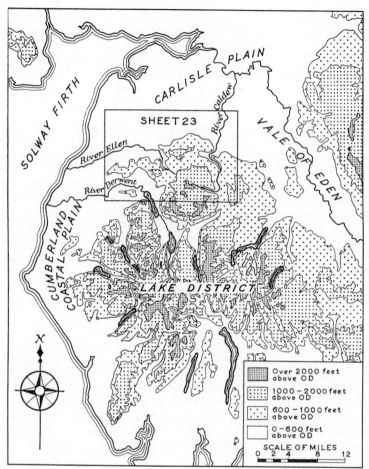

Fig. 1. *Sketch map showing the relation of the Cockermouth district to the sur-*
rounding country

River Derwent. They range in altitude between 600 ft and 850 ft O.D., and are
composed of Ordovician Skiddaw Slates and intrusive igneous rocks. Notable
prominences are Watch Hill and Elva Hill. To the north of the wide valley of
the River Derwent the foothills are mainly of Carboniferous rocks and extend
from the neighbourhood of Tallentire Hill eastward past the north of Binsey
to the River Ellen, with summits lying between 700 ft and 900 ft O.D. including
Moota Hill at 825 ft O.D. To the east of the River Ellen the foothills run
east-north-eastward, for the most part above 1000 ft O.D., to Warnell Fell,
which falls steeply to the River Caldew, with Seat at 1129 ft O.D. on Faulds
Brow as the most prominent summit. To the east of the River Caldew the foothills trend to the south-south-east at altitudes of about 800 ft to 1100 ft, notable
prominences being Hewerhill and Berrier Hill that lies just beyond the eastern
margin of the map on the Penrith (24) Sheet. The foothills are patchily covered
by Glacial Deposits.

   The low-lying tract. To the north of the foothills, and occupying about
two-fifths of the district, is ground varying in altitude from about 500 ft to

100 ft O.D. It is almost completely covered with superficial deposits and it is characterized by numerous half cigar-shaped mounds that in mass show the 'basket of eggs' topography typical of a suite of drumlins. The drumlins sweep in an arc across the area, their long axes changing direction progressively from north-west through west to south-west as they are followed from east to west.

Most of the rivers emanate from the mountains and the high upland surface, and all by devious courses enter the Solway Firth. The chief is the River Derwent in part of the valley of which is situated Bassenthwaite Lake. This river rises in the region to the south, though some of its tributaries have their headwaters in the area under description, the most important being the Glenderamackin which rises in the high ground to the south-west of Mungrisdale. Another important stream, the River Caldew, rises on Skiddaw, flows north-east and east to Mosedale and then turns north eventually to join the River Eden at Carlisle. A noteworthy feature is the presence of a broad peaty hollow extending roughly south to north from Mungrisdale through Mosedale, which is traversed both by the Caldew and the Glenderamackin, though one turns to the north and the other to the south. A substantial tributary from the west (the Caldbeck of Six-inch maps) formed in its higher reaches by the confluence of Parkend Beck and Dale Beck, joins the River Caldew to the north of Hesket Newmarket, and Roe Beck joins the river near Gatesgill from the south-south-east.

Another stream of importance is the River Ellen, which rises on the western slopes of Great Sca Fell, flows first to the west, then to the north, swings again to the west near Allhallows and Aspatria, and finally turns to the west-south-west to enter the sea at Maryport.

Several streams rise on the northern slopes of the central foothills and unite to form the River Waver which flows in a general north-westerly direction eventually to join the Solway in Moricambe Bay. Chalk Beck, another stream rising on the northern slopes of the central foothills, is the main headwater of the River Wampool which also drains into Moricambe Bay. From its source north of Caldbeck the Chalk Beck flows northwards until about one mile beyond the northern margin of the district it reaches the west to east valley of the River Wampool.

INDUSTRIES

The area is not heavily populated and contains only two medium-sized towns, Cockermouth in the south-western corner and Wigton near the middle of the northern margin of the area, although Aspatria on the coalfield and Caldbeck in the fell country are local centres of some importance.

Farming is now the principal industry. It is broadly related to the physical features and geology of the country. The low-lying northern area stretching northwards beyond the confines of the One-inch sheet into the Carlisle Plain, is characterized by soils derived from Glacial Drift. Here mixed farming (arable and grassland husbandry) flourishes. Milk production and the rearing of dairy cattle are important, with the greatest dairy cattle density around Wigton, an area famous for outstanding cattle of excellent market value.

The foothills yield soils of qualities varying from loamy soils, derived from limestone, to heavy soils, difficult to work, derived from boulder clay. Although there are some good arable lands, grassland and open heathland predominate in the fells. On the former, cattle rearing and milk production go hand in hand, whilst the open heathland is devoted to sheep rearing.

The mountainous highlands are devoted almost exclusively to stock raising, essentially sheep of the hardy Herdwick variety. Within recent years some of the fells in the neighbourhood of Bassenthwaite Lake, formerly used for sheep grazing, have been given over to afforestation by the Forestry Commission.

GEOLOGICAL SEQUENCE

The formations represented on the map and dealt with in this memoir are summarized in the following table:

Superficial Deposits

RECENT AND POST-GLACIAL
   Hill and basin peat
   Fluviatile alluvium
   River terrace deposits
   Alluvial fans
   Warp deposits (marine)

GLACIAL
   Fluvio-glacial gravel
   Laminated clay
   Morainic drift
   Sand and gravel
   Boulder clay

Solid Formations

PERMO-TRIASSIC (NEW RED SANDSTONE)
   Stanwix Shales: red and green clays and shales
   Kirklinton Sandstone: orange-red sandstones with rounded grains of quartz
   St. Bees Sandstone: buff-red micaceous sandstones with grey-white bands near
      base; subordinate dull-red shale bands
   St. Bees Shales: dull-red shales and sandy mudstones, micaceous, with thin
      veins of gypsum
   Penrith Sandstone: red coarse rounded-grained sandstones

Great unconformity

CARBONIFEROUS
   UPPER CARBONIFEROUS
   Upper Coal Measures: red and purple sandstones and shales
   Middle and Lower Coal Measures: shales and sandstones with workable
      coals and fireclays, reddened in places

Non-sequence

   Millstone Grit Series (Hensingham Group): sandstones and grits with
      subordinate limestone bands and occasional thin coal seams; reddened
      in places
   LOWER CARBONIFEROUS (CARBONIFEROUS LIMESTONE SERIES)
   Chief Limestone Group: limestones with subordinate sandstones and shales
      and a few thin coals
   Cockermouth Lavas: basalts
   Basement Conglomerate: conglomerates with bands of shale

Great unconformity

ORDOVICIAN
   DRYGILL SHALES: shales
   BORROWDALE VOLCANIC SERIES
      High Ireby Group: andesitic lavas with some rhyolitic flows and tuffs
      Binsey Group: andesitic lavas, tuffs, ashes and agglomerates
   SKIDDAW SLATES
      Slates: black slates and shales with minor bands of siltstone
      Slates and Sandstones: striped slates, siltstones and flaggy sandstones
      Grits: massive grits, blocky sandstones and subordinate striped slates

INTRUSIVE ROCKS
   SKIDDAW GRANITE: intrusion into Skiddaw Slates
   CARROCK FELL COMPLEX: acid and basic intrusive rocks including gabbros and
     granophyres
   MINOR INTRUSIONS: basic and acid rocks including picrite of Dash and the
     Embleton 'Granite' (a quartz-diorite) and numerous dykes

METAMORPHIC ROCKS
   Aureole of Skiddaw Granite: inner zone of crystalline hornfels; intermediate
   zone and outer zone of chiastolite and spotted slates. Hardened and spotted
   slates around minor intrusions.

GEOLOGICAL DESCRIPTION

The 'solid' formations conform to the topography in that they fall broadly
into three natural divisions: a southern area, consisting of Ordovician and
igneous rocks and in general forming the mountainous country; a central belt
comprising Carboniferous rocks; and a northern belt of Coal Measures and
Permo-Triassic (New Red) rocks.

Ordovician Rocks. The oldest sediments are the Skiddaw Slates. They pass
from gritstones through flagstones to slates becoming progressively less arenaceous and more argillaceous in upward succession.

The Slates give place, with interbedding, to the lavas and ashes of the
Borrowdale Volcanic Series, which series falls naturally into two groups.
The Lower or Binsey Group consists of andesites, with types varying from
fine-grained flinty to coarsely porphyritic lavas, interbedded with ashes, tuffs
and an agglomerate. The Upper or High Ireby Group consists essentially of
lavas, with several flows of the well-known Eycott type of andesite at the base
and rhyolites at the top of the sequence.

Upper Ordovician strata are represented by a small and narrow outcrop of
calcareous mudstones known as Drygill Shales of Caradocian age. It is inferred
that these mudstones lie above the Borrowdale Volcanic Series, but all their
contacts with adjacent rocks are either faulted or intrusive junctions.

Neither Silurian nor Devonian sedimentary rocks are known in the district,
and, during the vast period of time between the cessation of Ordovician and
the onset of Carboniferous sedimentation, the older rocks were subjected to
strong compression that has given rise to folding along east-north-east lines
and thrusting, and that later impressed a slaty cleavage on the softer strata.
Extensive and widespread igneous intrusion followed the formation of the
cleavage and since none of the intrusions affects Carboniferous rocks it is
inferred that all are of pre-Carboniferous age. Of the two major intrusions,
the Carrock Fell complex of gabbro, granophyre and diabase was emplaced

before the Skiddaw Granite. Numerous other intrusions are classed together as dioritic lamprophyres and show considerable variation in composition, the Embleton mass and that at Dash representing the acid and basic extremes of this suite. Some of the minor intrusions are contemporaneous with the Carrock Fell complex, others are of later date.

Although all of the intrusions have metamorphosed the country rock to varying degrees the most impressive thermal metamorphism is the extensive aureole in Skiddaw Slates which surrounds the Skiddaw Granite.

Carboniferous Rocks. The Carboniferous rocks rest upon the Ordovician suite with striking unconformity and in the west at least, where these younger rocks lie upon the Skiddaw Slates, thousands of feet of the latter had been denuded away before the Carboniferous sea flooded a land that had been weathered and deeply reddened under oxidizing conditions. It is not surprising, therefore, to find that the Basement Conglomerate, which marks the onset of Carboniferous sedimentation, has a red muddy matrix.

The Basement Conglomerate is directly overlain by the Chief Limestone Group (of Upper Viséan age), except in the west around Bothel where olivine basaltic lavas intervene between the Conglomerate and the limestones. The late date of submergence in this area contrasts with the early submergence in the geosynclinal area of the Mid-Northumberland Trough to the north, where thousands of feet of Tournaisian and Lower Viséan sediments were accumulating whilst the Cockermouth area remained land. In the west the Chief Limestone Group is represented almost completely by limestones, albeit of shallow-water type, but elsewhere in the district a Yoredale type of sedimentation is developed with repeated alternations of sandstone, limestone and shale, and a few thin coals. The detrital sediments thicken towards the east and north-east, and it is evident that the central and eastern areas during Upper Viséan times came under the influence of a large river that entered the district from the north-east.

This river exercised a still greater influence during Namurian times when the Millstone Grit Series was deposited. In this series arenaceous and argillaceous sediments predominate, the limestones are thin and scarce, and there are several coal seams, one of which reaches economic thickness in the east. These rocks are, however, of basal Namurian (Pendleian and Arnsbergian) age (E_1 and E_2), and are separated from the Coal Measures by a non-sequence. The non-sequence represents a period of time that covered at least the deposition of the Chokierian (H_1) to Yeadonian (G_1) stages of the Millstone Grit Series as well as the *Anthraconaia lenisulcata* Zone of the Coal Measures.

Deltaic and lacustrine conditions with rare marine incursions mark the formation of the Lower and Middle Coal Measures. The sediments consist of sandstones, mudstones, coal seams, fireclays and clay ironstones. The Upper Coal Measures consisting of red and purple mudstones occur at the surface only as two small faulted outliers, so that there is no evidence within the district to determine their relationship with the Middle Coal Measures.

Permo-Triassic (New Red Sandstone) Rocks. The Carboniferous period was terminated by earth movements, and in the prolonged period that followed several orogenies have elsewhere been recognized. Here these cannot be separated and they are grouped as the Hercynian earth-movements. During this prolonged period of crustal instability the Carboniferous and older rocks were elevated thousands of feet above sea level and were folded and severely faulted. The Hercynian upheavals were followed by prolonged denudation during which in places thousands of feet of Carboniferous sediment were removed under oxidizing climatic conditions with consequent reddening of the rocks upon and beneath the pre-New Red Sandstone land surface. Thus not only are Millstone Grit and Coal Measures rocks reddened but in places the oxidization has destroyed coal seams. Because of the severity of the Hercynian earth movements, the New Red Sandstone rocks follow those of the Carboniferous with pronounced unconformity, and because of the prevailing oxidizing conditions these younger rocks are red. Sedimentation commenced first in the depression to the east and south-east of the district—the Vale of Eden—with conglomerates or Brockrams, and these basal rocks were followed by the accumulation of aeolian sands that today form the Penrith Sandstone which crops out in the north-east of the Cockermouth district near Gatesgill and Highbridge.

A widespread subsidence ushered in the St. Bees Shales, and these shales with a thin local conglomerate or grit at their base are the oldest Permo-Triassic sediments west of the Gatesgill–Highbridge area as far as the Solway Firth. They pass upwards conformably into the water-laid St. Bees Sandstone. This formation yields building stones which have been used extensively in the past. The St. Bees Sandstone is followed by the Kirklinton Sandstone, a formation containing an abundance of aeolian material and lithologically similar to the Penrith Sandstone. The Kirklinton Sandstone passes upwards into the Stanwix Shales—a series of variegated grey, green, blue and red shales and marls that, because of thick drift, have been proved within the area only in boreholes.

These last-mentioned rocks are the youngest representatives of 'solid' rocks in the district. Lower Liassic rocks are present in the Carlisle (17) district to the north, and it is probable that there and in the Cockermouth district later Jurassic rocks were deposited, but have been subsequently removed by denudation. Possibly the Cretaceous rocks were also deposited and similarly removed during the earth movements and denudation of Tertiary age—the Alpine orogeny—that affected the rocks of Northern England and Southern Scotland.

A lead–zinc–copper mineralization is present and is post-Triassic in age.

Glacial Deposits. The glaciation of the area occurred in three episodes. Each comprised an advance and a retreat of the ice. Of the First we have little evidence except in the form of a boulder clay in the Caldew Valley. This is inferred to be the Lake District representative of the Early Scottish Glaciation. The Second or Main Glaciation consisted of combined Lake District and Scottish ice. It has left widespread records in the form of corries in the mountainous area, ground moraines and drumlins on the plains, and retreat phenomena such as end moraines, overflow channels, and the deposits of glacial lakes. The effects of the Third Glaciation can be seen on the ground below 400 ft O.D., which has been covered by the Scottish Readvance ice. The ground moraine of the ice-sheets consists of boulder clays of varying composition and texture. The outwash deposits of the retreat phases are composed of sands and gravels.

Recent Deposits. In the valleys are tracts of alluvium and river terraces, notably those of the rivers Caldew, Waver, Ellen and Derwent. Other Post-Glacial deposits consist of hill-peat in the mountainous areas of Broad End, Great Calva and Bowscale Fell, and basin peat, which lies for the most part in the low-lying ground to the west of Blencogo and to the north of Westnewton.   F.M.T.

Geology of Cockermouth (*Mem. Geol. Surv.*)

Elva Hill and Skiddaw (A 6630)

Plate I

(A 6626)

A. GRITS OF SKIDDAW SLATES

Geology of Cockermouth (*Mem. Geol. Surv.*)   PLATE II

B. FOLDING IN METAMORPHOSED SKIDDAW SLATES

(A 6673)

A. PASSAGE BEDS
BETWEEN
SKIDDAW SLATES
AND BORROWDALE
VOLCANIC SERIES
(A 6739)

B. DYKE IN
PORPHYRITIC LAVA
OF EYCOTT TYPE
(A 6613)

A. Granophyric veins in gabbro

(A 6747)

Geology of Cockermouth (*Mem. Geol. Surv.*)   PLATE IV

B. Banded gabbro

(A 6743)

(A 6597)

A. Clints limestone crags

Geology of Cockermouth (*Mem. Geol. Surv.*)　　PLATE V

B. Rhythmic unit of Five Yard Limestone

(A 6742)

Geology of
Cockermouth
(*Mem. Geol. Surv.*)

PLATE VI

A. GORGE IN
 PENRITH SAND-
 STONE, ROE BECK
 NEAR HIGHBRIDGE

 (A 6590)

B. QUARRY IN
 ST. BEES
 SANDSTONE
 (A 6588)

(A 6621)

A. Bowscale Tarn

Geology of Cockermouth (*Mem. Geol. Surv.*)   PLATE VII

B. Dash Beck Valley and Dash Waterfall

(A 6653)

Chapter II

STRUCTURE

THE STRUCTURES within the district may be divided into several major groups, each possessing its own characteristics. In the pre-Carboniferous rocks steep dips are accompanied by acute folding, and inversion is not infrequent; slaty cleavage is found only in these rocks and igneous intrusions are confined to them. In the Carboniferous and later rocks, dips are in general moderate, and folding, when present, is of a broad open type. Certain structures in the Carboniferous rocks, such as faults and folds, pass beneath the New Red Sandstone rocks without affecting them, thereby demonstrating their age as pre-New Red Sandstone. Other faults, as for example the great group of north-westerly-trending faults, displace both Carboniferous and New Red strata and clearly post-date the New Red Sandstone.

These three clearly recognizable periods of earth movement are referable to the pre-Carboniferous or Caledonian orogeny, the pre-New Red Sandstone or Hercynian orogeny, and the post-Triassic orogeny (usually regarded as Tertiary, and thus falling within the Alpine orogeny).

Prior to these three orogenies considerable folding accompanied by uplift and erosion occurred in the southern part of the Lake District between the time of deposition of the Borrowdale Volcanic Series and that of the succeeding Coniston Limestone Series. In the Cockermouth district the latter is represented by the Drygill Shales, but these are never seen in their original relationship to the Borrowdale Volcanic Series, and the nature of the original junction is thus not certain. A marked unconformity between the two formations in the district was advocated by Green (1917) and, although his view that grits of basal Bala age are present is no longer tenable, there is a distinct possibility that there is an unconformity resulting from pre-Bala uplift and erosion.

The three main orogenies are each capable of subdivision. Thus among the Caledonian movements, representing a long period of mountain building, some dislocations are earlier than the major intrusions, and others are later than them. Again, there are gentle intra-formational movements within the Carboniferous, which are precursors of the main Hercynian period.

CALEDONIAN OR PRE-CARBONIFEROUS MOVEMENTS

The main folding of the Ordovician rocks in the Cockermouth and Caldbeck Fells area is considered to result from the Caledonian earth movements, which folded the Silurian rocks in the southern part of the Lake District and generally impressed a regional east-north-easterly strike on the pre-Carboniferous rocks. Within the district there are many departures from this typical direction of Caledonian strike and the earth movements of this orogeny clearly took place at more than one time.

9

It would appear that the sequence of events was as follows: at first intense compression led to the development of isoclinally folded strata, the general trend of the major folds being east-north-east. Thrusting and faulting are associated with this phase and locally there is pronounced departure from the regional direction of strike. At a late stage of this phase, or possibly in a somewhat later phase, slaty cleavage of east-north-easterly trend was impressed upon the rocks. Next came the intrusion of the Carrock Fell complex (see p. 110); it is demonstrably later than the east-north-easterly folding and cleavage. Minor intrusions such as Dash and Embleton appear to belong to the same phase of igneous activity. Then followed the main north-south tear-faulting, which is associated with the development of some local cleavage, and also possibly some changes in the local strike. The intrusion of the Skiddaw granite (p. 128) is referable to the last phase of the Caledonian orogeny. It post-dates all other phases, but age determinations by the potassium-argon method place it still within that orogeny (p. 129).

FOLDING

The general direction of the Caledonian earth pressures was from south-south-east to north-north-west and their primary result was the production of a great and complex anticlinorium, the denuded core of which is represented by the main outcrop of the Skiddaw Slates. Owing presumably to greater resistance to the pressures at depth, the anticlinorium is decidedly asymmetric with a steeper northern limb that is locally overturned. This is best illustrated by the outcrops of the Borrowdale Volcanic Series. On the northern limb, which lies almost entirely within the district, these rocks are steeply inclined and locally overturned but with no repetition by folding, thus contrasting with the comparatively gentle rolling of the Borrowdale Volcanic rocks immediately south of the Skiddaw Slates outcrop in the Keswick district. A plunge to the anticlinorium in a general easterly direction is indicated by the tendency of the northern and southern outcrops of the Borrowdale Volcanic rocks to approach each other in the east, with Eycott Hill, $1\frac{1}{2}$ miles east-south-east of Mungrisdale, as a connecting link.

In the Skiddaw Slates the anticlinorium is made up of several steep-sided major folds and it includes much minor folding of considerable complexity. Both major and minor folds usually possess an asymmetry analogous to that of the main anticlinorium. Both types of folding display considerable variation in the trend of their axes and, moreover, the major folds cannot be traced throughout the outcrop. Thus the anticlinal cores, as indicated by outcrops of the Slates and Sandstones group and the Grits, commonly appear as elongated dome structures that are not aligned, as for example, the Broad End Anticline and the central Caldew upfold. This may partly be due to several transverse tear-faults which traverse the Skiddaw Slates outcrop, and along which the amount of horizontal displacement, although difficult to estimate precisely, is nevertheless probably of the order of miles.

The more massive sandstones and grits do not display small-scale folding but, these beds apart, minor folding of considerable complexity is widespread in the Skiddaw Slates. It varies from crumpling and knotting-up of the beds on hand-specimen scale and frequently with no definable orientation, to regular small-scale folds, the amplitude of which may be measured in inches to yards,

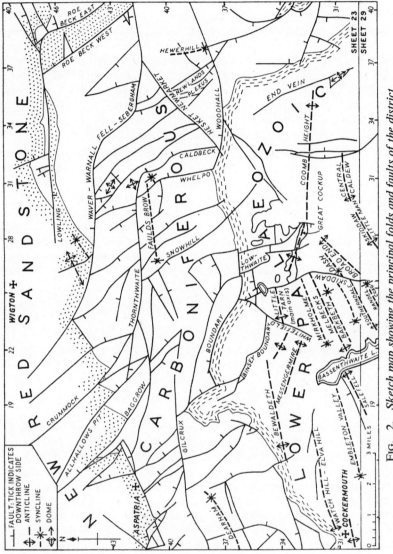

FIG. 2. Sketch map showing the principal folds and faults of the district

that have definite strike and pitch. The fold axes are usually parallel to the regional strike, but many cases are known in which the minor folding has a steep to vertical pitch oblique to or transverse to the general strike.

Before describing the major folds in detail it is desirable to mention briefly the departures from the east-north-easterly strike. Following the outcrop of the Borrowdale Volcanic rocks from west to east, the strike is east-north-easterly at Bothelcrags, east-south-easterly from Whittas Park to Binsey, thence easterly to the north of Over Water, after which it changes to east-north-easterly, and then back again to east-south-easterly in the Caldew valley and at Greystoke Park in the Penrith district. There is thus variation in strike amounting to at least 45° along the main outcrop. In the outcrop one mile east of Mungrisdale the strike is south by east. Similar and closely related changes of strike occur in the Skiddaw Slates, on both large and small scales, and are found mainly in the northern part of their outcrop nearest to the Borrowdale Volcanic Series, some becoming less pronounced southwards.   F.M.T., S.E.H.

The major folds can be conveniently described from west to east (see Fig. 2). There is a northerly trending upfold of sandstones to the west of Forth House, about 1½ miles north-east of Cockermouth. In the extreme south-west a sharp anticlinal fold brings up Grits west of the River Cocker at Cockermouth. This outcrop ends eastward against a northerly trending fault, beyond which are the outcrops of the Grits in the complex anticlinal area of Watch Hill-Elva Hill, in which both thrusting and faulting are probably present, accompanied exceptionally by overfolding to the south. A deep infold of black slates of the Slates group along the west to east Embleton valley separates this anticline from the Sale Fell Anticline which brings up arenaceous beds to the south. The latter structure, which shows overfolding both to the north and to the south, probably terminates against a tear-fault that may pass along Bassenthwaite Lake.   T.E., W.C.C.R.

North of Bassenthwaite Halls and west of the important Whitefield Fault, the structure is much obscured by drift. There is an inlier of Slates and Sandstones—the Messengermire Dome—to the north-west of Kilnhill. It is flanked to the north by a syncline in black slates that may be separated by a lag fault from a broad anticlinal belt of Slates and Sandstones, here termed the Bewaldeth Anticline.

East of Bassenthwaite Lake and between the Whitefield and Skiddaw faults the following folds of east-north-easterly trend are recognized from south to north: (a) the Randel Crag Syncline, which lies for the most part in the Keswick (29) district, but continues east-north-eastward on to Bassenthwaite Common; (b) the Southerndale Anticline, also mostly in the Keswick district; (c) the Barkbeth Syncline (all three folds are visible in black slates); (d) the Melbecks Anticline marked by a narrow outcrop of the Slates and Sandstones in the core of the fold; (e) the Mirkholme Syncline; (f) the Little Tarn Anticline. The last-mentioned is probably a compound fold, for in it the outcrop of the Slates and Sandstones is more than a mile wide and the dips are high.

East of the Skiddaw Fault there is another set of east-north-easterly trending folds; they cross the boundary separating One-inch sheets 23 and 29 and are best exposed on the western side of the Skiddaw massif. The southernmost of these is an anticline which brings up the Grits on Skiddaw Little Man (in Sheet 29); only the northern flank appears within the Cockermouth district, along the uppermost reaches of the River Caldew. The shallow syncline to the north on Skiddaw Man is possibly separated from the Broad End Anticline by a lag fault, though this has not been shown on the One-inch map. Nevertheless a considerable amount of strata appears to have been cut out on the southern limb of the Broad End Anticline. This anticline trends north-eastwards past Broad End towards Dash Beck, its core being marked by an outcrop of the Slates and Sandstones. The Dash Syncline is the complementary syncline (in the Slates group) to the north.

Farther north lie the ruptured anticline of Great Cockup and Burn Tod, and the overthrust mass on Great Sca Fell (see p. 14).   F.M.T.

There is a periclinal uplift of the Slates and Sandstones centred about the main granite outcrop in the Caldew valley. It is truncated to the east by north to south faults. This dome is flanked on the north and south by synclines in the Slates group. Farther north about Coomb Height are arenaceous slates, brought up in a complex fold here termed the Coomb Height Anticline. These beds continue eastwards along the Caldew valley where at least three asymmetric anticlinal folds with synclinal infolds of the overlying Slates group are developed between Bowscale Tarn and the Carrock complex. Bowscale Tarn is situated astride a west to east anticline in black slates of the Slates group that is separated from the folds to the north by a 'lag' or low-angled normal fault. South-east of this anticline and south-west of Mungrisdale is a broad area of black slates in which a synclinal axis trending to the east-south-east can be recognized. North of that village a well-defined anticlinal core of the Slates and Sandstones trending to the east, is thrust against black slates of the overlying Slates to the west.   S.E.H.

FAULTING

In the west, between Cockermouth and Elva Hill, the outcrops of the Grits and of the Slates and Sandstones are broken by a number of transverse faults; thrusting probably plays an important though obscure part in the Watch Hill area. In the Embleton valley west of Bassenthwaite Lake the Slates and Sandstones of the Sale Fell Anticline are separated from the Slates of the Embleton Valley Syncline by a reversed fault. It is probable that a tear-fault trends along Bassenthwaite Lake. If present its course is obscured by the lake waters and by the drift deposits that occur to the north of the lake.   T.E.

The Binsey Boundary Fault. In the central area, except for a small area west of Over Water, the boundary between the Skiddaw Slates and the Borrowdale Volcanic Series is faulted. In the west the separating fracture is the Binsey Boundary Fault, a tear-fault trending south-east from the Borrowdale rocks of Bothelcrags past the southern flank of Binsey to the Whitefield Fault. In this part of its course it displaces the Lower Eycott Lavas and overlying tuff from Bothelcrags to Binsey, a distance of 2 miles to the south-east. East of the Whitefield Fault the faulted boundary swings eastward and maintains this trend towards Lowthwaite where it ends against a low-angle dislocation— the Lowthwaite Fault. This latter forms the western boundary of an area of Borrowdale Volcanic Series that has been thrust, relative to the area to the west, south-south-eastwards over Skiddaw Slates for about two-thirds of a mile. The front of this overthrust mass of Borrowdale rocks on Skiddaw Slates trends eastward across Uldale Fells, the thrust junction disappearing beneath the Great Sca Fell thrust mass.

Northerly trending tear-faults. In the Whittas Park–Binsey area several tear-faults branch from the Binsey Boundary Fault in directions varying from north-west to north-east; they are considered to be adjustment fractures associated with this major tear-fault.

The Whitefield Fault and the Skiddaw Fault have already been mentioned. Both displace the Binsey Boundary Fault and both have considerable horizontal displacements in the Skiddaw Slates to the south of it. Two other northerly trending faults of this group cross the western flank of Great Cockup; both have relative displacements northwards on their western sides. They cut the Lowthwaite thrust mass and the more westerly fault also shifts the thrust mass on Great Cockup. There is reason to believe that the formation of these tear-faults was separated from that of earlier tear-faults by a considerable time interval, and that it post-dates the development of cleavage and also the emplacement of some of the intrusions. The Skiddaw Fault does not, however, displace the outer limit of the metamorphic aureole of the Skiddaw Granite; it is therefore earlier than that intrusion.   F.M.T.

The north-south faults crossing Grainsgill are provisionally assigned to the Caledonian earth movements, because they are mineralized by emanations from the granite, though they cut, and are clearly later than, that igneous intrusion.

The Great Cockup–Great Sca Fell Overthrust. The boundary between the mass of highly sheared grits of Burn Tod and Great Cockup and the slates to the south is seen to be vertical at and just above stream-level in Burntod Gill (of Six-inch map). The northern boundary of these grits, for the most part, appears as a low-angle plane with grits overlying the Slates group, and it is significant that not far to the north is the great overthrust mass of slates and associated sandstones and grits, centred about Great Sca Fell, which rests on Borrowdale Volcanic Series in the north along an approximately horizontal plane of junction; to the south, where it rests on slates, the precise limits of this overthrust mass and its relations to the Burn Tod area are not so well defined and are also complicated by faulting and erosion. There is, however, little doubt that the Burn Tod–Great Cockup grit belt represents the 'root zone' of the overthrust masses to the north.   S.E.H., F.M.T.

Some movement probably occurred along the Roughton Gill Faults before the intrusion of the Skiddaw Granite.

The age relations of the thrust fault at Mungrisdale are not definitely known, but the structure is probably linked with the northerly trending tear-faults and the Great Sca Fell overthrust.   S.E.H.

CLEAVAGE

The distribution of cleavage is decidedly irregular. The massive lavas and tuffs of the Borrowdale rocks are generally uncleaved apart from certain vesicular lavas in the Greystoke Park inlier (One-inch Sheet 24). The grits and the more massive sandstones and flagstones in the Slates and Sandstones group also are rarely cleaved although the interbedded slaty bands often develop local slip cleavage. Nevertheless an area of intense cleavage is developed on the eastern flank of Great Cockup, affecting massive grits and sandstones as well as the softer slates. Cleaved sandstones are also developed locally within the overthrust masses about Great Sca Fell.

Generally there is a progressive increase in cleavage in passing stratigraphically from sandstone through striped slate to black slate; but locally, as for example on Bassenthwaite Common, the Slates group—in an isoclinally folded condition—shows little or no cleavage.

The effect of the cleavage on the fracture of the rocks depends largely on its relation to the bedding, and where there has been any quarrying for slates the cleavage and bedding are approximately coincident; elsewhere the combined effects of cleavage and bedding tend to make the slates break into pencil or stick-like fragments.

The general strike of the cleavage varies from east-west to east-north-east, but there are variations and deviations. On Cockup, for example, it is north-westerly and locally even northerly; these changes are probably associated with the thrusting and tear-faulting of that area.

The Skiddaw Slates are cleaved on both sides of Dash Beck, both outside and within the metamorphic aureole of the Skiddaw Granite. To the south of the Beck, on the upland surface of Broad End, chiastolite-bearing slates rendered blocky by the metamorphism, display, on weathering, closely packed cleavage planes which presumably were in existence before the metamorphism.

Farther east there is a general change in the direction of the strike of the cleavage from east-north-easterly, through easterly to east-south-easterly in the Mungrisdale area, which is approximately paralleled by the change of strike of the beds. Against the reversed fault north of Mungrisdale it becomes southeasterly and parallel to the thrust plane. In the volcanic rocks of Greystoke Park several miles farther east, the cleavage strike is east-south-easterly, parallel to the strike of the bedding. There can be little doubt that these associated changes in strike of the bedding and cleavage are due to a common cause. As departures from the regional trends they may perhaps be attributed to the effect of a resistant barrier to the north-east; but whether the changes of strike are due to rotation of a pre-existing strike as the strata came up against the barrier, or to the development of folding and cleavage more or less tangential to that barrier, or to a combination of these two processes, is not clear.

This change of strike is independent of the intrusion of the Carrock complex and would therefore appear to antedate it. If so the complex is later than the cleavage, and the Drygill Shales received their cleavage before being down-faulted into their present position; for it is unlikely that they could have been cleaved subsequent to the emplacement of the igneous rocks that surround and protect them in their present position.

The dip of the cleavage is generally to the south at angles between 50° and vertical, but exceptionally inclinations of as low as 20° have been recorded. Locally the dip of the cleavage is northward at high angles. Nowhere, however, is the cleavage folded.

The diorite-picrite suite of intrusions of Dash and the Bassenthwaite Fells appears to be later than the cleavage, as the hardened slates in contact with the intrusions are in places heavily cleaved while the intrusions are not. Other intrusions, for example that 1000 yd west by north of Mungrisdale, appear to be somewhat cleaved. As there appears to be some evidence for a local recrudescence of cleavage effects at the time of the north-south tear faulting, the existence of cleavage which in places pre-dates, and in other places post-dates, minor intrusions does not necessarily indicate two periods of intrusion.

F.M.T., S.E.H.

POST-CARBONIFEROUS MOVEMENTS

The Caledonian movements were followed by a prolonged erosional epoch and the denuded Lower Palaeozoic rocks were eventually submerged beneath the Carboniferous sea. In general thereafter sedimentation continued until brought to a close by the important Hercynian earth movements. Following the Hercynian orogeny and subsequent extensive erosional epoch, the Permo-Triassic rocks were deposited. At a later date these were also uplifted by one or more earth movements, which are here grouped for convenience under the heading of post-Triassic. Within the Carboniferous outcrop, however, it is frequently impossible to separate the Hercynian and post-Triassic movements, and in the following account these movements are described together, individual structures, wherever possible, being assigned to the appropriate orogeny.

In broad outline the Carboniferous Limestone Series forms an arcuate outcrop dipping off the Lower Palaeozoic rocks. To the north it is overlain by a belt of Upper Carboniferous rocks in which the arcuate strike is partly obscured by faulting. Nevertheless, the general direction of dip swings from north-west in the west to north-east in the east. The general dip in the belt of Permo-Triassic rocks is between north-west and north-north-west.

FOLDING

On the western edge of the district the Carboniferous Limestone outcrop between Bridekirk and Plumbland is the eastern portion of a westerly plunging syncline that forms part of the Dearham Basin of the country farther west. The folding is much interfered with by faulting, but the general axial direction is approximately parallel to the Gilcrux Fault which forms the northern boundary of its outcrop.

The main structural feature of the central part of the area, displayed in the Carboniferous Limestone Series, is the Faulds Brow Syncline, the east-west axis of which lies parallel to and south of the Thornthwaite Fault. To the east the syncline abuts against and is terminated by the Caldbeck Fault; to the west it fades into gently dipping or horizontal strata on the fell 1½ miles east of Sandale. It is crossed by several north-westerly faults that terminate against the Thornthwaite Fault, and one of these, the Whelpo Fault, shifts the westerly-trending axis on Faulds Brow almost ½ mile to the south. The syncline has a plunge of 12° to 15° to the west at its eastern end, where the northern limb dips to the west-south-west and the southern limb to the north-north-west.

A north-south shallow syncline, here termed the Hewerhill Syncline, 2½ miles east of Hesket Newmarket, is brought out by the outcrop of the Little Limestone Coal. The structure is terminated to the south by the Woodhall Fault and it appears to die out northwards, but the rocks are mantled by drift in that direction.

At Waverhead, 1½ miles north-west of Caldbeck, a dome-like structure is indicated by the outcrop of the Little Limestone Coal, and half a mile farther north at Brocklebank there is an anticline of north-westerly trend, in the uppermost beds of the Carboniferous Limestone Series, bounded on four sides by faults.

The inlier of the Carboniferous Limestone and Millstone Grit Series around Lowling and eastwards beyond Chalk Beck is probably an elongated dome faulted along its southern margin, but the northern margin of the structure is hidden beneath the overlapping New Red rocks. At its western end the dip is 20° to the north-west, and in Chalk Beck, at the eastern end of the inlier, the dip is eastwards at 20° to 25°. The dip of the overlying New Red rocks is to the north-west and the structure is thus referable to the Hercynian orogeny.

The only known example of post-Triassic folding occurs near Westward, about 2 miles south-south-east of Wigton, where there is a small dome of St. Bees Shales with a core of Coal Measures. The structure is broken by two north-westerly faults that let down a wedge of St. Bees Sandstone. It is inferred that a complementary syncline lies to the south with an axis trending north-east-wards through Church Hill, but the infolded St. Bees Sandstone is drift covered.

T.E., F.M.T.

FAULTING

The fractures that disrupt the outcrops of the Carboniferous and Triassic rocks are too numerous to receive individual mention and information concerning the more important is to be found in the details of the Carboniferous Limestone, Coal Measures, and Permo-Triassic rocks.

These faults fall into two main groups trending generally to the north-west and to the east respectively. Several of the former set have a north-north-westerly direction, and included in the latter group are faults running to the east-south-east and to the east-north-east. There are a few faults trending to the north-east but these are relatively unimportant except for the Hesket Newmarket Fault, which is noteworthy because it divides the northern crop of the Carboniferous Limestone Series, with a general north-north-westerly dip, from the eastern crop, with an east-south-easterly dip. Thus to the west and north-west of the Hesket Newmarket Fault, in general the north-north-west faults are dip-faults and the east-north-east ones are strike-faults, whereas to the south and south-east of that Fault the north-westerly are strike-faults and the easterly are dip-faults.

East to west faults. Although the east to west faults are the less numerous, they include major fractures against which many of the north-westerly faults terminate. The chief faults of this set are enumerated below.

The Gilcrux Fault, with a northward throw, runs eastwards from Gilcrux to Ireby, and brings Coal Measures and Millstone Grit against the Carboniferous Limestone Series. Its continuation to the west is the Gilcrux Fault of the Maryport district (Eastwood 1930, pp. 7–10).

The Woodhall Fault trends east-north-east from Woodhall, south of Cald-beck, and throws down to the north, bringing Borrowdale Volcanic rocks and the Basement Conglomerate against the Carboniferous Limestone Series at its eastern end.

In the west a complicated fan-like system of north-westerly faults joins up, east of Allhallows, to form the Thornthwaite Fault which with northerly downthrow extends eastwards to Waverhead. Here it turns sharply and runs to the south-south-east as the Caldbeck Fault. In the west it brings Coal Measures against the Millstone Grit Series; farther east cross-fractures join it from the north-west and south-east, the general effect being to bring the Millstone Grit Series against the Carboniferous Limestone Series, although there is an outcrop of the latter to the north on the downthrow side of the fault and an outcrop of the former on the upthrow side.

The Waver–Warnell Fell–Sebergham Fault trends to the south-east from Waverton where it displaces the Trias, to Boltonwood Lane and from thence eastwards as far as Broadmoor, where it again turns to the south-east, but resumes its easterly trend from Sebergham to the eastern margin of the One-inch sheet. It throws down to the north and north-west and in the west near Westward it brings the Trias against the Carboniferous; farther east Coal Measures lie to the north and Carboniferous Limestone beds to the south of it.

The Lowling Fault trends from near Red Dial eastwards to Gatesgill. Here it splits into several branches which trend to the east-north-east; here also the Roe Beck East and the Roe Beck West faults branch from it to the south-east. Along its eastward course it repeats the outcrop of the St. Bees Shales. To the north of the fault, the St. Bees Shales rest on the Carboniferous Limestone and the Millstone Grit Series, but immediately to the south of the fault they rest on Coal Measures. Thus, the fault has a pre-Triassic, as well as a post-Triassic, throw: the pre-Triassic throw is down south, the post-Triassic downthrow is to the north.

The three last-mentioned east-west fractures have three points in common which throw some light on their age: (a) all three faults affect the Triassic rocks; (b) they display along different lengths of their courses an easterly trend; (c) north-west and south-east faults end against them. The Lowling Fault has moved in Hercynian and post-Triassic times and it is probable that this also applies to the other two faults.

The Hesket Newmarket Fault, although trending to the north-east, links itself with the easterly trending faults mentioned above because so many faults of north-westerly trend end against it or branch from it.

North-west to south-east faults. Many of these affect the Permo-Triassic rocks, notably the Baggrow Fault, the Allhallows Pit Fault, and the Roe Beck West and East faults, which together let in a trough of Penrith Sandstone. Other north-westerly faults are found only in the Carboniferous. They may be terminated to the south as well as to the north by easterly trending fractures, and there is a consequential alteration in the amount of throw along the courses of the latter. Many of the north-westerly faults are of considerable magnitude. They are not evenly spaced but tend to occur in belts, the individual members of a belt being joined by small cross-fractures. The longest belt runs from the Hesket Newmarket Fault past Caldbeck to the Waver–Warnell Fell–Sebergham Fault. It includes a trough some 600 ft deep at the southern end; farther north it embraces the dome at Brocklebank. Another fault belt—that of Denton Side—joins these two bounding faults and although the throw of the western member is 240 ft to the south-west, the belt as a whole throws 600 ft down north-west. The Newlands fault-plexus, trending from the Woodhall to the Hesket Newmarket Fault (see fig. 2), consists of a series of step-faults having a combined throw of 1000 ft to the south-west. Another fault-belt ending at the Woodhall Fault repeats much of the limestone sequence and brings up an inlier of Borrowdale Volcanics to the south-east in Greystoke Park.

T.E., F.M.T., S.E.H.

REFERENCES

EASTWOOD, T. 1930. The Geology of the Maryport District. *Mem. Geol. Surv. Gt Br.*

GREEN, J. F. N. 1917. The age of the chief intrusions of the Lake District. *Proc. Geol. Ass.* **28**, 1–30.

Chapter III

ORDOVICIAN: SKIDDAW SLATES

THE SUBDIVISION and correlation of the Skiddaw Slates have long been the subject of considerable controversy, for structural complexities make it difficult to unravel the lithological sequence with certainty. It is customary to make extensive use of fossil evidence to resolve such difficulties, as comparison with structurally simpler areas may then enable the order of succession and the overall structure to be determined. Unfortunately the occurrences of graptolites, to date the most useful fossils in the Skiddaw Slates, are so few as to limit their usefulness.

In general, individual workers have concentrated on restricted portions of the outcrop, and on either the lithological or the palaeontological sequence. It is accordingly convenient to treat these latter aspects separately in the early part of this chapter.

LITHOLOGICAL SEQUENCE

EVOLUTION OF TERMINOLOGY

The first lithological subdivisions were suggested by Ward (1876, p. 47), though he did not use them on the Old Series geological sheet of the region, for which he was largely responsible. He recognized the following five formations in descending order: 5. Black slates of Skiddaw; 4. Gritty beds (including those of Great Cockup and Watch Hill); 3. Dark slates; 2. Sandstone series of Grasmoor and Whitside; 1. Dark slates of Kirk Stile. Rastall (1910), however, recognized only three divisions, considering the sequence to be: 3. Black slates; 2. Flags; 1. Grits.

During the resurvey of the Whitehaven (28) district, Dixon (1925, pp. 70–1) at first considered that four formations could be distinguished. These he named: 4. Mosser Slates including the Skiddaw or Watch Hill Grit; 3. Loweswater Flags; 2. Kirk Stile Slates; 1. Blake Fell Mudstones. Although there was no exact equation with Ward's groups, in a general way the Kirk Stile Slates and Blake Fell Mudstones represented Ward's lowest group, the Loweswater Flags were the beds formerly referred to as the Sandstone series, while the Mosser Slates embraced the remainder of Ward's succession. As the mapping proceeded, however, Dixon's views changed, and ultimately he considered (Dixon *in* Eastwood and others 1931, p. 38) that some of the lithologically distinctive groups were lateral facies variants of the others, and that the strata could not be subdivided beyond two major groups, these being: 2. Mosser Slates including the Kirkstile Slates, together with the Watch Hill Grit; 1. Loweswater Flags and Blake Fell Mudstones. In addition Hollingworth (*in* Eastwood *op. cit.*) pointed out the presence of a local arenaceous formation, the Latterbarrow Sandstone, which overlies these two major groups.

The lithological sequence established by the resurvey of the present district was first set out as follows (Eastwood 1933, p. 59): "an arenaceous phase (Skiddaw Grit and its correlatives) in the lower part, passing upwards through grey sandy slates and striped siltstones (Mosser Slate type), and dark shales with occasional banding, to blue and black shales (Kirkstile Slate type) towards the top". This threefold classification was thus much the same as that of Rastall, and was employed on the Six-inch maps that first became available in 1938–9 and later on the One-inch sheet. Dixon's nomenclature was dropped and the three subdivisions were termed: 3. Slates; 2. Slates and Sandstones (Slates with Sandstones on the Six-inch maps); 1. Grits.

In a review of the geology of the Lake District Hollingworth (1954) made use of this nomenclature, but Rose (1954) retained Dixon's two major groups, calling them the Loweswater Flags and the Mosser-Kirkstile Slates. More recently Jackson (1961; 1962), dealing essentially with an area between Lorton Fells and Oughterside, has also used Dixon's later terminology, adding the Hope Beck Slates to cover those slates below the Loweswater Flags, and the Latterbarrow Sandstone for the arenaceous formation above the Mosser-Kirkstile Slates.

Simpson (1967) has recently revived Dixon's original terminology, and, in a description of the western half of the Skiddaw Slates outcrop, has subdivided the sequence into eight formations. These are: 8. Sunderland Slates; 7. Watch Hill Grits and Flags; 6. Mosser Slates; 5. Loweswater Flags; 4. Kirkstile Slates; 3. Blakefell Mudstones; 2. Buttermere Flags; 1. Buttermere Slates. Of these the uppermost three formations are subdivisions of Dixon's original 'Mosser Slates', the underlying three equate with Dixon's formations, and the lower two are new terms. Simpson also considers that the Latterbarrow Sandstone is best grouped with the Borrowdale Volcanic Series.

ROCK TYPES

The Skiddaw Slates comprise shales, siltstones, sandstones and grits, including distinctive types comprising rhythmic alternations of these sediments.

The shales are grey-green to blue-black in colour. One distinctive type is a hard, pale greenish grey mudstone with minute spots, and it is this variety that was at first thought by Dixon to have stratigraphic significance, and that was named by him the 'Blake Fell Mudstones'. This rock-type is, however, commonly found in the immediate vicinity of minor intrusions. Two specimens of slate were accordingly collected: one, of the pale spotted variety, from an outcrop immediately adjacent to the Barkbeth dioritic intrusion; the other of normal aspect from about 40 yd away. Comparative chemical analyses were made of these, together with a further one from a second specimen of normal mudstone. The results are given in Table 1, and it can be seen that, while all three analyses vary in detail, the essential peculiarity of the bleached mudstone is its almost complete loss of carbon, which has presumably been driven off by the heat of the intrusion, resulting in the colour change from dark to pale grey.

TABLE 1

*Chemical analyses of altered and unaltered slate from
Barkbeth and unaltered slate from Mungrisdale*

	Bleached slate, immediately adjacent to Barkbeth intrusion	Slate, unaltered, 40 yd from Barkbeth intrusion	Slate, unaltered, south-west of Mungrisdale
	I	II	III
Slide No.	E 17554[1]	E 17553	E 17555
Lab. No. ..	1035	1034	1036
SiO_2 ..	55·45	54·95	58·41
Al_2O_3 ..	23·29	23·33	20·25
Fe_2O_3 ..	0·70	0·60*	0·63*
FeO ..	6·26	7·04*	8·05*
MgO ..	2·45	1·85	2·02
CaO ..	0·40	0·36	0·41
Na_2O ..	0·71	0·98	0·68
K_2O ..	3·96	3·02	2·50
$H_2O > 105°C$	5·10	5·32	4·87
$H_2O < 105°C$	0·35	0·69	0·46
TiO_2 ..	1·07	1·07	1·00
P_2O_5 ..	0·20	0·11	0·23
MnO ..	0·20	0·42	0·07
S	tr	tr	tr
BaO ..	0·09	0·05	0·04
C	0·02	0·39	0·39
	100·25	100·18	100·01

*Owing to the presence of carbonaceous matter these figures should be regarded as approximations.

Analyst C. O. Harvey (see Guppy 1956, pp. 53-5).

The slates from Barkbeth were also examined in thin section, and Dr. K. C. Dunham reports on them as follows:

"An examination was made of slates from the contact-zone of the hornblende–picrite of Barkbeth. The apparently unaltered slate at 40 yd from the intrusion (E 17553) has the normal dark grey colour, and is composed predominantly of pale chlorite, partly in tiny rosette-like growths, mixed with fine-grained white mica and some carbonaceous matter. Adjacent to the intrusion the slate is pale grey (E 17554) and appears under the microscope to contain more white mica. The white mica is of decidedly coarser grain-size and has probably been recrystallized. The chlorite has been segregated into distinct spots, similar to those which in the Skiddaw granite aureole prepare the way for the formation of cordierite (p. 121). Definite evidence of the presence of cordierite here was not, however, obtained. The only significant difference shown by the chemical analyses is the reduction in carbon-content. Evidently

---

[1]Numbers preceded by the letter E refer to sliced rocks in the English Sliced Rock Collection of the Institute of Geological Sciences.

this is the main cause of the bleaching. Some potash may have been added, but the difference might also be due to a primary difference in composition. Albitization has not occurred."

Since both the chemical and microscopic examinations show that a Blake Fell type of mudstone can be produced by local thermal metamorphism, it is thought unwise to assume that the presence of this rock-type has any stratigraphic significance.

Many of the shales are noticeably striped, and where silty layers are absent or only thin and infrequent such shales are referred to below as of Kirk Stile type, for these are typical of Dixon's 'Kirk Stile Slates'. Associated ferruginous nodules are not uncommon, and more rarely cone-in-cone structure has been noted. In mass the Kirk Stile type mudstones are dark grey, and have been called 'black slate', 'slate' being a term applied somewhat loosely in the Lake District to shales, striped shales and mudstones that have been cleaved.

Where the striping in the mudstones is closely spaced and includes bands of silt, the rock is referred to below as of Mosser type, after the 'Mosser Slates' of Dixon. Commonly the dark grey to blue argillaceous layers are of the order of $\frac{1}{8}$ to $\frac{1}{4}$ in thick, and the light grey silty bands rather thinner.

As the thickness, grain-size and frequency of the silty bands increases, the Mosser type slates merge into flagstones. The sandy bands in the flagstones may be intercalations an inch or so thick in striped slates, as is the case near Bassenthwaite Hall; or they may be 6 in thick, or more rarely up to 3 ft, as in the 'Loweswater Flags' of Loweswater in the Keswick district. They show ripple-marked surfaces and a variety of small-scale sedimentary structures picked out by wisps of argillaceous material (Jackson 1961).

The grits normally form massive posts up to 10 ft thick. They vary from fine- to coarse-grained, and commonly grade upwards within an individual post from a coarse, locally conglomeratic, grit at the base to a fine-grained siltstone. Many posts contain small phosphate nodules at, or close above, their bases.

Rhythmic deposition has been noted throughout much of the more arenaceous parts of the sequence. The complete rhythmic unit consists of a flagstone or grit band, commonly with a basal plane of erosion, that passes upwards through striped shale into blue-black shale. This sequence was used by Dixon (*in* Eastwood and others 1931, p. 26) to indicate the order of deposition within his 'Loweswater Flags'. False-bedding has also been used for this purpose, for the inclined portions of many beds have been truncated before the deposition of the overlying sediments. This method was first used in the Lake District by Hartley (1925, p. 206), in a study of the tuffs of the Borrowdale Volcanic Series.

The development of cleavage is clearly dependent on lithology. The Mosser and Kirk Stile types of mudstone are commonly cleaved. Where cleavage and bedding coincide the rocks break into large slabs that have been used as roofing slates: otherwise they fracture into small pieces or pencil-like fragments. Thin flagstones may be cleaved, and commonly show strain-slip cleavage. Generally arenaceous beds over 3 to 4 in thick are uncleaved. Exceptionally in the Great Cockup area, even massive grits are cleaved.

B

SUCCESSION AND DISTRIBUTION

The nomenclature adopted on the One-inch and Six-inch sheets has been built up from the limited number of lithological sequences that can be established within, or closely adjacent to, the district. Of these the most important localities are Skiddaw, the Bassenthwaite Halls–Bassenthwaite Common area, and Mungrisdale.

Skiddaw. The fullest sequence is exposed on the western face of Skiddaw, including Skiddaw Little Man a short distance within the Keswick district. It shows a gradual upward passage from coarse arenaceous beds to fine argillaceous measures and is as follows:

3. Slates. This is essentially a shale group converted for the most part into slates. Typically the shales are of Kirk Stile type, striped shales or slates passing upwards into blue-black shales or slates in which banding is only faintly discernible. Near the base a few bands of Mosser type slates are locally present. The thickness of the group is considerably more than 2000 ft.

2. Slates and Sandstones. This group consists of striped slates or shales, thin flagstones, silty sandstones and sandstones; so both the 'Loweswater Flags' lithology and Mosser type slates are present. The estimated thickness is 1500 to 2000 ft.

1. Grits. Some 200 to 300 ft of massive grits and sandstones interbedded with silty sandstones and striped slates are present. They apparently represent only the uppermost part of the group that in Burntod Gill is more than 600 ft thick.

The Grits crop out in the core of the Skiddaw Anticline on Skiddaw Little Man, this being the type locality of Ward's 'Skiddaw Grit'. The Slates and Sandstones group is present on both limbs of the anticline on Little Man. On the southern limb it passes up into the Slates group, but on the northern limb the contact is a faulted one. The Slates and Sandstones reappear in the core of the Broad End Anticline at the northern end of Gibraltar Crags, while farther north the Slates group crops out in the complementary Dash Syncline.

Bassenthwaite Common area. From near Barkbeth southwards to the margin of the district and beyond it, to Randel Crag and Ullock Pike in the Keswick district, an upward sequence from the Slates and Sandstones group to the Slates group can be recognized on either side of the dale named Southerndale on the Six-inch sheet. In the Caldew and Blackhazel Beck valleys an anticlinal core of the Slates and Sandstones is overlain by striped slates that pass upwards into black slates of the Slates group. To the north the Slates and Sandstones group reappears along Grainsgill Beck and on Coomb Height, also lying in the cores of steeply dipping overturned anticlines near Bowscale Tarn.

Mungrisdale. An anticlinal core of the Slates and Sandstones is upfaulted to the north of Mungrisdale, and a deep synclinal fold in blue-black slates is recognizable in the Keswick district south of the village, within a broad outcrop of the Slates Group.

PALAEONTOLOGICAL SEQUENCE

The fauna of the Skiddaw Slates is predominantly one of graptolites, and, by virtue of the complexity of stratal sequence and structure, correlation with other areas, both within the Lake District and elsewhere, rests almost entirely upon the placing of individual graptolite faunas in a zonal sequence largely established elsewhere. The following account considers first the graptolite zones of that part of the stratigraphical column to which various authors have attributed the Skiddaw Slates, viz. the Upper Cambrian and Lower Ordovician (Tremadoc, Arenig and Llanvirn Series), secondly, previous research upon the position of the Skiddaw Slates in the graptolite zonal sequence, and thirdly, the zonal position and implied correlation resulting from collections made during the present survey. Most of the graptolite faunas quoted in this and other studies have been collected from natural screes but the use of this material is considered permissible by virtue of the considerable thickness of rocks included in each graptolite zone (cf. Jackson 1962, p. 302).

The standard graptolite zonal succession for the Tremadoc, Arenig and Llanvirn Series is still largely that first established by Lapworth (1879–80) and subsequently revised and extended by Elles (1904, 1922, 1925, 1933) and Elles and Wood (1901–18). As early as 1931 (Dixon *in* Eastwood and others, pp. 31–6) it was, however, subject to adverse criticism and suggested revisions have since been made. These have recently been summarized by Bulman (1958) and Skevington (1963), but it is pertinent here to consider briefly a number of points bearing closely upon the zonation of the Skiddaw Slates.

The Tremadoc zones of *Bryograptus* and *Dictyonema flabelliforme* of Elles and Wood (1914, p. 526) are now believed to represent only the Lower Tremadoc of the type area (Bulman 1958, pp. 162–4), the Upper Tremadoc in Britain being devoid of graptolites. Though a suggested Upper Tremadocian fauna is recorded from Norway, Australia, Texas, Newfoundland, Argentina and the Yukon (Skevington 1963, p. 315) its value for any correlation with supposed British Tremadocian faunas, those from the Skiddaw Slates in particular, raises the problem of provincialism in Tremadoc/Lower Ordovician graptolite faunas.

The post-Tremadocian graptolite zones were established in Wales, first by Lapworth (1880, p. 197) who recognized three zones: those of *Tetragraptus*, *Didymograptus bifidus* and *D. murchisoni* in ascending order. Elles (1904) later substituted the two zones of *Didymograptus extensus* and *D. hirundo* for Lapworth's *Tetragraptus* Zone. Yet later Elles and Wood (1901–18) introduced a *Dichograptus* Zone below the *extensus* Zone, proposed essentially for a part of the Skiddaw Slate succession, and in consequence having no stratigraphical continuity with the previously established zones. Its diagnostic graptolites were listed by Elles (1925), and its occurrence in the Skiddaw Slates elaborated upon by Elles (1933). Jackson (1961, 1962) has, however, shown that at all Elles' (1933) localities of both the *Dichograptus* Zone and the Upper *Tetragraptus* Subzone of the *D. extensus* Zone, the fauna can be interpreted as being no older than the *deflexus* Subzone of the *D. extensus* Zone. He concludes (p. 311) that "the presence of *Bryograptus* or *Dichograptus* on a scree should not be taken as indicating the existence of their respective zones when from the same scree an associated fauna of tetragraptids and didymograptids is also collected". Furthermore, as Bulman (1958) remarks, the *Dichograptus* Zone has never been recorded elsewhere and (p. 164) "there is no stratigraphical evidence for its existence. Nor does there seem strong evidence as yet for the occurrence of any marked concentration of *Tetragraptus* in the lower portion of the British Arenig". Indeed, the absence of a *Tetragraptus approximatus* fauna—a distinctive zonal assemblage at the base of all but the British Arenig— indicates that the early Arenig, like the Upper Tremadoc, is in Britain devoid of graptolites (Skevington 1963, p. 299).

Elles' (1933) subdivision of the *D. extensus* Zone into, in ascending order, the subzones of Upper *Tetragraptus*, *Didymograptus deflexus*, *D. nitidus* and *Isograptus gibberulus* was also based on Skiddaw Slate collections. Jackson (1962) confirms on both faunal and stratigraphical evidence the existence of the upper three subzones, but there is as yet no published independent confirmation of their presence elsewhere in Britain.

The currently accepted zonal scheme is as follows, and it is within this framework that the faunas of the Skiddaw Slates must be assessed.

Llanvirn $\left\{ \begin{array}{l} \textit{Didymograptus murchisoni} \\ \textit{D. bifidus} \end{array} \right.$

Arenig $\left\{ \begin{array}{l} \textit{D. hirundo} \\ \textit{D. extensus} \left\{ \begin{array}{l} \text{Subzone of } \textit{Isograptus gibberulus} \\ \text{Subzone of } \textit{D. nitidus} \\ \text{Subzone of } \textit{D. deflexus} \end{array} \right. \\ \textit{(Tetragraptus approximatus)}^1 \end{array} \right.$

Tremadoc $\left\{ \begin{array}{l} \text{(Anisograptidae and ?Graptoloidea)}^1 \\ \textit{Dictyonema flabelliforme} \text{ and Anisograptidae } \textit{(Bryograptus)} \\ \textit{D. flabelliforme} \textit{ (D. sociale)} \end{array} \right.$

PREVIOUS GRAPTOLITE ZONATION AND CORRELATION

Marr (1894, p. 128) was the first to make use of Lapworth's researches and classify the *Graptolite-bearing portion* [his italics] of the Skiddaw Slates or Skiddavian largely on the basis of their fauna. He did so as follows:

(2) $\left\{ \begin{array}{l} \text{d. Milburn Beds} \\ \text{c. Ellergill Beds} \\ \text{b. } \textit{Tetragraptus} \text{ Beds} \\ \text{a. } \textit{Dichograptus} \text{ Beds} \end{array} \right.$ $\left. \begin{array}{l} \\ \end{array} \right\}$ Upper with *Didymograptus nanus*
Lower

(1)   *Bryograptus* Beds

He classified (1) as Tremadoc and (2) as Arenig.

Elles (1898) modified Marr's sequence by placing the *Dichograptus* Beds between the Upper and Lower *Tetragraptus* Beds, and later Elles and Wood (1914, p. 526) implied that the Skiddaw Slates (Skiddavian) embraced the zones of *Dichograptus* to *Didymograptus bifidus* inclusively.

Dixon (*in* Eastwood and others 1931, pp. 31–6) believed that the graptolite sequence established in Wales, i.e. basically that employed by Elles and Wood (1901–18), was not applicable to the Skiddaw Slates, but that the fauna of the Lévis Shales of Quebec, Canada, afforded a more useful standard of comparison. Rather than subdividing the group into Arenig and Llanvirn he advocated the retention of Marr's (1905) term 'Skiddavian'.

---

[1]Zones not recorded in Britain.

Elles (1933) strongly disputed Dixon's conclusions and maintained that graptolite zones are of world-wide application. She amplified her former scheme and produced, essentially for the Skiddaw Slates, the following zonal classification:

5. Zone of *Didymograptus bifidus* (sensu stricto)

4. Zone of *D. hirundo*

3. Zone of *D. extensus*	d ⎰	Subzone of *I. gibberulus*
	c ⎱	Subzone of *D. nitidus*
	b ⎰	Subzone of *D. deflexus*
	a ⎱	Upper Subzone of *Tetragraptus* (reclined)
2. Zone of *Dichograptus*	⎰	Lower Subzone of *Tetragraptus* (horizontal)
	⎱	Lower part (unnamed)

1. Zone of *Bryograptus kjerulfi*

She favoured placing (1) and (2) in the Tremadoc.

Bulman (1941) in dealing with the Dichograptids of the Tremadoc and Lower Ordovician expressed the view that the Bryograptids ranged upwards into the Arenig and that the Tremadoc (which he regarded as Ordovician) was not represented in the Skiddaw Slates.

Hollingworth (1954) indicated that during the mapping of the Cockermouth district it was not found possible to apply Elles' detailed zonal scheme; and it has already been shown (p. 25) how Jackson (1961, 1962), dealing chiefly with an area of Skiddaw Slates between Lorton Fells and Oughterside, has shown that Elles' scheme can no longer be upheld in detail. Jackson concluded that the lowest graptolite zone certainly present in the Skiddaw Slates was that of *D. extensus* (Subzone of *D. deflexus*), but that a single specimen provisionally assigned to the *Tetragraptus approximatus* group pointed to the possible presence of older beds (Jackson 1964). He was also of the opinion that in his area at least the highest zone was that of *D. hirundo*, for he failed to find any evidence for the *D. bifidus* Zone recorded by Elles (1933, p. 105) at Oughterside. He did, however, confirm the existence of the *D. deflexus, D. nitidus* and *I. gibberulus* subzones of the *D. extensus* Zone.

Most recently Temple (*in* Simpson 1967) has suggested that the oldest beds in the Skiddaw Slates lie within the Zone of *D. extensus*—probably to be correlated with the Norwegian Zones of *D. validus* and *D. balticus* of Monsen (1937); whilst the youngest belong either to the uppermost Arenig (Zone of *D. hirundo*) or range into the Lower Llanvirn.

PRESENT ZONATION AND CORRELATION

It has already been pointed out above that during the present resurvey it was not found possible to apply Elles' (1933) detailed zonal scheme. Others (e.g. Jackson 1962) have since reached the same conclusion, but as Elles' work was based to a considerable extent on collections made mainly by Mr. S. W. Hester during the resurvey of the Cockermouth district, it is pertinent to consider the difficulties closely, and outline the evidence that necessitates the revision of Elles' zonal sequence and correlation.

The main difficulty in formulating an acceptable zonal scheme for the Skiddaw Slates has been the presence within particular faunal assemblages of

graptolites elsewhere considered individually typical of different zones of the
Tremadocian and Lower Ordovician. To date, most of these assemblages
(see Fig. 3) have been collected from screes, and they may thus be interpreted either as mixed collections from different zones or as the fauna of one
zone into which members of lower faunas have ranged upwards. For example,
the assemblage from Barf (Sheet 29) which includes *Bryograptus kjerulfi*
Lapworth, *Bryograptus sp.*, *Tetragraptus bigsbyi* (Hall), *T. quadribrachiatus*
(Hall), *Dichograptus octobrachiatus* (Hall), *Phyllograptus angustifolius* Hall,
Didymograptus protobifidus Elles and *D. nitidus* (Hall) may be taken to indicate
the presence of the zones of *B. kjerulfi*, *Dichograptus* and *D. extensus* as
accepted by Elles, but the alternative explanation is that the *D. extensus* Zone
only is present (cf. Jackson 1962, p. 310). Similarly, the assemblage from the
screes of Randel Crags (Sheet 29) (see p. 34) may indicate the presence of the
Dichograptus, *Didymograptus extensus* and *D. hirundo* zones, or of the last-
mentioned only. Again the screes from a small crag east of Barkbeth (Great
Knott of Six-inch map) have yielded a few graptolites at four separate places (see
pp. 35–6); considered separately these restricted assemblages appear to indicate
the presence of the subzones of Upper *Tetragraptus*, *Didymograptus nitidus*
and *Isograptus gibberulus*, but taken as a whole, the fauna may be interpreted
as that of the *I. gibberulus* Subzone.

Bryograptus kjerulfi, the eponymous graptolite of Elles' lowest zone, is found
at only one locality—on the screes of Barf—where its associated fauna (see
above) includes forms typical of the *D. extensus* Zone, possibly up to the
Isograptus gibberulus Subzone (cf. Elles 1933, p. 104; but see Jackson 1962,
p. 310). The species is one of the index fossils of the uppermost zone of the
Dictyonema Shales of Scandinavia (Tjernvik 1958), and its presence might
be held to suggest the existence of Tremadocian rocks at Barf (cf. Elles 1933,
p. 103). However, this form occurs on the same slab as its variety *cumbrensis*
(Elles and Wood 1902, p. 89, pl. xii), which in turn has been found by Elles
(1898, p. 472) on the same slab as *Tetragraptus bigsbyi*, a form that makes its
first appearance in the *D. extensus* Zone. Thus the occurrence of the species
is by no means certain evidence of the presence of a *Bryograptus* Zone in the
Lake District.

The doubts expressed over Elles' *Dichograptus* Zone have been reviewed
above (see p. 25). These are supported by the fact that at all the localities
included in Elles' (1933, p. 103) distribution for the zone, i.e. "round the flanks
of Skiddaw by Randel Crag, Carlside, Ullock Pike, to Mire House and thence
across to Brackenthwaite, by Barf, Braithwaite and Grisedale Pike", the
faunas include fossils characteristic of higher zones (cf. Jackson 1962, p. 310).
A distinct assemblage for a *Dichograptus* Zone has been found only at Hodgson
Howe Quarry, near Portinscale (Sheet 29), and it is doubtful whether this one
fauna at one locality can be said to establish the existence of the zone. Indeed,
Jackson (1962, p. 310) has recorded a fauna from this same locality which he
believes indicates an horizon no lower than the *D. nitidus* Subzone.

Likewise, Elles' upper Subzone of *Tetragraptus* is recognized only on the
screes below a crag on Great Knott, east of Barkbeth. These screes are small,
and if the graptolites found at other places on these screes are considered
then the fauna as a whole indicates the presence of the *I. gibberulus* Subzone
only.

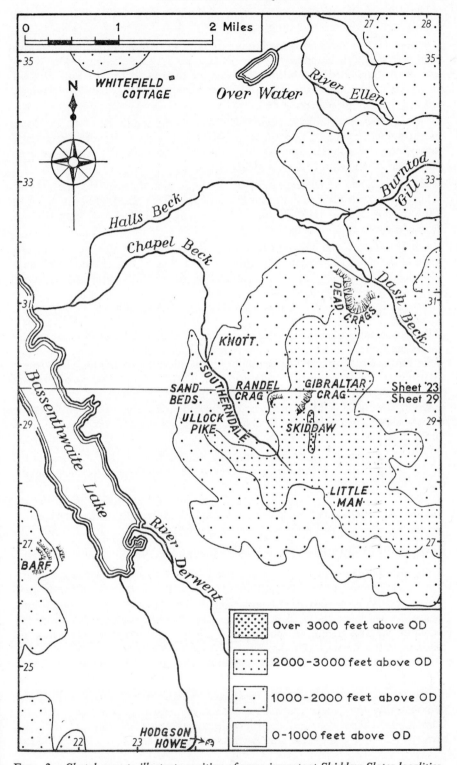

FIG. 3. *Sketch map to illustrate position of some important Skiddaw Slates localities*

The *Didymograptus deflexus* Subzone is found within the district only at a locality near Undercrag, Mungrisdale (see p. 44).

A distinct *D. nitidus* Subzone fauna has been recognized at several localities along the southern boundary of the district, notably on Bassenthwaite Common at the Sand Beds just within the Keswick district, at Little Knott 1200 yd E. of High Side, at White Horse 1¼ miles E. of High Side, at Mungrisdale, and in Jonah's Gill W.S.W. of Isel Old Park.

The *I. gibberulus* Subzone occurs at Great Knott ¾ mile E. of Dyke Nook and at a small crag east of Barkbeth. It is also known at Randel Crag, Barf, Sand Beds, Hazelhurst and in the Glenderamackin Valley south-west of Mungrisdale, all within the Keswick district.

The *D. hirundo* Zone is present in the beck near Scalegill to the east of Sunderland, in the beck to the west of Dead Crags (Dead Beck of Six-inch map), 400 to 600 yd S.E. of Dyke Nook, and also at Randel Crag and Sand Beds in the Keswick district.

The *D. bifidus* Zone has been recorded with certainty, *in situ*, on the eastern slope of Souther Fell (Sheet 29) about 1 mile S. of Mungrisdale and ¼ mile S. by E. of Hazelhurst. The fauna, recently re-identified by Professor O. M. B. Bulman, is: *Didymograptus* cf. *artus* Elles and Wood, *D. bifidus* (Hall), *D.* cf. *climacograptoides* Bulman, *D. leptograptoides* Monsen, *D.* cf. *leptograptoides*, *D.* cf. *miserabilis* Bulman and *Glyptograptus* cf. *dentatus* (Brongniart), and this supports Elles' (1933) determination of the horizon as the base of the *D. bifidus* Zone. This is one of only two confirmed records of the zone in the Lake District outcrops of the Skiddaw Slates, the other being at Haweswater (Skevington 1964). Jackson (1962) was unable to confirm Elles' record of the zone at Oughterside, and Simpson (1967) failed to prove its existence in Scalegill Beck [203 356], in beds he considered to be among the youngest in the Skiddaw Slates. The only record in the present district is a very doubtful one in Dead Beck (see p. 37).

In summary, therefore, on the basis of the accepted graptolite zonal sequence, the fossiliferous parts of the Skiddaw Slates of the district and of the immediately neighbouring area to the south fall within the zones of *D. extensus* (subzones *D. deflexus*, *D. nitidus*, *I. gibberulus*), *D. hirundo* and *D. bifidus* (basal part) and are thus essentially Arenigian in age, but just range into the Llanvirnian.

EQUATION OF LITHOLOGICAL AND PALAEONTOLOGICAL SEQUENCES

The lithological sequence here advanced, and shown on the Cockermouth (23) One-inch Sheet (viz. in ascending order, Grits group, Slates and Sandstones group, and Slates group), can in some measure be equated with the palaeontological sequence on the evidence of the graptolite assemblages from various localities, notably from Bassenthwaite Common, from the western face of Skiddaw in the Keswick (29) district, and from the Mungrisdale area.

Grits group. The Grits group has yielded no fossils within the district. Consequently the correlation of the grits at Watch Hill, Great Cockup and Burn Tod with one another and with those of Skiddaw Man, where the grits are demonstrably the oldest rocks in the exposed sequence, is based solely on lithological comparison and on the general structural interpretation of the area (see Ch. II). The coarse massive grits of Great Cockup and Burn Tod are confined to a limited area, and they do not appear to be present farther south in the ground described by Rose (1954) and Jackson (1961, 1962). They may well be older than anything exposed elsewhere along the Skiddaw Slates outcrop, and Rastall (1910) even suggested that they might be Pre-Cambrian in age. In contrast Green, who originally (1917) favoured a Bala age for certain of the grits, later (1925) abandoned this view, when beds believed to be the correlatives of his 'Watch Hill Grits' yielded *Glyptograptus dentatus* indicating an Upper Arenig or Llanvirn age. It is possible that this discrepancy in interpretation results from the presence of a stratigraphic break within the Grits group of the Cockermouth district, and that the sequence at Watch Hill lies above this break whilst the Great Cockup–Burn Tod grits lie beneath it. If so, the shales which appear to underlie the grits at Watch Hill may equate with the upper part of the Hope Beck Slates of Jackson and be unrepresented elsewhere in the Cockermouth district. The resulting correlation between the sequence here described and that of Jackson is illustrated in Fig. 4.

Correlation with the sequence proposed by Simpson (1967) is not clear. Broadly, however, Simpson assigns all the various outcrops of arenaceous beds that extend from Cockermouth towards Bewaldeth to his 'Watch Hill Grits and Flags' which thus includes beds here referred to the Grits group and the Slates and Sandstones group. Those outcrops of the Slates group lying north of this belt form his 'Sunderland Slates', and those immediately to the south comprise his 'Mosser Slates'. The Slates and Sandstones outcrops on the western side of Bassenthwaite Lake, Simpson includes in the 'Loweswater Flags'. His lower formations are not, as yet, claimed to be present within the Cockermouth district, though even the lowermost one, the Buttermere Slates, is still considered to lie within the *D. extensus* Zone (see p. 27).

Slates and Sandstones group. The Slates and Sandstones group contains the oldest beds from which fossils have been obtained within the district. In the Mungrisdale area assemblages occur indicative of the *D. deflexus* Subzone, the lowest subzone of the *D. extensus* Zone, and elsewhere assemblages from the overlying *D. nitidus* Subzone are known. There is thus broad agreement between the faunas from this group and those from the arenaceous part of the sequence (Loweswater Flags) described by Jackson (see Fig. 4).

Slates group. The lowest beds of the Slates group also belong to the *D. nitidus* Subzone, whilst the higher beds contain faunas establishing the presence of the *I. gibberulus* Subzone, the *D. hirundo* Zone and possibly also the basal part of the *D. bifidus* Zone, an undoubted *D. bifidus* fauna occurring in the upper part of the group in the Keswick (29) district, about ¼ mile S. by E. of Hazelhurst. Again there is general agreement between these faunas and those recorded farther south by Jackson from the argillaceous part of the sequence (Mosser–Kirk Stile Slates). A minor discrepancy is that whilst in the present district the lower part of the Slates group lies within the upper part of the *D. nitidus* Subzone, the lowest known faunas in the argillaceous beds farther south belong to the *I. gibberulus* Subzone (see Fig. 4). This suggests that there is limited diachronism of the facies change, and that deposition of the argillaceous facies began in the Cockermouth district slightly earlier than in the district to the south.

Near Over Water along the northern boundary of the Skiddaw Slates outcrop dark grey-blue mudstones are interbedded with lavas which are in con-

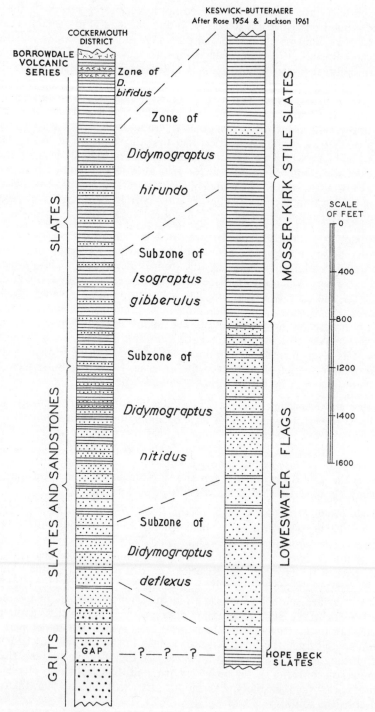

FIG. 4. *Vertical sections illustrating sequence of Skiddaw Slates*

Erratum: On scale of feet, for 1400 read 1600 and for 1600 read 2000

tinuous sequence with the Borrowdale Volcanic Series. They have yielded no fossils but almost certainly lie at no lower an horizon than the *D. bifidus* Zone, representing passage beds into the Borrowdale Volcanic Series comparable with the Milburn Beds (also of *D. bifidus* Zone age) of Cross Fell (Sheet 24). Unfortunately these mudstones are separated from the main outcrop of the Skiddaw Slates by a fault, so their relationship to the upper part of the Slates group is uncertain.

DETAILS

Cockermouth to Sunderland and Setmurthy. The greater part of the ground is drift covered and for the most part the outcrops of bare rock are restricted to Watch Hill and Elva Hill.

Grits varying from fine to coarse outcrop in the Cocker [1223 3037][1] to the north of the railway bridge at Cockermouth, and also in a tributary from the east joining the main stream, just below the bridge. At the mouth of the tributary they are seen to lie in sharp folds and there also appears to be some faulting of a minor character. These grits are closely associated with slates of the Mosser type which in the banks of the Cocker to the south are highly contorted. The exact relationship between the two is in doubt but it is probable that the grits occupy the crest of an anticline. Outside the valleys of these two streams the outcrop is largely concealed by boulder clay, but to the west grits reappear at the surface [110 297]—from ¾ mile W. 20° S. of South Lodge—after being shifted to the south about 300 yd by a fault. To the east of the Cocker the grit seems to be faulted, for the trend of the Watch Hill outcrop lies over ½ mile to the north at the rifle range.

The outcrops on Watch Hill and Elva Hill present many items of interest: the rocks range from coarse grits to fine sandstones with one or two intercalations of shale; a considerable development of shaly material appears to underlie the main grits and there are several intrusive masses of diorite. The general dip varies from northwards to north-westwards but there is some sharp folding with steeper limbs to the south. As a rule the plunge is to the northeast. The folding is associated with minor faulting.   T.E.

Embleton Valley. The sides of the valley are mostly drift covered but exposures of dark blue and striped slates associated with quartz-dolerite intrusions are to be seen to the north-east of Strawberry How. Other exposures in the Slates group are to be seen in an elongated outcrop (associated with diorite intrusions) lying to the north of Embleton Station. In these exposures the strike of the slates is to the east-north-east; there is much isoclinal folding but the general direction of dip is north-north-westwards at a steep angle, and this is also the direction of the dip of the cleavage.

The southern side of the valley appears to be bounded by a fault, on the southern or upthrow side of which flaggy sandstones, grits and subordinate slates (usually cleaved), of the Slates and Sandstones group, crop out on an east-north-easterly strike, and although in places isoclinally folded, the general direction of the dip is to the south-south-east. To the south of this arenaceous outcrop there is a synclinal infold of strongly cleaved blue-black slates of the Slates group that is shifted to the north by a north-westerly trending fault and disappears beneath Bassenthwaite Lake, ¾ mile S.S.E. of Bassenthwaite Lake Station.   W.C.C.R.

Kilnhill and Bewaldeth. Lying to the east of Isel Old Park this area extends from the north end of Bassenthwaite Lake northwards to the Binsey Boundary Fault and eastwards to the Whitefield Fault.

In general the beds are vertical and the strike undulates along a general W. 5° N.–

[1]All Grid References in this account fall within the 100 kilometre square denoted by the letters NY (or the number 35); these prefixes are omitted from the Grid References throughout. The Grid References are restricted to geological localities e.g. sites of exposures, boreholes etc. Where a geological locality can be indicated to within an area of 10 metres square an eight-figure reference is given, where the locality is within a 100 metre square a six-figure reference is used. For other localities Grid References are not used.

E. 5° S. direction. Near the Binsey Boundary Fault, however, the strike is to the north-north-east and this marked deviation from the general trend is probably the result of lateral movement along the tear-fault. The strike of the cleavage is more or less constant at a few degrees north of east. The detailed structure, however, is in doubt. The Slates and Sandstones group and possibly the upper beds of the Grits group occur in a dome north-west of Kilnhill, and shales with sandstones are again seen farther north where the outcrop, wide in the neighbourhood of Bewaldeth, narrows to the east-south-east. These beds would be regarded as the Slates and Sandstones group but for the fact that there appears to be an upward sequence northwards from the slates and sandstones of the above mentioned dome through slates to the slates with sandstones of the Bewaldeth area. A possible explanation may be that there is here a local development of blue slates in the Slates and Sandstones group.

This apparent upward sequence is best seen in the stream that flows from High Bewaldeth to Bassenthwaite Lake near Ouse Bridge. Exposures [2115 3309] of striped slates, silty sandstones and grits are first seen 400 yd W. of the bridge, where the the main road through Bewaldeth crosses the stream. A 12-ft grit is seen in the same stream at a point [2134 3321] east of a north-south fault, 250 yd west of the road bridge, and a grit of similar thickness, possibly the same bed, crops out [2169 3325] 250 yd N.E. of the bridge. The latter is succeeded by cleaved, silty-banded slates that pass up into cleaved blue-black slates. The blue-black slates are exposed intermittently to a point [2203 3388] 600 yd S.W. of High Bewaldeth, and upstream from here the rocks consist of alternations of thinly bedded, fine-grained sandstones, and blue-black slates, the former from 5 to 20 ft thick and the latter from 40 to 80 ft. At High Bewaldeth cleaved blue-black slates are again visible. To the north-west there are isolated exposures of striped slates with thin sandstone bands as far as the Binsey Boundary Fault. Particular reference may be made to 20 to 25 ft of soft feldspathic sandstone seen in a small quarry [2201 3468], 200 yd W.S.W. of Fellend, and traceable to the west-north-west for 300 yd.

Bassenthwaite Common–Over Water area. Bounded to the west and east by the Whitefield and Skiddaw faults respectively, this area stretches northwards from the southern margin of the district to the outcrop of the Borrowdale Volcanic rocks. The general direction of strike is to the east-north-east, and the following folds, which are overturned to the north, are recognized from south to north: the Randel Crag Syncline, the Great Knott Anticline, the Barkbeth Syncline, the Melbecks Anticline, the Mirkholme Syncline and the Little Tarn Anticline (see Figs. 2 and 5). The existence of the first three of these folds is deduced mainly from the evidence provided by fossils; the shales although isoclinally folded are uncleaved and graptolites are relatively abundant. The last three structures lie within a belt of cleavage and are based on stratigraphy.

The best exposures of the Randel Crag Syncline lie in Sheet 29 on Ullock Pike and Randel Crag. The black slates of Randel Crag [255 295], 1½ miles S.E. of High Side, dip 40° to 60° south-south-eastwards without apparent folding. At the eastern end of the crag chiastolite crystals are developed in the slates but the greater part of Randel Crag lies outside the metamorphic aureole. This crag is a well-known graptolite locality and the screes have yielded a prolific fauna indicative of the *D. hirundo* Zone and probably the *I. gibberulus* Subzone. The faunas from the various exposures are as follows: *Dichograptus octobrachiatus* (Hall) including hexad type, *Didymograptus extensus* (Hall), *D. hirundo* Salter, *D. nitidus* (Hall) including a form near *D. hirundo*, *D. pennatulus* (Hall), *D. protobifidus* Elles, *D. simulans* Elles and Wood, *D. suecicus* Tullberg, *D. uniformis* Elles and Wood, *Glyptograptus dentatus* (Brongniart), *Isograptus gibberulus* (Nicholson), *Phyllograptus angustifolius* Hall, *P. ilicifolius* Hall, *P.* cf. *typus* Hall, *Tetragraptus amii* Elles and Wood, *T. headi* (Hall), *T. quadribrachiatus* (Hall), *T. serra* (Brongniart), *Cyclopyge* spp., *Eurymetopus cumbrianus* Postlethwaite and Goodchild, *E. harrisoni* Postlethwaite and Goodchild. '*Niobe*' *doveri* Etheridge, '*Ogygia*' *sp.*, *Caryocaris marri* Hicks and *C. wrighti* Salter.

The Great Knott Anticline crosses Ullock Pike Edge some 700 yd S.E. of Dyke Nook and trends via Great Knott [247 300] and

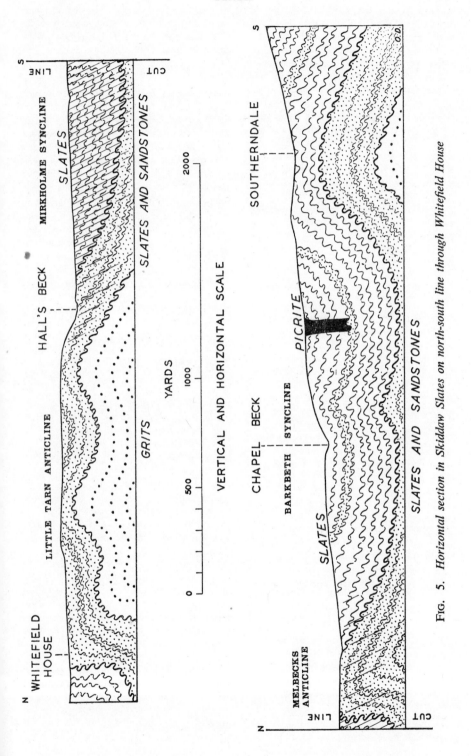

FIG. 5. *Horizontal section in Skiddaw Slates on north-south line through Whitefield House*

Buzzard Knott, respectively 1400 yd E. and 1560 yd E. 10° S. of Dyke Nook, to White Horse, 1 mile S.E. of Barkbeth. At these four localities the beds are in the Slates group, possibly near its base, and consist of isoclinally folded blue slates with striped slates that fall within the *D. nitidus* to base of *I. gibberulus* subzones. The fossils are listed below. Ullock Pike Edge: *Cryptograptus hopkinsoni* (Nicholson), *Didymograptus extensus* including a small early form, *D. extensus-nitidus* transient, *D. nitidus*, *D. nitidus-hirundo* transient, *D. suecicus*, *Tetragraptus bigsbyi* (Hall), *T. crucifer* (Hall), *T. headi*, *T. quadribrachiatus*, *T. serra*. It is possible that this assemblage includes forms from a zone below the subzone of *D. nitidus* as well as from that subzone. Buzzard Knott [250 297]: *D. extensus*, *D. nitidus*, *D. suecicus*, *D. uniformis*, *T. serra*. White Horse [255 304]: *D. extensus*, *D. uniformis*, *P. angustifolius*, *T. amii* and *T. serra*.

The Barkbeth Syncline probably contains a subsidiary anticline (see Fig. 5). The beds are isoclinally folded and normally consist of blue-black slates with occasional thin belts of striped slates. Exceptionally, igneous intrusions are margined by a belt, a few yards wide, of hardened, light grey, minutely spotted slates. These hardened slates are best seen on the margins of the Little Knott Picrite, about ½ mile S. of Barkbeth. Graptolites of the *D. hirundo* Zone have been collected [238 296] 400 to 600 yd S.E. of Dyke Nook and include *D. extensus*, *D. hirundo*, *D. suecicus*, *D. uniformis*, *Glyptograptus dentatus*, *Isograptus gibberulus*, *P. angustifolius* and *T. crucifer*. Farther north [239 299], 400 to 480 yd E. of Dyke Nook, lower beds appear to be present as indicated by the following fauna: *D. extensus*, *D. extensus-nitidus* transient, *D. nitidus*, *D. nitidus-hirundo* transient, *Glyptograptus dentatus*. *G. dentatus* and *D. nitidus* are relatively abundant on Watches of the 6-in map [240 304], 600 to 700 yd E.S.E. of High Side.

The Slates and Sandstones group, with fine-grained 3-in sandstones in striped and blue slates, is brought up by the Melbecks Anticline, and is well exposed in the stream to the west of Melbecks and ½ mile to the east of that place.

In the Mirkholme Syncline to the north, blue-black shales of the Slates group are strongly cleaved, the dip of the cleavage varying from 20° to 80° to the south-south-east. The best exposures are in Dash Beck east-north-east of Bassenthwaite Halls.

The Slates and Sandstones occupy a wide belt of country in the Little Tarn Anticline and this structure may include several minor folds. Exposures are good in Dash Beck, to the south of, and in, Park Wood. There are many small sections farther north and mention may be made of a 6-ft quartzitic sandstone interbedded with cleaved slates in a quarry [2386 3345] 1500 yd N. 37° E. of Bassenthwaite Halls.

The Slates and Sandstones are flanked to the north by the Slates group which extends to the faulted junction with the Borrowdale Volcanic rocks, but sections are too few to decide whether these slates occupy a syncline.

Skiddaw–Cockup. This area extends northwards from the southern margin of the district to the outcrop of the Borrowdale Volcanics. It is bounded to the west by the Skiddaw Fault and to the east by a north to south line through the triangulation point, 2014, ¾ mile W. of Great Calva. It lies to the north of the main Skiddaw Anticline and is crossed by a series of folds that trend to the north-east in the south, and to the east in the north. The southern part of the area falls within the metamorphic aureole of the Skiddaw Granite, and the beds of the Slates group in a syncline on Skiddaw show chiastolite and rounded spots that are probably incipient cordierite.

The Slates and Sandstones group comes up in the core of the Broad End Anticline some 250 yd south of the sheet boundary and 600 yd north of the summit of Skiddaw (Sheet 29). Beds on the south-eastern limb occupy the greater part of Gibraltar Crag [260 294] on the margins of Sheet 29, where bedding and cleavage both dip to the south-east. The coincidence favours the preservation of fossils and on these crags specimens may be obtained showing graptolites in association with chiastolite crystals. From this locality the following forms have been identified: *Didymograptus extensus*, *D. nitidus*, *D. patulus* (Hall), *Tetragraptus bigsbyi*, ?*T. headi*, *T. serra*, indicating the presence of the *D. nitidus* Subzone. On the north-western limb of the anticline at Gibraltar Crag there is isoclinal folding on a vertical dip; the cleavage, however, is to the south-south-east and tends to obscure the details of the folding. The slates are dominantly chiastolite-bearing though there are thin belts of spotted slate without chiastolite. The needles of chiastolite follow the argillaceous layers and are not affected by the cleavage planes which they commonly cross at high angles. The width of the outcrop of the Slates and Sandstones on the north-western limb of the Broad End Anticline is 800 yd as against 150 yd on the opposite limb, and possibly a thrust or a lag-fault may cut out beds on the south-eastern limb.

The axis of the Broad End Anticline trends towards Randel Crag but is separated from the latter by the Skiddaw Fault; the anticline is in Slates and Sandstones with a *D. nitidus* Subzone fauna, whilst the blue-black slates of the Slates group at Randel Crag yield an assemblage that indicates the presence of the *D. hirundo* Zone. Hereabouts the line defining the outer limit of the metamorphic aureole is not displaced by the Skiddaw Fault thus providing clear evidence that this fault was present before the metamorphism of the slates, caused by the intrusion of the Skiddaw Granite, had taken place.

Within the metamorphic aureole, the Slates and Sandstones of the Broad End Anticline may be traced to the north-east and the beds of this group are again well exposed on the eastern side of Dead Crags and in Dash Beck. At both places the cleavage is to the south-south-east and it has been sealed by the metamorphism. The cleavage is not distinct on freshly broken rock, but on weathered surfaces the slates display cleavage planes of paper thickness cutting across the bedding. Furthermore uncleaved chiastolite crystals are commonly seen cutting across the cleavage planes. The metamorphism is clearly later than the cleavage.

The Slates group occupies the Dash Syncline to the north of the Broad End Anticline, and the beds are well exposed within and beyond the metamorphic aureole on the western side of Dead Crags. Here vertical beds with undulating strike can be followed 400 ft up the crags, but on the extreme north-western corner there is much isoclinal folding. The screes have yielded

Schizograptus tardifurcatus? Elles, and an Acidaspid [suggestive of *A.* (*Selenopeltis*) *buchi* Barrande] that Sir James Stubblefield has reported to be the first record of the family from the Skiddaw Slates. To the west there is a continuous exposure of black slates in the stream (Dead Beck) where [2627 3153], 450 yd E. 15° N. of the summit of Cockup, an assemblage was collected, and identified by Dr. G. L. Elles as follows: *Didymograptus acutidens* Elles and Wood, *D. bifidus* (Hall), *?D. hirundo*, *D. nicholsoni?* Lapworth and *Glyptograptus dentatus*. Elles considered that the assemblage indicated either the top of the Zone of *D. hirundo* or the base of the Zone of *D. bifidus* and suspected the presence of both.

The Didymograptids from this locality were recently (1962) submitted for re-examination to Professor O. M. B. Bulman, who confirmed the probable presence of *D. hirundo*. The *D. acutidens* and *D. nicholsoni?* identifications he suggests might be *D. nicholsoni planus* Elles and Wood, and the *D. bifidus* of Elles could be that form or *D. protobifidus*, but identification with either is uncertain. Bulman considers that the assemblage is inconclusive; it might be referred to the *D. hirundo* Zone.

Other localities in the Dead Beck have yielded *?D. hirundo* and *Glyptograptus dentatus*.

Blue-black slates are also well exposed on the crags between Dash and the waterfalls, ¾ mile to the south-south-east. Here the dip at 70° to 80° to the south-south-east coincides with the cleavage to give rise to large smooth slabs of slate.

On the margins of the picrite, 400 yd N.E. of Dash, the blue-black slates are altered to a grey hardened rock that shows cleavage only on the weathered surface, i.e. the cleaved rock has been subsequently hardened and bleached by the intrusion.

Two veins of quartz of north-north-west trend, and numerous quartz strings traverse a crag of hardened cleaved slate 170 yd E. 15° N. of Brocklecrag. The slate was probably cleaved prior to the injection of quartz-bearing solutions that have hardened the slate.

Farther north, an outcrop of the Grits group, consisting of coarse grits with subordinate bands of sandstone and slate

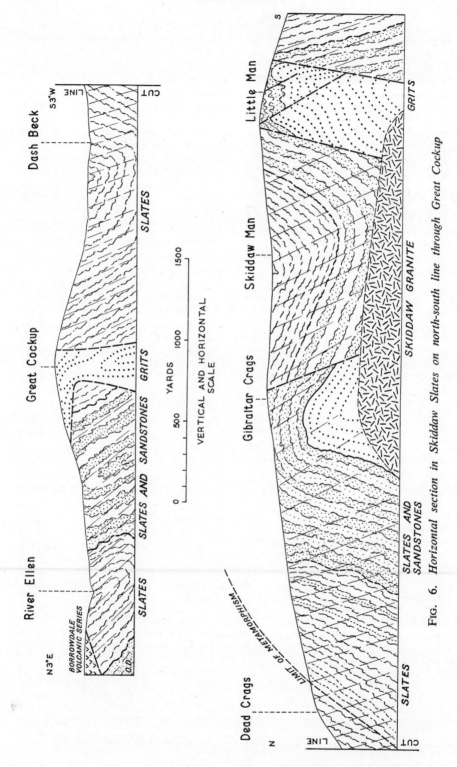

FIG. 6. *Horizontal section in Skiddaw Slates on north-south line through Great Cockup*

strikes approximately west to east from near Horsemoor Hills to Great Cockup, where it is shifted to the south by a north-south fault. Thence it extends south-eastwards on to Burn Tod. This outcrop of grit seems to be bounded by dislocations: the southern margin appears to be a steep-angled fault, but from ¼ mile E. of Horsemoor Hills *via* Little Cockup (name of hill on 6-in map, 1100 yd E. 30° S. of Orthwaite) to the stream that flows north-west towards Stockdale, the Grits group maps as a gently inclined mass resting on highly inclined slates and has been clearly thrust into that position. In this area the disposition of the grits and associated measures is interpreted as a ruptured anticline (see Fig. 6) from which the grits have been thrust outwards and northwards on to Little Cockup and on to Castle How (name of hill on 6-in map 500 yd E. of Orthwaite). The rocks in the gill (Burntod Gill of 6-in map) 1½ miles E.S.E. of Orthwaite show what are believed to be the roots of the thrust mass. In this gill the grits and associated arenaceous measures of the Grits group are vertical, and they are highly cleaved which is exceptional for rocks in this group. It was probably for this reason that a Pre-Cambrian age was suggested for the grits of this area by Rastall (1910, pp. 121–2). A section [2758 3296] at the southern end of the Grits exposure in Burntod Gill, is as follows in descending order.

	Thick-ness ft
Grit passing upwards into sandstone	10
Cleaved slate with included blocks of sheared grit up to 4 in long ..	4
Grit passing upwards into sandstone	8
Striped slates	1
Flagstones with minor bands of slate	2
Grit passing upwards into flaggy sand-stones	2½
Slate, grey blue, with minor silty bands	2
Sandstones and flags interbedded with slates, partly obscured	9
Grit, coarse and in thick posts in lower part, less coarse in top part ..	19
Not exposed: some slate debris ..	9
Grit, coarse; base conglomeratic and containing fragments of slate up to 3 in long	15

The beds are practically vertical with the lowest grit faulted against cleaved slates on the south, the fault plane being occupied by vein-quartz. The section contains five cycles of sedimentation each commencing with a grit. Since the beds are vertical the order of deposition has been determined by the grading upwards from coarse to fine in the arenaceous beds of each cycle.

Heavily cleaved slates of the Slates group lie to the north of the Grits, and these are followed upstream by Slates and Sandstones. These are brought by a north-north-westerly trending fault against slates of the Slates group which, at a locality [2792 3353] 830 yd N. 27° W. of the summit of Burn Tod, have yielded *Didymograptus nitidus*, *Tetragraptus amii* and *T. quadribrachiatus*.

The Slates and Sandstones are well exposed, at high angles in an inverted position (giving an appearance of overlying the Slates group) in the River Ellen about 1200 yd E.S.E. of Stockdale. Although the beds are undulating and in places contorted, they have on average a north-easterly strike, towards the overthrust Borrowdale Volcanic rocks. The cleavage on the other hand maintains the normal east-north-easterly trend.

Striped slates are seen to be faulted against Borrowdale Volcanic rocks in the reservoir section [2590 3551], 1 mile S.S.E. of Uldale.   F.M.T.

Around Great Sca Fell. The outcrops of massive sandstones and coarse grits on Great Sca Fell, Little Sca Fell ¼ mile to the north, and Meal Fell ¼ mile to the east have the appearance of outliers capping the hills. They are interpreted as beds of the Grits group that have been thrust from the ruptured anticline upwards and then north-wards along a low-angled plane, eventually on to the Borrowdale Volcanic Series. In the western arm of the gill (Thief Gill of 6-in map) east of Great Sca Fell, pale buff to grey, somewhat hardened sandy mud-stones pass downwards into brecciated mudstones and grits resting on intensely sheared andesite. Mapping shows the contact to be an approximately horizontal plane.

Exposures high on the western side of the valley, E. by N. of Great Sca Fell, show contorted slates and grits above Borrowdale andesites and tuffs. Plunging masses of grit and overturned minor folds are indicative of pressure from the south. The contact is partly hidden by peat and debris, but is generally traceable by a line of springs around the north-eastern flank of Great Sca Fell into the upper part of the gill (Swinburn Gill of 6-in map) north of the mountain, where both slates and andesites are intensely sheared and crushed as their contact is approached. At the head of the gill [293 348], ¾ mile N. of Great Sca Fell, stained and crushed grits and slates rest on tuffs but their relationship is complicated by an intrusion of porphyrite (p. 140). In the gill (Charleton Gill of 6-in map) south-south-west of Brae Fell summit the junction is again associated with intense crushing of slates and lavas.

Farther south, where the thrust plane lies wholly in Skiddaw Slates, evidence of movement is visible at the head of the gill (Frozen Fell Gill of 6-in map), about 250 yd S. of Great Sca Fell, where massive posts of grit have been broken into rounded and polished blocks, embedded in slate, and resembling gigantic augens. Downstream minor thrust-planes are marked by layers of crushed slate and impervious clay that are traceable more or less horizontally along crags of steeply dipping slates. The southern limit of this upthrust core of grits is the fault south of Burn Tod (p. 14).

The mudstones of Thief Gill appear to be continuous with similar rocks to the south that form the summit of Knott. These commonly carry garnets, and lie within or close to the outer part of the aureole of the Skiddaw Granite, but are quite unlike the normal rocks of that aureole. On the other hand they resemble lithologically both the altered Skiddaw Slates near the Carrock Fell mass north-west of Mosedale, and pale types allied to the Blake Fell mudstone type, that are formed by the alteration of black slates near certain minor intrusions (p. 21). It seems possible that these pale, hardened, blocky 'mudstones' have been produced by a thermal metamorphism independent of the Skiddaw aureole.

Around Great Calva. This area lies almost wholly within the aureole of the Skiddaw Granite. Apart from stream cours s, exposures are poor owing to widespread boulder clay and peat. Structurally the area consists of a broad east-west syncline between the Skiddaw Little Man Anticline to the south and the Burn Tod–Coomb Height axis to the north, with subsidiary upfolds, one of which trends eastwards through Great Calva.

Along the River Caldew south of Great Calva striped cordierite-hornfels[1] with sandstones and occasional bands of black andalusite-cordierite-hornfels strikes W. 5° S. to E. 5° N.

On the southern slope of Great Calva black cordierite-hornfelses predominate on the lower ground; there are, however, subordinate bands of andalusite-cordierite-hornfels, and silty banding is variably developed in both types. On the higher slopes andalusite-bearing hornfelses are more abundant until the summit is reached where there is a recurrence of cordierite-hornfels, here grey and somewhat hydrothermally altered. The dominance of andalusite-hornfels appears to represent a synclinal infold.

The degree of metamorphism decreases rapidly north-westwards, and unaltered blue-black slates form the lower crags of the corrie-like recess, 1 mile N.W. of Great Calva. These blue-black slates are presumed to occupy a syncline between the subsidiary anticline, pitching and dying out eastward through Great Calva, and the disrupted major anticline through Burn Tod.

On the southern slopes of Knott silty banded hornfels of the Slates and Sandstones group forms an easterly trending belt some 600 yd wide. Continuous stream exposures reveal closely packed symmetrical minor folds with vertical axial planes. To the west this belt is terminated by converging faults; eastwards it is traceable along the southern and south-eastern slopes of Coomb Height.

The upper parts of the gill draining the southern slope of Knott (Little Wiley Gill of 6-in map) show that there is widespread

---

[1] 'Andalusite-cordierite-hornfels' in this account refers to rocks with conspicuous macroscopic andalusite needles and cordierite 'spots'; 'cordierite-hornfels' to rocks without macroscopic andalusite.

hydrothermal alteration of the mildly metamorphosed slates, with the formation of soft claystone along certain bands. Magenta, buff, and deep brown colours are commonly developed and a typical 'birds-eye' appearance results from concentric zoning of the oval 'spots' of cordierite. This hydrothermal alteration is associated with quartz-veining and decreases towards the Skiddaw Granite outcrop.

Blackhazel Beck and Grainsgill Beck. The area includes the metamorphosed sediments around the Skiddaw Granite outcrops in the valleys of the Caldew and Grainsgill. Hydrothermal alteration is slight except in close proximity to the granite and also adjacent to two north–south mineralized faults lying to the east of the main granite outcrop. Where hydrothermal alteration is present, arenaceous beds are selectively affected; perhaps the best example is west of the Caldew where, close to the granite, siltstones include much fairly coarsely crystalline white mica (part of Ward's central zone of mica-schist, p. 121).

The eastward continuation of the upfold through Great Calva brings up an oval-shaped outcrop of the Slates and Sandstones group that crosses the middle reaches of Blackhazel Beck and its eastern branch, where the beds are well exposed and where a sequence is recognizable in the core of this periclinal fold. It is convenient first to describe this sequence, then to deal with the rocks to the south of the periclinal fold and finally those to the north of it. Outwards from the core of this fold, in and about Blackhazel Beck the sequence is as follows:

(6) Andalusite-cordierite-hornfels with bands in which andalusite is rare or absent; some fine silty banding

(5) Cordierite-hornfels, andalusite rare; little or no banding

(4) Andalusite-cordierite-hornfels with a little fine silty banding

(3) Cordierite-hornfels with fine silty banding, increasing downwards

(2) Cordierite-hornfels with broad silty banding approaching siltstone locally and with occasional thin sandstones

(1) Sandstone and striped silty cordierite-hornfels interbedded.

On the southern limb of the periclinal fold the dip and cleavage change from south-south-easterly to nearly due south as the southernmost headstreams of Blackhazel Beck are ascended. Minor folding with overturning to the north is generally recognizable in the sandy and striped beds. On the north side of the periclinal fold a general succession from arenaceous cordierite-hornfels to argillaceous andalusite-bearing types can also be traced on the hillside north-east of the outfall of Blackhazel Beck.

A distinct belt of andalusite-bearing hornfels, probably a synclinal infold continuous with that north-west of Great Calva, is traceable across the gill (Burdell Gill of 6-in map) draining south from Coomb Height, and is followed to the north in the Burdell Gill and Caldew valley by a variable series of hydrothermally altered cordierite-hornfelses. These range from black rocks, with cordierite up to ⅛ in across, to fine-grained bluish grey to pale greenish grey micaceous rocks with small inconspicuous spotting. The latter appear to represent a distinct lithological type of silty mudstone. Downstream along the Caldew these cordierite-hornfelses are separated from a broad east–west belt of more arenaceous, conspicuously silty banded cordierite-hornfels by a narrow outcrop of andalusite-bearing hornfels. The latter appears to correspond with (4) of Blackhazel Beck (see above), while the silty banded cordierite-hornfels represents the upper part of the arenaceous series of that sequence, reappearing on the southern flank of the Burn Tod–Coomb Height Anticline. The outcrop of this silty banded group, which includes lenticular beds of sandstone and grit on Coomb Height, is interrupted by Skiddaw Granite.

In Grainsgill the metamorphic condition differs in some cases from that of apparently similar rocks found farther south, and it seems probable that this, and their disturbed character, are related to events which took place at the time of the intrusion of the Carrock complex (p. 89).

Garnetiferous, metamorphosed grits and sandstones are developed in the upper part of Grainsgill. Westwards they are concealed beneath 'head' and peat.

Bowscale Fell to Mosedale. West of a north–south line, a quarter of a mile east of

Swineside, the rocks lie within the metamorphic aureole of the Skiddaw Granite; those on the north side of the Caldew valley east of this line have been hornfelsed by the Carrock mass to the north, while the rest are unaltered. The Slates and Sandstones group, which is traceable eastward from Coomb Height, forms most of the lower slopes of the Caldew valley and is brought up in the cores of anticlinal folds as far south as Bowscale Tarn. The overlying Slates group occupies the intervening synclines and forms the higher ground about and south of Bowscale Fell.

Tough, silty-banded, cordierite-biotite-hornfelses are well exposed along the River Caldew for several hundred yards below Grainsgill Beck. The dominant direction of the small-scale folding is north-easterly, but folds about vertical axes, and others with horizontal axial planes, are by no means rare. The river bed and numerous blocks commonly show sharply angular folds.[1] The glaciated knobs of hornfels in the vicinity of Swineside include interbedded sandstones and appear to be the lowest strata hereabouts. The crags [332 320] 900 yd W.S.W. of Swineside are in rather higher beds—principally of fairly low metamorphic grade—consisting of broad-silty-banded slates alternating with a massive grey to black spotted hornfels with subordinate silty banding such as commonly occurs near the junction of the Slates and Sandstones and Slates groups. These beds dip to the south-south-east at high angles. There is a considerable amount of minor folding with overturning to the north and, on a larger scale, inversion is clearly shown by the false-bedding. In the southern wall of the corrie-like recess [334 320], 700 yd S.W. by W. of Swineside, southerly dipping beds show a southward passage from slates to sandstones. This inverted succession, and the false-bedding, both indicate that the beds lie on the southern limb of an overturned syncline.

Again, at the northern end of the crags forming the western wall of the Bowscale Tarn corrie, there is a southerly dipping sequence of, from north to south, spotted slates with minor silty banding associated with more argillaceous chiastolite-slates, massive blue-black cordierite-hornfels, and silty banded cordierite-hornfels with sandstone bands. The latter form the northern limb of a sharp anticlinal fold somewhat overturned to the north. Massive sandstones in the core of this fold are clearly exposed in the crags [333 316] 350 yd W.N.W. of the outlet of Bowscale Tarn. The northern limb here dips south at 70°–80° and the southern limb at 20°–40° to the south-east, the fold having a pitch E. 20° S. at 30°. The cleavage in the softer beds between the sandstones dips southwards at a gentler angle than the bedding in the northern limb, and at a steeper angle than it in the southern limb, and so provides a good example of local cleavage induced by the folding of bedded rocks of differing competence.

The blue-black cordierite-hornfelses of the overturned southern limb of this fold appear to be of rather higher metamorphic grade than the softer, more argillaceous chiastolite-slates on which they now rest. This appearance may be due in part to the fact that the cordierite-hornfels was originally a more massive mudstone, but there is some possibility of a reversed fault bringing rocks of two distinct metamorphic grades into juxtaposition.

The normal upward succession of silty cordierite-hornfels followed by black andalusite-cordierite-hornfels with subordinate silty banding on the southern limb of this anticline is succeeded to the south by andalusite-hornfels, dipping at 70° to the north and forming the steep northern limb of a broad east-west anticlinal fold excellently displayed in the western crags [334 313] at Bowscale Tarn. Here some 500 ft of virtually continuous section reveal:

(4) Flaggy, black, andalusite-cordierite-hornfels.

(3) Interbedded andalusite-cordierite-hornfels and bluish grey, cordierite-hornfels.

---

[1]Such characters were interpreted by Green (1918, p. 133) as indicative of metamorphism prior to the folding. In accord with the views adopted here as to the sequence of events, it is considered that the peculiar folding is perhaps related to pressures acting at the time of the intrusion of the Carrock mass, and before the metamorphism due to the Skiddaw Granite. It is improbable that the complex folding shown could have taken place after metamorphism.

(2) Massive, bluish grey to black, cordierite-hornfels with beds of black, flaggy, andalusite-rich type.

(1) Hard, black, andalusite-cordierite-hornfels.

Silty banding is subordinate and is often absent. No sandstones are present, nor is there any indication in the core of the fold of the arenaceous silty beds which usually succeed them. This necessitates a fault, with a downthrow south, between this anticline and that to the north. Its course probably follows a 'slack', corresponding approximately with the syncline between the two anticlines, where the slates are crushed and penetrated by innumerable strings of quartz.

There is much minor rolling of the beds on the flanks and crest of the Bowscale Anticline and intense contortion of highly altered hornfels in the core near the south-western edge of the Tarn. The metamorphic grade of the latter rocks is in striking contrast to that of the soft chiastolite-slate at the top of the corrie-wall. There is also a rapid decrease in the degree of metamorphism eastwards, for in the comb (Dry Comb of 6-in map) ½ mile E. of the Tarn, folded silty-banded mudstones are low grade spotted rocks with isolated crystals and radiating clusters of chiastolite. Unmetamorphosed lower beds of more arenaceous character come in towards the Caldew.

Near Mosedale striped slates, locally approaching siltstones, are closely folded about axes approximately parallel to the line of contact with the gabbro to the north. The metamorphic effect of the latter is slight and is restricted to a belt about 200 yd wide; the inner portion of this belt forms a distinct ridge alongside the gabbro 500 yd W.N.W. of Mosedale. Welded junctions of gabbro and slate hereabouts appear to rule out a post-intrusion faulted contact.

Mungrisdale and the Glenderamackin Drainage. In this area the outcrops are wholly of the Slates group except for a small upfaulted area of Slates and Sandstones, north of Mungrisdale.

In the valleys west of Mungrisdale the outer limit of metamorphism declines eastwards at 10°–15°, probably steepening before it disappears below the surface.

Around Bowscale Fell the general direction of the strike and the cleavage swings from east-by-north to east-by-south, but the detailed structure is obscure because of the predominantly argillaceous lithology. Black, silty-banded andalusite-hornfels interbedded with massive, blue-grey, cordierite-hornfelses in the valley-head east of Bowscale Fell probably occupies a low position in the Slates group, thereby suggesting an easterly extension of the upfolded pericline (p. 41) of Blackhazel Beck.

South of Bowscale Fell the fine exposures in the crags (Bannerdale Crags of 6-in map) are of low to medium grade metamorphosed slates, in which silty banding, where present, is usually fine and subordinate. The prevailing dip of both bedding and cleavage is south-south-easterly. Where, as commonly happens, these coincide, a slate results and has been used locally for rough roofing. Folding is present, but in the absence of a reliable succession its effect is not clear.

Cordierite-hornfelses with and without prominent porphyroblasts of andalusite are present. These two main types occur as distinct belts and are intimately interbedded. Since there is some evidence that the supposed anticlinal belt of silty-banded hornfels of the Sinen Gill area persists to the northern spur of Saddleback (in Sheet 29), the Bannerdale rocks probably form a broad compound syncline.

The outer edge of the metamorphic aureole is excellently exposed in the crags on the southern side of Bannerdale (Sheet 29). There is clear evidence that the incoming of chiastolite marks a decidedly lower grade of metamorphism than the spots which represent incipient cordierite. Bedding and isometamorphic planes approximately coincide and there is an apparent upward succession: spotted chiastolite-slate; spotted slate without andalusite (= low grade cordierite-hornfels); chiastolite-slate with the spotting dying out upwards; chiastolite-slate without spotting; passing up into unaltered slate. It is estimated that the belt with only chiastolite has a thickness of 300 to 500 ft measured perpendicular to the outer edge of the aureole.

Minor variation in the unmetamorphosed Slates group permits the recognition of a south-easterly trending syncline west of the Glenderamackin in the crags ¾ mile W.S.W.

of Mungrisdale, where the following up-ward succession is present: thin bedded, shaly, black slate with a little fine silty banding; black and grey striped slates; black mudstones with a vague, rather broad, colour banding.

A broad outcrop of black mudstones on the eastern slope of Souther Fell (Sheet 29) about 1 mile S. of Mungrisdale is of par-ticular interest for it provides an assemblage *in situ* of the *Didymograptus bifidus* Zone. An exposure [3630 2930] on the roadside ¾ mile S. of Mungrisdale church yielded a collection, which has been recently (1962) re-identified by Professor O. M. B. Bulman as follows: *Didymograptus* cf. *artus* Elles and Wood, *D. bifidus, D.* cf. *climaco-graptoides* Bulman, *D. leptograptoides* Mon-sen, *D.* cf. *leptograptoides, D.* cf. *miserabilis* Bulman and *Glyptograptus* cf. *dentatus*. These identifications, although not identical with those of Dr. Elles, support her determination of the horizon as the base of the *D. bifidus* Zone.

Screes [360 289] below a small crag (Sheet 29) 1 mile S. 13° W. of Mungrisdale church, yield an assemblage identified by Dr. Elles as indicative of the subzone of *Isograptus gibberulus*. It includes *Crypto-graptus? antennarius* (Hall), *C. hopkinsoni, Didymograptus extensus, D. gracilis* Törn-quist, *?D. hirundo, D. nicholsoni, D. nichol-soni planus, D. protobifidus, Glyptograptus dentatus, Phyllograptus angustifolius, ?Tetra-graptus quadribrachiatus* and *Trigonograptus ensiformis* (Hall).

Within the upthrust inlier to the north of Mungrisdale, Raven Crag comprises several hundred feet of fine-grained quartzitic silt-stones with beds of massive sandstone of the Slates and Sandstones group. This upthrust mass of arenaceous beds may possibly mark the continuation of the Blackhazel anticlinal. In the core of the fold 250 yd N.W. of the church the beds dip to the north and to the south at 70°–80°, with indications of local overturning to the south. On the northern flank minor folding is markedly asymmetric with gentle dips to the south-west, and steep, commonly vertical, northern limbs. These minor folds usually pitch to the north-west. There are examples of graded and truncated bedding; small scale 'balling' and irregular isoclinal folding due to contemporaneous slipping are also present.

In the quarry [3633 3058] at Undercrag, N. by W. of Mungrisdale, silty-banded slates dip south at 70°–80°; they are inter-bedded with sandstones at and beyond the southern edge of the quarry. The relation of these beds to those in the hill-side above is obscure, but it is possible that the anticlinal core of sandstones has been displaced southward along an easterly-trending reversed fault. There is clear evidence in the quarry of lateral movement along minor tear-faults that displace small east to west dykes in the slates, and along small thrusts from the north that cause local overturning of the slates.

The fauna from a section [3626 3064] on the southern limb of the anticline 150 yd west of Undercrag, Mungrisdale, includes *Didymograptus deflexus* Elles and Wood, *D. extensus, D. v-fractus* Salter, and *Tetra-graptus serra*, indicative of the subzone of *D. deflexus*. A slaty band between two sandstones 50 yd farther west yielded *D. extensus, D. nitidus* and *D. uniformis;* these are considered to mark the subzone of *D. nitidus*.

In the black slates of the Slates group to the west of the upthrust anticline the cleavage is parallel to, and doubtless intimately related to, the movements along the bounding thrust-fault.

East of the Mungrisdale-Stone Ends road, exposures are rare. Black slate of the Slates group with quartz strings was proved in a shaft [3555 3339] sunk 300 yd S. of Stone Ends, and on this evidence much of the area east of Carrock Fell has now been mapped as Skiddaw Slates.   S.E.H.

REFERENCES

BULMAN, O. M. B. 1941. Some Dichograptids of the Tremadocian and Lower Ordo-vician. *Ann. Mag. nat. Hist.* (11), **7,** 100–21.

———— 1958. The sequence of graptolite faunas. *Palaeontology,* **1,** 159–73.

DIXON, E. E. L. 1925. In *Summ. Prog. Geol. Surv. Gt Br.* for 1924, 70–1.

EASTWOOD, T. 1933. In *Summ. Prog. Geol. Surv. Gt Br.* for 1932, Pt. I, 59.

————, DIXON, E. E. L., HOLLINGWORTH, S. E. and SMITH, B. 1931. The geology of the Whitehaven and Workington district. *Mem. Geol. Surv. Gt Br.*

ELLES, Gertrude L. 1898. The graptolite-fauna of the Skiddaw Slates. *Quart. Jl. geol. Soc. Lond.*, **54**, 463–539.

———— 1904. Graptolite zones in the Arenig rocks of Wales. *Geol. Mag.*, **41**, 199–211.

———— 1922. The graptolite faunas of the British Isles. *Proc. Geol. Ass.*, **33**, 168–200.

———— 1925. The characteristic assemblages of the graptolite zones of the British Isles. *Geol. Mag.*, **62**, 337–47.

———— 1933. The Lower Ordovician graptolite faunas with special reference to the Skiddaw Slates. *Summ. Prog. Geol. Surv. Gt Br.* for 1932, Pt. II, 94–111.

———— and WOOD, Ethel M. R. 1901–18. A monograph of British graptolites. *Palaeontog. Soc.* [*Mongr.*].

GREEN, J. F. N. 1917. The age of the chief intrusions of the Lake District. *Proc. Geol. Ass.*, **28**, 1–30.

———— 1918. The Skiddaw Granite: a structural study. *Proc. Geol. Ass.*, **29**, 126–36.

———— 1925. In *Summ. Prog. Geol. Surv. Gt Br.* for 1924, 71.

GUPPY, Eileen M. (Compiler) 1956. Chemical analyses of igneous rocks, metamorphic rocks and minerals, 1931–54. *Mem. Geol. Surv. Gt Br.*

HARTLEY, J. J. 1925. The succession and structure of the Borrowdale Volcanic Series as developed in the area lying between the Lakes of Grasmere, Windermere and Coniston. *Proc. Geol. Ass.*, **36**, 203–26.

HOLLINGWORTH, S. E. 1954. The geology of the Lake District—a review. *Proc. Geol. Ass.*, **65**, 385–402.

JACKSON, D. E. 1961. Stratigraphy of the Skiddaw Group between Buttermere and Mungrisdale, Cumberland. *Geol. Mag.*, **98**, 515–28.

———— 1962. Graptolite zones in the Skiddaw Group in Cumberland, England. *J. Palaeont.*, **36**, 300–13.

———— 1964. Observations on the sequence and correlation of Lower and Middle Ordovician graptolite faunas of North America. *Bull. geol. Soc. Am.*, **75**, 523–34.

LAPWORTH, C. 1879–80. On the geological distribution of the Rhabdophora. *Ann. Mag. nat. Hist.* (5), 3, 245–57; 4, 333–41; 5, 273–85; 6, 16–29, 185–207.

MARR, J. E. 1894. Notes on the Skiddaw Slates. *Geol. Mag.*, **31**, 122–30.

———— 1905. Anniversary address of the President. *Proc. geol. Soc. Lond.*, Session 1904–5, lxi–lxxxvi.

MONSEN, A. 1937. Die Graptolithenfauna im unteren *Didymograptus*-Schiefer Norwegens. *Norsk geol. Tidsskr.* 16, 57–226.

RASTALL, R. H. 1910. The Skiddaw Granite and its metamorphism. *Quart. Jl. geol. Soc. Lond.*, **66**, 116–41.

ROSE, W. C. C. 1954. The sequence and structure of the Skiddaw Slates in the Keswick–Buttermere area. *Proc. Geol. Ass.*, **65**, 403–6.

SIMPSON, A. 1967. The stratigraphy and tectonics of the Skiddaw Slates and the relationship of the overlying Borrowdale Volcanic Series in part of the Lake District. *Geol. J.*, **5**, 391–418.

SKEVINGTON, D. 1963. A correlation of Ordovician graptolite-bearing sequences. *Geol. För. Stockh. Förh.*, **85**, 298–319.

———— 1964. A new occurrence of the *Didymograptus bifidus* Zone in the Skiddaw Group. *Nature*, Lond., **202**, 585.

TJERNVIK, T. 1958. The Tremadocian Beds at Flagabro in south-eastern Scania (Sweden). *Geol. För. Stockh. Förh.*, **80**, 259–76.

WARD, J. C. 1876. The geology of the northern part of the English Lake District. *Mem. Geol. Surv. Gt Br.*

Chapter IV

ORDOVICIAN:
THE BORROWDALE VOLCANIC SERIES

GENERAL ACCOUNT

THE END OF THE DEPOSITION of the Skiddaw Slates was marked by the incoming of volcanic deposits over the old sea floor. In the area here described the earliest volcanic outbursts were submarine in character. Sedimentary fragments and ash were blown into the air, fell into the sea and were interstratified with deposits of mud; lava flowed over the sea bottom and was overlain by muds. This submarine phase did not last long, for the volcanic action was accompanied by gradual elevation of the sea floor, the sea became shallower, and finally the floor emerged as land. It would appear that the main mass of lavas and tuffs constituting some 8000 ft of rock accumulated sub-aerially. Nevertheless these volcanic rocks show many examples of stratification; flow-banded lavas, with up to 30 bands per inch, persist for miles; and interbedded tuffs and ashes show signs of internal stratification. Well-bedded volcanic ash of recent date, laid down sub-aerially, can be seen in the neighbourhood of Naples, so that stratification in volcanic ash is not diagnostic of deposition in water. It is the total absence of sedimentary deposits through a sequence of volcanic rocks 1½ miles thick which favours the suggestion that they were deposited sub-aerially.

The volcanic rocks herein described occur on the northern limb of the Skiddaw Anticline and with the exception of a brief description of the sequence on Eycott Hill (Ward 1877) no description of the Borrowdale Volcanic Series of the district has been published.

The series consists of a large number of lava flows with subordinate bands of ash, tuff and agglomerate. The recognition of individual lavas in the sequence has not been without difficulty. Ward·(1877) regarded most of the rocks of the Borrowdale Volcanic Series now known to be auto-brecciated lavas as altered ashes. Green's (1917) contribution to the interpretation of the Borrowdale volcanics was important in that he clearly recognized the character of individual lava flows, pointing out that fragments from the underlying flow or flows may be caught up in the base of a lava, that the main part of lava is normally massive, and that its top may be heavily brecciated and scoriaceous.

Among the lavas of this district dark bluish green to dark grey andesites predominate; but the succession includes rocks ranging in composition from rhyolite to olivine-basalt. Differences in the degree of crystallinity, and in the nature, size, and abundance of the phenocrysts give rise to a great variety of rock types, and the individual flows normally exhibit massive fluidal-banded rocks in the centre, with flow-brecciated and/or vesicular scoriaceous rocks on the upper and lower margins. The lavas possess well-developed systems of joints of both local and regional character, but cleavage is absent except in the Greystoke Park area on the eastern margin of the district.

In this account the diagnostic character of a tuff or ash is considered to be the presence of contained rock fragments or debris of explosive origin. Fine-grained well-bedded flinty ash is readily recognizable as of explosive origin, as at the other extreme are coarse tuffs and agglomerates containing several varieties of fragmental rocks. Intermediately the determining factor in the rocks is the presence of exotic fragments, since these cannot be regarded as having been picked up during flowage over underlying lavas or formed by auto-brecciation; the exotic fragments must be the result of explosive vulcanicity. All of the tuffs, except the basal one, contain much fragmental andesitic material. The two lowest mappable tuffs contain fragmentary sedimentary rocks including varieties of Skiddaw Slate and Latterbarrow Sandstone, and although the upper of these develops a glassy matrix towards the west the presence of the exotic fragments of sandstone and slate distinguish these rocks as tuffs. The next four tuffs in the sequence are designated as such because they all contain (with andesite fragments) fragments of rhyolite. Subordinate in thickness to the andesites and basic andesites with which they are inter-bedded and underlain, they nevertheless persist for several miles in a sequence that is completely devoid of rhyolitic lavas; the rhyolite fragments in these four tuffs are thus clearly exotic and of explosive origin.

The beds appear from beneath the Carboniferous in the neighbourhood of Bothel, and occupy a belt of country one to $1\frac{1}{2}$ miles wide, trending eastwards by Binsey and High Pike to beyond Linewath, where they disappear beneath the Carboniferous. The series reappears in two detached areas in the south-east. That at Greystoke Park, 2 miles north of Berrier and partly within the Penrith (24) Sheet, represents an eastward continuation of the northern out-crop; and an inlier centred about Eycott Hill, which falls partly within the Keswick (29) Sheet, forms a link between the northern outcrop and the Ulls-water portion of the main outcrop of the central Lake District. Lavas south-west of Bothel that were previously regarded as belonging to this formation, have been shown to be of Carboniferous age (Eastwood 1928, p. 22).[1]

Where the outcrop of the Borrowdale Volcanic Series has suffered marked erosion during Glacial times (as for example in the detached hills of Binsey and Eycott) exposures are good, and it has been possible to map the bands of tuff and individual lava flows. Here regular craggy features are developed. The massive central parts of the lava-flows offer considerable resistance to erosion and weathering, in contrast to the softer rubbly and vesicular upper parts which decompose and are easily eroded. In other areas detailed mapping of individual lava flows is not possible, either because of a covering of drift, as for example east of Bothel, or, as in much of the high ground between Longlands Fell and West Fell, because glacial action has not completely removed the skin of weathered debris that is possibly of pre-glacial origin. Here smooth feature-less outlines are typical. Furthermore, this region is much broken by faults,

---

[1]From the parallelism of the outcrop of these supposed Borrowdale rocks to that of the over-lapping Carboniferous Limestone, it was formerly inferred (Green 1917) that the Volcanic Series and the underlying Skiddaw Slates had a low sheet-dip hereabouts—a conclusion that no longer can be sustained.

many of which are mineralized or associated with belts of hydrothermal decomposition, often of considerable width. In general this area lies just beyond the outer edge of the metamorphic aureole of the Skiddaw Granite (p. 119), but it seems possible that the rocks have suffered widespread alteration by juvenile solutions that have rendered them less resistant to weathering, and less likely to produce a craggy topography (compare for example the absence of 'trap-featuring' within the limits of pneumatolysis in Mull described by Bailey and others, 1924).

The main portion of the northern outcrop shows no minor folding; the dip is northerly and at high angles, except where it becomes locally vertical or reversed. Some transverse and oblique faults are present, but these do not affect the general upward succession northwards. In the south-east, however, where the dip is north-east to east-north-east, part of the sequence on Eycott Hill appears to be repeated in the Greystoke Park inlier, (p. 50). The post-Carboniferous faulting responsible for the latter inlier does not seem adequate to account for the repetition of the Borrowdale sequence.

VOLCANIC SEQUENCE

The greatest thickness of beds is found in the area south of High Ireby where it is estimated that 8000 feet of strata—the greatest known thickness of the Borrowdale Volcanic Series—are present. It is in this part of the northern outcrop that the details of the succession are most fully apparent, and here also the relation of the volcanic rocks to the underlying Skiddaw Slates is most clearly displayed. For these reasons the ground south of High Ireby has been chosen as the type area for the whole of the northern outcrop.

Among the many lava types present the rock with a fine-grained matrix containing porphyritic feldspars up to one inch in length so well known from Eycott Hill, and referred to here as the 'Eycott type', is of outstanding value for mapping and correlation purposes, since a belt of such lavas is traceable at two distinct horizons. The Borrowdale Volcanic Series is divided into a lower (Binsey) and an upper (High Ireby) group, the Eycott type of lavas occupying a basal position in each group. There is a third occurrence of the Eycott type of lava high in the High Ireby Group, but it cannot be widely traced at this horizon.

In the western part of the outcrop in the neighbourhood of Binsey the sequence is as follows:-

	Approximate thickness in ft
High Ireby Group	
Lavas, mainly fine-grained andesites but including the Upper	
Eycott Lava west of High Ireby	3500
Middle Eycott Lavas	700
Binsey Group	
Lavas, mainly pyroxene-andesites	1600
Andesites and tuffs	2000
Lower Eycott Lavas, with interbedded slates and tuffs	300

Binsey Group. There is a much greater development of this Group in the Binsey–Over Water area than farther east. In this, the type area, the lowest strata are lavas of Eycott type interbedded with slates and mudstones carrying thin tuffaceous layers, and they appear to constitute passage beds from the Skiddaw Slates up into the Volcanic Series. These passage beds may be seen in the reservoir section north of Over Water and in old quarries ½ mile west-north-west of Whitefield House. In the first-mentioned locality they are faulted against Skiddaw Slates. The interbedded Lower Eycott Lavas comprise three flows characterized by pale green feldspar phenocrysts up to ¾ inch in length. The interbedded slaty mudstones and slates are of variable thickness and they contain gritty tuffaceous bands. On Binsey the upper of these two sedimentary bands is represented by a fine well-bedded ash. The Lower Eycott Lavas and associated sediments are cut out by faulting to the east and west of the Binsey–Over Water area and are not seen again. They probably die out in an easterly direction.

The overlying beds consist of lavas and tuffs. The lavas are blue-black aphanitic or sparingly porphyritic, fluidal-banded basic andesites (or basalts), interbedded with greenish, freely vesicular, porphyritic types with feldspar phenocrysts up to an ⅛ inch in length. The intercalated pyroclastic rocks vary from fine to coarse andesitic tuffs with many scattered fragments of rhyolitic material. That which lies immediately above the Lower Eycott Lavas is note-worthy in that it also contains 'pebbles' of slate and sandstone which can be matched in the Skiddaw Slates and Latterbarrow Sandstone respectively. Rocks of Latterbarrow Sandstone type, however, are not known in the Skiddaw Slates succession in this area. These 'pebbles' are up to an inch or so in length in the Over Water area. Eastwards, however, they increase in size and in number until south of Longlands Fell elongated fragments attain lengths up to one foot.

The third tuff above the Lower Eycott Lavas (the second rhyolite-bearing tuff) is exceptionally coarse, with 'boulders' of flow-banded basic andesite, pyroxene-andesite and of rhyolite, up to 3 ft in length, being in this respect in striking contrast to the other tuffs in which the fragments of andesite and rhyolite seldom exceed an inch in length. This tuff becomes markedly less coarse towards the east.

Tuffs associated with the andesitic lavas near the head of Dale Beck probably correspond with the andesites and tuffs above the Lower Eycott Lavas of the Binsey area.

The thick series of lavas above the highest tuff is not sufficiently well exposed to permit the mapping of individual flows in the Binsey area, or in the regions to the east and west of it. It comprises a varied suite of andesitic lavas in which flows with small phenocrysts of feldspar and pyroxene are common.

The lowest rock in the Eycott Hill area is a red and green mottled tuff that probably corresponds to a horizon in the upper part of the type area of Binsey. The tuff appears to thicken south-eastward becoming quite coarse west of Greenahcrag (Sheet 29) where it includes rhyolitic material. It is overlain by an indivisible mass of bluish andesite some 300 ft thick.

To sum up: vulcanicity both effusive and explosive commenced earlier in the west around Binsey than in the east at and near Eycott Hill.

High Ireby Group. The Middle Eycott Lavas at the base of the High Ireby Group comprise several flows in the Binsey area. Here, and as far east as the stream valleys west of High Pike, they are interbedded with fine-grained, rather pink-tinted acid andesites. In the Caldew section about Linewath, however, these lavas of Eycott type attain a thickness of 1000 ft and include at least five flows. In this area a massive andesite with conspicuous phenocrysts of pyroxene but without large feldspars comes in above the lowest flow. South-eastwards these lavas attenuate fairly rapidly, and on Eycott Hill two flows only can be recognized, with a total thickness of 200 ft.

On the northern slopes of Binsey the lavas above the Middle Eycott Lavas are some 3000 ft thick, but cannot be mapped individually. They consist of porphyritic pyroxene-andesites interbedded with dark blue fine-grained flinty basic andesites with occasional flows of more acid types of keratophyric and dacitic affinities and at least one flow of Eycott type, representing the Upper Eycott horizon.

Farther east, from Longlands Fell to the River Caldew, the lavas consist, through a thickness of 1000 to 2000 ft, of fine-grained, bluish black flow-banded andesites.

Individual flows have been mapped in the admirably exposed ground about Eycott Hill. Here the fine-grained flow-banded type alternates with variably porphyritic pyroxene-andesites through a thickness of 1000 ft or more. There are occasional thin bands of interstratified tuff, and two thin acid flows. Southwards the proportion of the porphyritic type increases, and the flow-banded lavas appear to decrease in thickness.

In the Greystoke Park inlier the exposed succession resembles and probably corresponds with that above the Middle Eycott Lavas; but there are con-siderable variations from the sequence seen in the Caldew section and that on Eycott Hill. A useful horizon is provided by a 300-ft thick rhyolitic lava that appears in the middle of a thick series of porphyritic pyroxene-andesites, and seems to correspond with a thin flow stratigraphically some 800 ft above the Middle Eycott Lavas on Eycott Hill. A band of coarse tuff 100 to 150 ft thick, not far above the rhyolite, also correlates with a tuff mapped at the northern end of Eycott Hill. Above the pyroxene-andesites is a series of flow-banded lavas, approaching 1000 ft in thickness, identical with those above the Middle Eycott Lavas along the Caldew, on the main outcrop.

SOURCES OF VULCANICITY

In the present area, no vents either linear or central have been detected, nor are there any intrusions that can be definitely assigned to the Borrowdale Volcanic epoch. Outside the area Ward (1877) regarded the igneous rock of Castle Head, Keswick, as a volcanic plug from which lavas may have flowed as far as Eycott Hill to the north-east and the outcrops around Binsey to the north-west. This suggested source seems an unlikely one for the rocks of the Binsey Group and for the overlying Middle Eycott Lavas, for during their extrusion the main eruptive centres appear to have lain to the north or north-west, in areas now overlain by Carboniferous rocks. In later Borrowdale Volcanic times, however, there appear to have been several centres of eruption.

The Binsey Group and overlying Middle Eycott Lavas are best developed eastwards from Binsey towards the Caldbeck Fells. Farther east the sequence is attenuated and to the south-east on Eycott Hill the greater part of the Binsey Group is absent. This marked easterly to south-easterly attenuation of the

Group as a whole points to a westerly or north-westerly source of origin. In the details of the sequence there is corroborative evidence.

The presence of sedimentary 'pebbles' in the two lowest tuffs, although evidence of a local source of origin, at first glance appears to indicate an easterly source as the sedimentary 'pebbles' are coarser in that direction. Many of the 'pebbles' are undoubtedly rolled, and as these two lowest tuffs are associated with the deposition of mudstones their formation in water is highly probable. The coarsening of the 'pebbles' towards the east may be an indication of a shore-line in that direction rather than a source of eruptive vulcanicity. A westerly source for the volcanic material in the upper of the two tuffs is suggested by the development of the glassy character of the matrix in that direction.

The source of the rhyolite fragments in all of the four succeeding tuffs is to be sought in the north-west, since the rhyolites are not found at the outcrop and no acid plugs are to be found in the Skiddaw Slates to the south. The second member of these four rhyolite-bearing tuffs is exceptionally coarse on Binsey (with rhyolite fragments up to the size of a man's head) but it becomes markedly less coarse to the east—further evidence of a westerly or north-westerly direction of origin.

The Eycott type of lavas in the Binsey area cannot be far from their source since they occur here at three widely separated horizons, whereas elsewhere on the northern crop they only occur at one. This type of lava is found only on the north crop of the Borrowdales. The persistent Middle Eycott lavas become attenuated and decrease in number in a southerly direction from five flows in the River Caldew section near Linewath to two flows on Eycott Hill.

After the effusion of the Middle Eycott Lavas there appear to have been more than one centre of vulcanicity. The centre to the north or north-west of Binsey continued to operate and gave rise to the thick series in that area. In the east the pyroxene-andesites of Eycott Hill and Greystoke Park appear to have a southerly or easterly origin, for they are only feebly developed in the Caldew sequence. Again in the east, variation in the fluidal-banded andesites of the High Ireby Group suggests a northern or north-eastern origin; and the rhyolites found only in the Greystoke Park Inlier presumably originated in the east or north-east.

CORRELATION

The sequence of Borrowdale Volcanic rocks described above is that which is found along the northern outcrop and in the detached outcrop at Eycott Hill. Across the Skiddaw Anticline, on the southern outcrop in the central Lake District, the Borrowdales cover a larger area and the question of correlating the sequences of the opposing outcrops naturally arises.

After the primary survey, Ward (1877) made no attempt to establish a detailed sequence; indeed in his view this was not practical since he considered that most of the lavas were altered ashes. Marr and Harker (Marr 1916) propounded a sequence for the volcanic rocks of the Lake District. It is necessary here to consider only the basal Falcon Crag Group and the overlying Ullswater and Eycott Hill Group. Eycott Hill was made the type area of the last-mentioned group and the whole of the northern outcrop of the volcanic rocks (including Cockermouth Lavas now known to be of Carboniferous age) was placed within it. However it has been shown that the greater part of the Binsey Group is absent at Eycott Hill. Where the Binsey Group is fully developed, as on Binsey, it probably broadly equates with the Falcon Crag Group described by Marr and Harker.

A sequence for the Borrowdale Volcanic Group was advanced by Green (1917, p. 168), but he did not apply it to the northern outcrop where, indeed, his subdivisions are inapplicable. Local sequences have been advanced for areas of the southern outcrop, notably by Hartley (1925) and Mitchell (1929, 1934, 1940 and 1956), which are basically similar to that defined by Green; these also are inapplicable to the northern crop. Recently Moseley (1960) has described a local sequence in the Ullswater area that lies in the north-eastern part of the southern outcrop and relatively near to the Eycott Hill outcrop. This sequence, whilst it can be correlated with other sequences of the southern outcrop, does not afford a correlation link with the northern outcrop.

Hadfield and Whiteside (1936) ascribed a sequence found on High Rigg, about 7 miles south-west of Eycott Hill, to Marr and Harker's Falcon Crag Group. If this be correct then these High Rigg volcanic rocks equate in general with the rocks of the Binsey Group. It remains true, however, that correlation of the rocks of the south and north outcrops across the Skiddaw Anticline is highly problematical and this is not surprising. Difficulties in correlation arise because of the frequent recurrence of individual petrological types in the succession, because of the great lateral changes in the sequence of lavas which may occur within short distances, and because of different sources of vulcanicity both effusive and explosive. For the rocks of the northern outcrop the main source of origin appears to have been from the north-west, north and north-east, and lavas from these sources, as for example the Eycott type, do not appear to have reached the southern outcrop.   F.M.T., S.E.H.

PETROGRAPHIC CLASSIFICATION

The classification of the lavas is set out below. This summary is followed in turn by a description of each of the major classes of lavas, and finally by a description of the tuffs.   K.C.D.

Rock Name	Phenocrysts or Porphyritic Crystals	Groundmass
Olivine-basalts	Olivine, augite, labradorite (hypersthene)	Labradorite, augite, chlorite, alkali-feldspar, iron-ore, glass, quartz.
Basalts without olivine	—	Labradorite, pyroxene, chlorite, alkali-feldspar, iron-ore, quartz.
Basic andesites	Labradorite,[1] augite, (hypersthene)	Labradorite, augite, iron-ore, glass, alkali-feldspar, quartz.

[1]The labradorite here may be macroporphyritic (Eycott type). The other porphyritic rocks are all microporphyritic (phenocrysts less than 2 mm long). Quantitatively, the predominant types in the series are the basic and acid andesites.

Rock Name	Phenocrysts or Porphyritic Crystals	Groundmass
Acid andesites	Oligoclase or andesine	Oligoclase, chlorite, iron-ore, glass, (quartz).
— Dacitic type	„	„ with essential quartz
— Keratophyric type	„	„ with essential microfelsite or cryptofelsite.
Soda-rhyolites	Oligoclase or albite, (quartz)	Microfelsite
Rhyolites	—	Microfelsite or cryptofelsite.

OLIVINE-BASALTS

Three specimens of lava from High Ireby and two from Linewath prove to be olivine-basalts. In hand specimen they are very dark grey fine-grained rocks, similar to the fine-grained basaltic andesites, and are seen to contain small black phenocrysts of pyroxene. Under the microscope the rocks show also microporphyritic feldspar, olivine and, in the case of the Linewath specimens, pseudomorphs after hypersthene. The porphyritic plagioclase forms automorphic prisms up to 1·5 mm long and is of labradorite composition with about An_{60}. It is marginally zoned to basic andesine and commonly replaced by white mica. Augite, a colourless aluminous variety, occurs in the Linewath specimens as clots of fresh individuals, up to 0·5 mm in length, but is less abundant and replaced by carbonate in the High Ireby rocks. The olivine is recognized by its shape and by the nature of its pseudomorphs which are usually aggregates consisting of quartz or chalcedony, chlorite, iron ore or carbonate. The cracks of the original crystal may be outlined by hematite. The more common replacement by serpentine is found however in specimen E 14581. These pseudomorphs are numerous in the High Ireby specimens, but less so in the Linewath rocks which, as noted above, also carry a few small chlorite pseudomorphs of orthorhombic pyroxene.

The groundmass of the olivine-basalts is composed of labradorite laths, numerous small prisms or prismatic grains of colourless augite, scattered octahedra of iron-ore and cementing material. The latter is intersertal to the plagioclase laths and includes chlorite, alkali-feldspar, devitrified glass and quartz. Though quartz occurs as a secondary mineral in the olivine pseudomorphs, it appears to be primary in the base. Except in High Ireby specimen E 15865, the minerals of the base are very much altered.

The olivine-basalts are represented in the Geological Survey Collection by specimens E 14581, E 15014, E 15015, E 15865, E 15867.

BASALTS WITHOUT OLIVINE

From the south side of Binsey comes a non-porphyritic basalt of very fine grain which is composed of labradorite laths, numerous faintly yellow pyroxene prisms, both turbid and clear, scattered octahedral iron-ore grains and interstitial material which includes chlorite, alkali feldspar and some quartz. The pyroxene prisms are about 0·05 mm long and seem to include two types, a clear aluminous augite and a less abundant clinoenstatite which is subject to fibrous alteration. This rock (E 15847) is fresh and has a striking resemblance to the olivine-free non-porphyritic basalts of the Thulean Tertiary province. About one and a half miles north-west of Binsey a similar but decomposed basalt (E 15862) crops out, and a number of specimens from the same neighbourhood are comparable but are albitized and contain a considerable proportion of acid mesostasis (E 15681, 15863, 15866, 15868).

BASIC ANDESITES

The lavas of the region are in the main basaltic andesites which show considerable mineralogical and textural variation. They include porphyritic and non-porphyritic types; in the former, plagioclase is a constant porphyritic mineral and orthorhombic pyroxene is generally present as phenocrysts. Porphyritic monoclinic pyroxene however shows no regular distribution. The groundmass of the rocks ranges from hyaline to holocrystalline and may be essentially feldspathic or may contain abundant microcrystalline augite; that is, the groundmass may be of definitely andesitic or definitely basaltic character. For descriptive purposes this large group has been separated into the following three divisions:-

(1) Rocks with large porphyritic feldspars—Eycott type.

(2) Rocks with numerous small seriately porphyritic feldspars—Berrier type.

(3) Non-porphyritic type.

Transitional varieties occur, but on the whole this method of grouping works well.

Eycott type: This division includes the well-known porphyritic lava from Eycott Hill which was described in detail by Teall (1888, p. 225) under the name labradorite-pyroxene-porphyrite. The labradorite phenocrysts form stout idiomorphic prisms with rounded corners up to 3 cm in length. In some specimens they are zoned, in others apparently homogeneous. The average composition is An_{65}, and such zoning and twinning as occur do not lower the anorthite content by more than 10 per cent. Tests of composition by the maximum extinction in the zone normal to (010) indicate, according to curves published by Berek, a difference in composition of adjacent parts of twins amounting to 8-10 per cent An.

Hypersthene altered to chlorite (see below), also forms stout idiomorphic prisms which rarely occur as individuals 3 to 4 mm in length, but usually form aggregates about 2 mm across. Monoclinic augite is usually fresh and may be grown around decomposed hypersthene (E 15787); it is always subordinate to orthorhombic pyroxene and in many slides is absent.

The groundmass of the rock varies. It may be composed of deep brown devitrified glass in which are embedded stout laths of labradorite (about An_{60}) with skeletal terminations, granular and skeletal augite and grains of iron-ore. Narrow prisms of chlorite, pseudomorphous after hypersthene, may be present. The glass is commonly replaced in ramifying patches by chlorite, and may also be altered to carbonate. Small vesicles filled with chlorite, calcite or various forms of silica are usually present. In the type with very large porphyritic feldspars, the groundmass has typical hyalo-ophitic texture. It may however be represented by a cryptocrystalline mixture of feldspathic and irony material, and may be microcrystalline in the lavas with numerous porphyritic feldspars of small size. The freshness of some of the lavas is, in view of their great age, remarkable, but in others alteration is widespread, the main effects being sericitization of the plagioclase phenocrysts, replacement of augite by calcite, and of the groundmass by calcite and chlorite. The alteration of the ortho-rhombic ferromagnesian mineral is always to chlorite but the textural variation of the latter is worth description (see also Bonney, 1885, and Harker, 1891, p. 517). The hypersthene crystal may be replaced by a single crystal of chlorite which preserves the idiomorphic outline of the pyroxene (E 15794). The pleo-chroism of the chlorite is X = faint pink, Z = clear pale green, and the section looks like one of fresh hypersthene. The chlorite is recognized by its refractive index, $\gamma = 1\cdot61$, and its low and slightly patchy birefringence. It is uniaxial negative with a birefringence of 0·007, and is, thus, an iron-rich magnesian chlorite. In other slides the chlorite has the fibrous structure of bastite. Generally, however, there has been alteration along cracks as well as the bastite type of change parallel to the prism axis. The resulting mesh structure resembles that of serpentinized olivine but usually the pyroxenic outline is sufficient to distinguish the original character of the mineral. In one slide (E 15785) a pseudomorph in chlorite and calcite has a definite olivine-like outline, though other phenocrysts which have undergone precisely the same type of alteration have equally definite pyroxene shape.

Typical sections of the Eycott type of andesite in the Survey Collection are E 15016, E 15794, E 15860, E 16233 and more altered examples E 14608, E 15017–8, E 15793, E 16203. Sections of lavas with smaller feldspar pheno-crysts are E 14544, E 15293, E 15774, E 15785–87, E 15843, E 16208. These generally show more augite, both as microphenocrysts and as microlitic grains, than the Eycott type.

Berrier type: Phenocrysts of feldspar and pyroxene are numerous. They rarely exceed 1·5 mm in length and range downwards to groundmass size in the same rock. The group is therefore essentially microporphyritic. The feldspar has been determined as basic labradorite (about An_{65}) in the fresher specimens, but it is usually albitized or sericitized. Hypersthene is always present as stout idiomorphic prisms which are commonly collected into groups measuring up to 2 mm across. It is pseudomorphed by chlorite and has been seen partly fresh in only one specimen (E 15857). Augite, pale brown or yellowish in colour, occurs as stout, rounded, cracked prisms which show lamellar twinning but it is not always present. Glomeroporphyritic augite in a basaltic specimen measures 3 mm across (E 15797).

The groundmass of the rocks is sometimes composed of glass containing microlithic prisms of acid labradorite and augite. The texture is then hyalo-ophitic, but in some specimens the proportion of base relative to phenocrysts is so reduced that the texture is almost intersertal (E 15841–2). Devitrification of the glass to cryptocrystalline or microcrystalline feldspathic aggregate is common, and the glass is locally replaced by chlorite. The groundmass may also be microcrystalline and with increase in the proportion of augite shows an approach to the intergranular texture of basalts. Ophitic relations between plagioclase and augite are very rare (E 15777). In these more crystalline varieties interstitial alkali-feldspar is always present and usually some quartz can be identified (E 15797). Fluidal structure is rare (E 15771–2, E 15780).

Typical sections of these lavas are: E 14555, E 14557, E 14559, E 14567, E 15019, E 15841–2, E 15859; specimens containing augite are E 14023,

E 14551, E 14606, E 15836, E 15857–8. Basaltic varieties include the following: E 14023, E 14551, E 14576, E 15775–6, E 15780, E 15783–4, E 15798, E 15832, E 15844, and certain specimens must be grouped as hypersthene-quartz-basalts (E 15777–8, E 15797). Transition to the Eycott type is shown by specimens E 14577–8, E 15774.

Non-porphyritic and sparsely microporphyritic andesite type: This group corresponds in appearance to the groundmass of the Eycott type of lava. Typically the rocks are dark grey in colour, of very compact texture and assume a more flinty appearance as the proportion of unaltered glass increases. Decomposition leads to a variety of tints which may be summarized as follows. When the pyroxene has altered to chlorite but the condition is otherwise normal the rock has a green tint. Glassy rocks in which the glass has oxidized are purple. When the ferromagnesian material is replaced by disseminated calcite and chlorite the colour is pale green, when by chlorite and leucoxenic material the colour is dark grey-green. Silicified rocks are granular in appearance and yellow-green or red in colour according to whether chloritic or ferruginous material permeate the rock.

The scarce phenocrysts, forming less than one per cent of this rock, are albitized plagioclase, originally basic andesine or labradorite. Small colourless augite (E 14604, E 14623) and chloritized hypersthene (E 14614, E 15782) are very scarce. The base consists of laths of plagioclase, often albitized or sericitized, and prismatic grains of pyroxene in a mesostasis which may be partly glassy, cryptocrystalline or holocrystalline. Feldspar, iron-titanium oxide granules, chlorite and quartz are in the latter event its constituents. While quartz has commonly been introduced after consolidation, it is in places definitely primary. There is moderate variation in the proportion of pyroxene and opaques to the feldspar. Fluidal texture is rare. The analysed rock (E 16234) is typical of these sparsely porphyritic lavas. Scarce small phenocrysts of andesine or labradorite, partly albitized and replaced by chlorite and sporadic augite crystals are present. The rock consists essentially of basic andesine laths, up to 0·1 mm long, and pyroxene prisms, up to 0·05 mm across, cemented by anhedral feldspar which appears to be oligoclase. The pyroxene is a colourless pigeonite with highly inclined extinction and low optic axial angle. There are also many prismatic grains altered to a fine fibrous aggregate of brown material with slightly varying absorption and high aggregate birefringence. The form suggests that these were originally pyroxene. Grains of iron-ore and needles of apatite are numerous, and interstitial quartz is not rare. An approximate quantitative mineral composition is given in Table II, but in such a fine-grained rock estimation is difficult.

Included with this group are two non-porphyritic lavas (E 14545, E14553) which are interbedded with lavas of Eycott type about half a mile south of Normans. These are composed of a plexus of albitized plagioclase laths and green slender prisms diversely arranged in a base of anhedral and ill-defined quartz, feldspar, and chlorite. Slender prisms of apatite, mostly about 0·2 mm long but some reaching fully 0·5 mm, are common. Iron-ore is comparatively scarce. The green prisms are about 0·1 to 0·2 mm long and are composed of chlorite but their shape suggests that they were originally hornblende, and these rocks may be classed as hornblende-quartz-andesite.

Chemical analyses: Specimens collected by F. M. Trotter from the type area of the Binsey Group as representative of the non-porphyritic type of andesite and of the Eycott type of andesite respectively have been analysed, with the results shown in Table II. The norms and modes are also given. The mode of the Eycott type was calculated partly by areal measurement over a polished surface of the rock to obtain the proportion of phenocrysts to base, and partly by micrometric measurement of the base. The mode of the non-porphyritic type was obtained by drawing the outlines of pyroxene and magnetite in an average field, and estimating their proportion by area, judging the amount of apparent quartz by reference to known areal proportions and obtaining feldspar, etc., by subtraction. The mode must be regarded as only approximate.

Chemical analyses of three lavas from Eycott Hill were made by John Hughes for J. Clifton Ward (1877). The specimens include one which from its short description seems to correspond with the Berrier type, to which the third also may belong, and one non-porphyritic type; the analyses are reproduced in Table III, Cols. E, A and D respectively.

An analysis of a pyroxene-andesite from low in the sequence of the Borrow-dale Volcanic Series of another district is reproduced in Col. B for comparison, and in Col. C is given the analysis of a Pleistocene labradorite-dacite from Montserrat, which is closely similar to that of the Eycott type.

Assuming that the composition of the plagioclase phenocrysts of the Eycott type of lava is $Or_4Ab_{33}An_{63}$ [cf. variations in composition of feldspars, H. L. Alling 1921] and that the composition of the hypersthene phenocrysts is given by the norm, the chemical composition of the base of the Eycott type has been calculated with the result shown in Col. IA. The agreement with the composition of the non-porphyritic lava (Col. II) is very close, and the conclusion is drawn that the non-porphyritic type represents a residual magma from which early formed phenocrysts have been removed. Since the non-porphyritic and the Eycott type flows are individually homogeneous and form an interbedded group, two chambers supplying the residual magma and the magma with accumulated phenocrysts must have been closely associated, and both equally available for eruption. Such magmatic circumstances were deduced also by W. Q. Kennedy (1931, p. 166) in his study of composite non-porphyritic and feldspar-phyric basaltic flows. It appears then that neither the non-porphyritic nor the Eycott type can represent the pre-differentiation magma, which would more probably correspond to the Berrier type in which the feldspars are seriate from tiny laths to considerable crystals.

The size of the phenocrysts, their conspicuous hiatal character, their comparative lack of zoning and corrosion, all indicate that they represent a plagioclase in equilibrium with the surrounding liquor. The calculated composition of the base shows, however, a normative plagioclase of An_{77} exactly the same as the normative plagioclase of the whole rock. Correspondingly, the determined composition of the plagioclase laths in the base is An_{60} which is close to that of the phenocrysts An_{70}. According to the experimental curves for melting of plagioclase, crystals of composition An_{70} should be in equilibrium with liquor in which the plagioclase ratio is $Ab_{74}An_{26}$ (Bowen 1913, p. 583). The analysis of the non-porphyritic andesite differs only slightly from the calculated composition of the base of the Eycott type. The differences correspond to a higher proportion of hypersthene and a lower proportion of feldspar in the latter, while the normative plagioclase of the non-porphyritic type is $An_{63\cdot6}$, the determined composition of the laths being about An_{48}.

TABLE II

Chemical analyses, norms, and modes of andesites

	I	II		I	II
Analyses				**Norms**	
SiO$_2$ ..	56·28	54·16	Q	13·86	11·64
Al$_2$O$_3$ ..	14·25	19·68	or	16·12	8·90
Fe$_2$O$_3$ ..	2·38	1·45	ab	20·96	20·96
FeO ..	7·36	4·38	an	19·46	36·97
MgO ..	2·55	2·90	C	—	0·41
CaO ..	6·53	8·78	wo	3·60	—
Na$_2$O ..	2·47	2·46	en	6·41	7·20
K$_2$O ..	2·75	1·45	fs	7·63	4·62
H$_2$O > 105°C	1·69	1·88	il	5·02	2·74
H$_2$O < 105°C	0·28	0·28	mt	3·48	2·09
TiO$_2$ ..	2·65	1·42	ap	1·34	0·67
P$_2$O$_5$ ..	0·48	0·23	ca	0·20	1·60
MnO ..	0·28	0·09	normative		
CO$_2$ ..	0·10	0·70	plagioclase	An$_{49}$	An$_{77}$
FeS$_2$ ..	0·11	0·09	total normative		
			feldspar	Or$_{28}$Ab$_{37}$An$_{35}$	Or$_9$Ab$_{21}$An$_{70}$
	100·16	99·94			

I	II
Volumetric Modes	
Feldspar + little chlorite .. 69	Phenocrysts:
Pyroxene 20	Labradorite, An$_{65}$ .. 38·0
Iron-titanium oxide 7	Hypersthene (pseudomorphs) 0·8
Quartz .. .. .. ?3	Groundmass:
Apatite .. .. .. ?1	Plagioclase, An$_{60}$ .. .. 16·4
	Pyroxene, including augite and chloritized hypersthene .. .. .. 1·3
	Iron-titanium oxide .. 4·7
	Glass devitrified .. .. 31·5
	Chlorite, calcite and obscure material .. .. 7·3
100	100·0

Localities

I   Sparsely microporphyritic andesite, Top of Binsey, 1466 ft. O.D. (E 16234, Lab. No. 951.)

II   Porphyritic basic andesite of Eycott type, 850 yd S. 30° W. of High Ireby Grange, High Ireby. (E 16233, Lab. No. 950.)

Analyst B. E. Dixon (*in* Guppy 1956, p. 17–8).

TABLE III Chemical analyses of lavas

	I	A	B	C	IA	II	D	E	F	G
SiO_2	54·16	53·300	53·38	56·75	56·7	56·28	52·600	51·100	57·39	53·05
Al_2O_3	19·68	20·990	18·49	18·36	14·0	14·25	17·315	22·051	19·24	19·18
Fe_2O_3	1·45	1·660	0·69	2·53	2·4	2·38	1·722	1·210	0·49	1·59
FeO	4·38	6·343	7·50	4·96	7·0	7·36	12·043	5·885	4·90	5·84
MgO	2·90	3·964	4·30	3·73	4·4	2·55	3·252	2·346	1·53	4·09
CaO	8·78	8·512	6·08	8·62	6·8	6·53	7·728	11·424	5·33	2·55
Na_2O	2·46	2·456	2·57	2·72	1·7	2·47	2·622	2·216	2·68	2·72
K_2O	1·45	0·926	1·34	0·72	2·0	2·75	1·486	1·022	3·51	2·72
H_2O+	1·88	Loss on ignition	2·86	0·44	1·7	1·69	Loss on ignition	Loss on ignition	1·49	0·46
H_2O-	0·28	1·120	0·39	0·23	0·3	0·28	1·160	0·710	0·24	5·19
TiO_2	1·42		0·49	0·71	2·4	2·65			0·56	1·99
P_2O_5	0·23	0·102	0·46	0·09	0·4	0·48	0·153	0·179	0·31	0·96
MnO	0·09		0·19	0·16	0·15	0·28			0·13	0·18
CO_2	0·70	0·320	1·63	nil	0·10	0·10	0·140	1·820	1·55	0·15
FeS_2	0·08				0·10	0·11			S = 0·03	BaO 0·03
	99·94	99·693	100·37	100·02	100·15	100·16	100·221	99·963	99·72	100·32

Sources of analyses in Table III

I Labradorite-hypersthene-andesite, lava of Eycott type, 850 yd S. 30° W. of High Ireby Grange, Cumberland. E 16233. *Anal.* B. E. Dixon.

A Lava, with many small porphyritic crystals, Eycott Hill. *Quoted from* J. C. Ward 1877, pp. 243 and 246. *Anal.* J. Hughes.

B 'Lowest Basic Pyroxene Andesite', North of William's Beck, 1000 ft contour. *Quoted from* Hadfield and Whiteside 1936, p. 51. *Anal.* G. S. Hadfield.

C Labradorite-dacite, Centre Hills, Montserrat. *Quoted from* A. G. MacGregor 1938, p. 74.

IA Calculated composition of the groundmass of Eycott type lava of Col. I. Water and CO_2 adjusted to correspond with values in analysis of non-porphyritic lava of Col. II.

II Sparsely porphyritic pyroxene andesite, top of Binsey, High Ireby, Cumberland. E 16234. *Anal.* B. E. Dixon.

D Lava, minutely crystalline, Eycott Hill. *Quoted from* J. C. Ward 1877, p. 243. *Anal.* J. Hughes.

E Lava, highly crystalline, plagioclase from the size of ordinary needles up to ¼ inch in length. *Quoted from* J. C. Ward 1877, p. 243. *Anal.* J. Hughes.

F Harter Fell Andesite, Nan Bield Road. *Quoted from* G. H. Mitchell 1930, p. 2.

G Middle High Rigg Andesite, near Moss Crag, above Sosgill, 900 ft contour. *Quoted from* Hadfield and Whiteside 1936, p. 51. *Anal.* G. S. Hadfield.

In summary, the geological and chemical data suggest that by crystal sorting two complementary eruptible fluids were formed, one non-porphyritic, the other feldspar-phyric. The microscopic and chemical study arrive at the conclusion that the phenocrysts and groundmass plagioclase are of approximately the same composition, and that the plagioclase of the non-porphyritic lavas, presumed to be the mother liquor of the phenocrysts of the porphyritic lava is a more sodic type, but that both the non-porphyritic magma and the groundmass fluid of the porphyritic lavas show a wide divergence from the composition which on theoretical and experimental grounds would be expected.

Classification: The classification of the basic andesites is troublesome. Teall designated the Eycott type a labradorite-pyroxene-porphyrite, using the term porphyrite as equivalent to altered andesite, but described the rock among the dolerites (1888, pp. 225–7, 258). Harker (1891, pp. 331–2) classed it as hypersthene-basalt. The transitional character of the rock is evident from the silica percentage 54·16 (Col. I, Table III) and 53·40, 52·73 (Bonney 1885, p. 80), the average of these values, 53·43, agreeing closely with the intersection, 53·7, of the frequency curves for basalt and andesite (Eyles and Simpson 1921, p. 437). On the basis of either optically determined or normative plagioclase, the fresh rocks should be relegated to the basalts. Chemically and mineralogically the porphyritic types agree with the labradorite-dacites, or bandaites, though in general the latter are somewhat richer in silica. It seems preferable to retain the Eycott type of lava among the andesites on the basis of the typically andesitic texture, the low proportion of ferromagnesian minerals, and the considerable content of quartz, often determinable microscopically. The basaltic affinities are, however, strong, and the non-porphyritic members grade into olivine-free basalts.   J.P.

ACID ANDESITES

Most of the rocks classified as acid andesite are microporphyritic types, with well-developed automorphic phenocrysts of sodic plagioclase, usually oligoclase, between 0·5 and 1·5 mm long. Rarely phenocrysts may reach 3·0 mm long (E 14617, E 14619) but the average length is still within the microporphyritic class (2·0 mm average). The composition commonly varies between An_{15} and An_{25}; in very few rocks is the oligoclase fresh and clear, but definite evidence that albitization has taken place, for example in the form of patchiness in the feldspar, is seldom forthcoming. Apart from the presence of cryptocrystalline clay material, which is assumed to be the cause of the cloudy appearance of the feldspars, some of these latter also show partial, or complete replacement by sericite, or by calcite. Phenocrysts of ferromagnesian minerals, or even pseudomorphs after such phenocrysts, are completely lacking from the andesites of this group.

In the normal acid andesites, the groundmass varies between a pilotaxitic felt of oligoclase laths, varying between 0·05 and 0·3 mm long (E 15807, E 15790), and a hyalopilitic suspension of still smaller laths in more or less devitrified glass (E 14565, E 14617). In a few instances the proportion of feldspar microlites is so small that the texture approaches the hyalo-ophitic (E 14619, E 14620). Interbanding of layers of hyalopilitic material showing pronounced parallel orientation of feldspar microliths with glassy layers, each of only a few tenths of a millimetre thick, may occur (E 15684). The rocks in question have a platy fracture. Chlorite is usually present as a secondary mineral in the groundmass of the andesites, and small amounts of opaque oxides are present.

Some varieties also show quartz as an essential mineral, and these may be regarded as transitional to dacite in composition (E 14534, E 14562, E 14618, E 15837, E 15870). In the rocks classified as dacitic andesites, the quartz is intergrown in the groundmass, or occurs as small phenocrysts. Andesites subjected to secondary silicification are also known (E 15682); sometimes introduction of epidote has accompanied the silicification (E 15010). Quartz also occurs as an amygdale filling in the andesites (E 14615).

A second distinctive type of acid andesite forms a link with the rhyolites. Here, cryptofelsite or microfelsite occurs along with oligoclase microlites in the groundmass (E 14535, E 14538–9, E 14540, E 14600). If the microfelsite is sufficiently coarse, the spherulitic arrangement of the alkali-feldspar fibres in it becomes evident from the shadowy extinction shown (E 14616).

RHYOLITES

The acid lavas may generally be distinguished in the field by their pale grey, pink or buff colour, accompanied in some places by a streaky character. The rocks here classified as rhyolites are predominantly composed of micro-felsite or cryptofelsite; that is, apparently a fine-grained, possibly fibrous and radial intergrowth of quartz and alkali feldspar. In the absence of chemical analyses of these rocks, it is not possible to say whether the feldspar involved is mainly orthoclase, or partly albite; but in view of the evidence of spherulitic intergrowth of albite and quartz in the Carrock Fell Granophyre (p. 101), it should not be assumed that the rhyolites are necessarily orthoclase-rich rocks here. The individual spherulitic units in the intergrowth have very irregular edges and vary up to about 0·2 mm across (E 14537).

Those rhyolites carrying phenocrysts of oligoclase or albite may conveniently be distinguished as soda-rhyolites (E 15020, E 15005, E 15781). Complete sericitization of the phenocrysts is not uncommon (E 14537, E 14657). The occurrences of orthoclase as phenocrysts are rare (E 14655).

A few examples of partly glassy rhyolites have been found, in which there are patches of glass and patches of microfelsite (E 15683). A little chlorite is present in many of the rocks, and in some it becomes relatively abundant (E 15838). Silicification of rhyolite produces a very white rock (E 14649–50), unless the silica is accompanied by iron oxides as it appears to have been in some places (E 14656, E 15047).

Transitions to the keratophyric type andesites are shown by the incoming of microlites or small laths of oligoclase in the groundmass (E 14542, E 14651, E 15872).

TUFFS

Among the lowest tuffs, bands of interbedded slate similar to the normal Skiddaw types occur (E 14548, E 14550). The beginning of volcanic activity leaves its mark upon the sediments by a marked increase of the coarseness and amount of chlorite present (E 14552), or by a scattering of feldspar crystals, elsewhere rare in the Skiddaw Slates, through the mudstone (E 14569). Sediments abnormally rich in iron-titanium oxide minerals also occur interbedded with the tuffs (E 14566).

The tuffs themselves are for the most part crystal-lithic or lithic tuffs in the terminology proposed by Wentworth and Williams (1932); that is to say, the fragmental constituents are either crystals and previously formed rocks, or solely previously formed rocks. Among the rock fragments it is a striking fact that acid andesite and rhyolite fragments are common, while basic andesite and basalt fragments are extremely rare in the 34 sliced rocks examined. The commonest fragments are of hyalo-ophitic and hyalopilitic andesite (E 14558, E 14019) or dacitic andesite (E 14575). A type of andesite with long very slender oligoclase crystals, rarely found among the lavas, occurs in the tuffs (E 14592, E 15789). Rhyolite fragments are also common (E 14572, E 14593–4, E 15035, E 15809) and usually they are mixed with fragments of acid andesite (E 15026).

The crystals in the tuffs are the same as the phenocrysts in the acid andesites and soda-rhyolites—well-formed automorphic sodic plagioclase (E 14582, E 14596, E 14605). Some have been albitized (E 15792). A little quartz occurs sporadically (E 14602).

The matrix of the tuffs varies considerably. A few are conspicuously glassy (E 15855–6, E 17503), but most have a hyalopilitic matrix, with tiny microlites of feldspar in dusty material, the nature of which is difficult or impossible to determine. Chloritization (E 14605), silicification and epidotization have affected the rocks in variable degree (E 15024–5), and calcite has been introduced in some places (E 16230).

Where several different kinds of rock fragments are present in a lithic tuff, it is not difficult to be sure of its nature. Where, however, the fragments are glassy varieties of the matrix of the supposed tuff, it is more likely to be the autobrecciated upper part of a lava (E 15779, E 15791).

Many of the lithic and crystal-lithic tuffs could be accounted for by supposing that the products of explosive vulcanism fell into liquid lava with phenocrysts, or that the lavas themselves carried solid rock fragments along with them. Lavas enclosing foreign fragments have been recorded from the Gosforth district (Hollingworth and others 1937, p. 32). Welded tuffs with flattened glass shards have not been found among the 49 pyroclastic rocks sliced from this sheet, except in one doubtful case, from a locality west of Scawthwaite Close (E 15809). The compact textures of the tuffs may nevertheless be the result of hot accumulation of crystals, rock-fragments and glass, with some welding, but chloritic and other forms of alteration have done much to obscure the evidence. K.C.D.

Details

Bothel. This region may be taken as extending from Bothel to near the Torpenhow-Bewaldeth road. Much of it is obscured by boulder clay but it is obvious that there must be considerable faulting.

The most important sections are near Bothelcrags. Here, to the east and north-east of the farm, the lowest rock exposed consists of a thick flow of coarsely porphyritic lava of typical Eycott aspect. To the north-west this rock appears to be succeeded by a series of hard fine-grained lavas which are followed in turn by a lava with small phenocrysts of feldspar and by a coarse red tuff. The outcrops of all of these rocks are cut off to the north by an east-west fault that brings in the fine splintery lavas seen at intervals towards High Barn; while to the west, they disappear, presumably beneath the Cockermouth Lavas exposed west of the road.

To the north-east, as the high ground is

approached, the porphyritic lava of Bothel-crags meets a fault which has the effect of thrusting a mass of Borrowdale rocks against the Skiddaw Slates seen in the low ground above Blackbeck. Most of the rocks between this fault and the Torpenhow road are fine-grained dark lavas. Some show flow-banding and auto-brecciation, and possibly on this account were mistaken for tuffs by Ward. To the south-east, near the 'Fort', there is a lava with small phenocrysts of feldspar which appears to be the same flow as one exposed north-east of the road junction, having been shifted by a north-north-west fault. T.E.

Whittas Park and Binsey to Lowthwaite. In this area the Borrowdale Volcanics

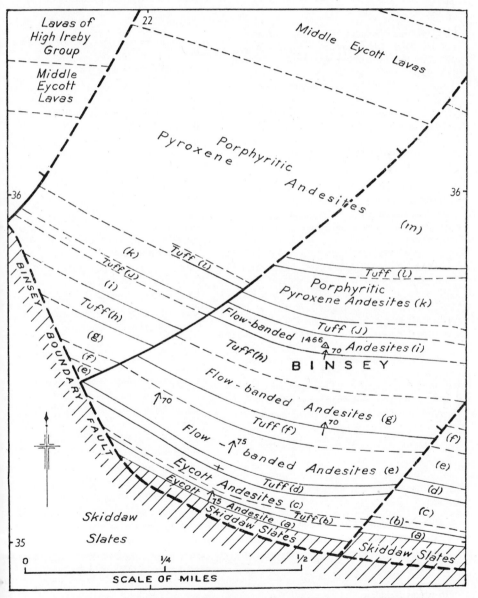

FIG. 7. *Sketch map of Borrowdale Volcanic Series on Binsey*

are separated from the Skiddaw Slates to the south by an important tear-fault, the Binsey Boundary Fault. Most of the north-easterly fractures in the Borrowdales end against this structure but some shift it, a notable example being the tear fault ½ mile E. of Over Water. Faulting apart, the main structural feature is the persistent high northerly dip (60° to 90°) along a strike that gently undulates between east-south-east and east-north-east.

The area includes the type localities of the High Ireby Group and the Binsey Group. The former is best seen in Whittas Park and northwards as far as High Houses, and again in the stream (Humble Jumble Gill of the 6-in map) to the west of that farm. The best sequence of the Binsey Group is seen on Binsey north of Fellend, but the lower beds are also well exposed as far east as the reservoir section south of Chapel House.

At least eight lava flows of the Binsey Group are seen in Whittas Park south of the outcrop of the Middle Eycott Lavas. All are green andesites with porphyritic pyroxenes and feldspars. Numerous exposures in Whittas Park serve to delimit the crop of the Middle Eycott Lavas with their characteristic labradorite phenocrysts up to one inch in length. To the north the High Ireby Group is covered by patches of thin drift and individual lava flows cannot be mapped, but numerous exposures indicate that two types of andesite are prevalent, a blue flow-banded, fine-grained to flinty lava, and a somewhat similar rock type with porphyritic lath-shaped feldspars up to a quarter of an inch long. Other rock types include a pink-banded rhyolite exposed [2128 3728] 500 yd W. 6° N. of High Houses and again in the gill [2213 3716] 450 yd E. 12° S. of that place, and an Eycott type lava (the Upper Eycott Lava) exposed in the same stream [2216 3722] 70 yd farther north.

The succession of the Binsey Group as exposed in crags and features on Binsey north of Fellend (see Figs. 7 and 8) is as follows:

		ft
m.	Green andesites; at least eight flows similar to *k*, thickness estimated at	1600
l.	Purple and green tuff; similar to *f*	100
k.	Green andesites; three flows, medium-textured with porphyritic pyroxenes and feldspars ..	380
j.	Purple and green tuff, similar to *f*; fragments up to one inch in length	150
i.	Blue flinty andesites; two flows similar to *e*; top of each flow markedly autobrecciated and vesicular	220
h.	Coarse agglomerates; blocks of rhyolite and of several varieties of andesite up to 3 ft in length ..	280
g.	Blue flinty andesites similar to *e;* two flows, each with top autobrecciated and vesicular; overlain by a third and similar flow; somewhat poorly exposed	300
f.	Green and purple tuff; matrix fine-grained with fragments of andesite and rhyolite, some fragments drawn out	180
e.	Blue flinty andesites; two flows of equal thickness, each markedly flow-banded (30 bands to 1 in)..	320
d.	Green and purple tuff; matrix fine-grained with fragments of rhyolite and andesite up to ½ inch in length	100
c.	Vesicular green andesites; two flows, each slaggy at base, and each with scattered large labradorite crystals near top (Eycott type)	140
b.	Ash; fine-grained, banded and silicified. Coarse layers near top[1]	75
a.	Vesicular green andesite with labradorite crystals up to ¾ inch in length. (Eycott type) ..	85

Lavas of *a* and *c* are grouped as the Lower Eycott Lavas.

To the north of the outcrop of the Binsey Group on Binsey, the Middle Eycott Lavas are seen ½ mile W.S.W. of Ruthwaite, in a

---

[1]In places Skiddaw Slate debris is found between *a* and *b*. This may represent thin inter-bedded slates. Slates occur above *a* north of Over Water.

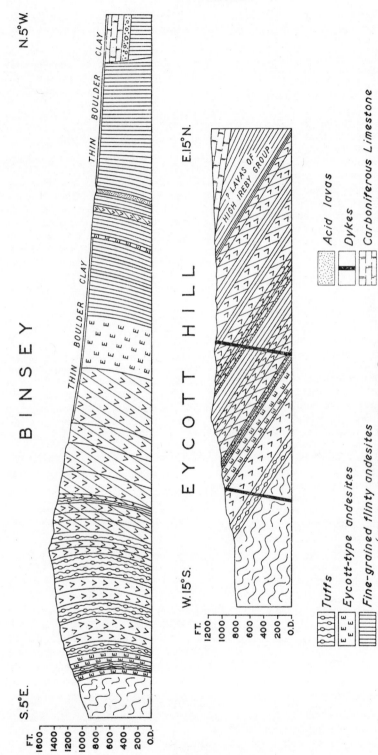

Fig. 8. Horizontal sections across (a) Binsey and (b) Eycott Hill

small stream (Mell Beck of the 6-in map) which also exposes overlying andesites of the High Ireby Group. The rocks are much decomposed, and are crossed by two veins of baryte, at points respectively [2338 3663] 460 yd W. 18° S., and [2338 3665] 400 yd W. 10° S. of the cross-roads at Ruthwaite. The former vein is 3 in thick in the bed of the stream; the latter, which occupies the east–west fault that brings in a small outlier of the Carboniferous Basement Conglomerate, is reported to be 3 ft thick. The northern boundary of the High Ireby Group is a fault that brings in the Carboniferous Limestone Series. At Ruthwaite this fault is mineralized by baryte and in opencast workings along the vein rotten andesites are seen forming the south-west wall whilst the opposite wall consists of red interbedded shales of the Carboniferous Basement Conglomerate.

To the south-east of Binsey a section in a small quarry at Whitefield Cottage [2377 3486] is of interest in that the interpretation here given differs from that of Green (1917, p. 10). Slates dipping at 50° to 60° to the north rest on some 18 ft of andesite, in which a thin irregular band of slate occurs some 3 ft below the slate-lava junction. Green considered this to be the junction of the Skiddaw Slates and the Borrowdale Volcanic Series, accounting for the relative positions of the beds by assuming them to be on the inverted limb of an overturned fold. The slates here, and farther to the east, are however interbedded with lavas, and from the numerous exposures available it is possible to map the following sequence of rocks in the neighbourhood of White-field Cottage and correlate it with the sequence on Binsey:

5. Andesite (bed e of the Binsey section); blue, fine-grained and flow-banded.

4. Tuff (bed d of Binsey) with fragments of andesite, rhyolite and quartzite.

3. Andesite (upper flow of c of Binsey); vesicular with large labradorite crystals.

2. Mudstone, grey-blue, slaty, with thin tuffaceous bands. 35 ft seen, estimated at 45 ft thick.

1. Andesite (lower flow of c of Binsey); vesicular with feldspars up to ⅜ inch in length. Thin lenticular bed of

slaty mudstone 3 ft from top of andesite.

To the east of Whitefield Cottage the Binsey Group is shifted by the Whitefield Fault half a mile to the north-east, and the basal members are well displayed on the hill (Latrigg on 6-in map) to the west of Scawthwaite Close. Mudstones again separate the upper and lower flows of bed c, and 20 ft of them with gritty tuffaceous layers are seen between lavas in a small quarry 200 yd [2485 3542] S. 10° E. of Scawthwaite Close. Pebbles and fragments of tuff (bed d of Binsey) include Skiddaw Slate, a quartzite indistinguishable from Latterbarrow Sandstone, and andesite. A circular boss, some 50 yd in diameter, of coarse-grained diorite with porphyritic feld-spars and pyroxenes, cuts across the crop of the flow-banded lavas that constitute bed e. Beds f, g and h also outcrop on Latrigg and display lithological characters identical with those seen on Binsey. Farther east a good section [2590 3551] is seen in the spillway of Over Water Reservoir 1000 yd W.S.W. of Longlands; there, Skiddaw Slates are faulted against the lowest beds of the Binsey Group. North of the fault the strata are approximately vertical and the sequence is as follows:

		ft
5. Mudstone .. .. at least		6
4. Andesite (lower flow of c of Binsey) coarse-grained and vesicular		30
3. Mudstone with tuffaceous layers..		8
2. Lava of Eycott type (bed a of Binsey), vesicular and coarsely porphyritic		16
1. Bedded tuff, composed almost exclusively of Skiddaw Slate fragments		8

Northwards for 200 yd there are no further exposures in the spillway, but beyond this point [2596 3590] there is a continuous section for 200 yd of lavas and tuffs dipping northwards at high angles. It commences with a banded tuff, coarse in its upper part, that is probably bed h. Green andesites intervene between this and a second tuff band which probably represents bed j, although it is much thinner than that bed on Binsey. Andesites extend from this tuff band to Chapel House where the section in the spillway ends. On the opposite bank of the stream and 200 yd N.E. of Chapel House there are some isolated exposures of pyroxene-andesites that recall the flows in *k* and *m* on Binsey.

Lowthwaite and Longlands. Along the western, southern and south-eastern flanks of the hill 500 yd S.E. of Lowthwaite, the boundary between the Borrowdale Volcanic Series and the Skiddaw Slates has been mapped as a low-angled thrust that dips to the north-east. The rocks above the thrust are referred to the Binsey Group, but good exposures are restricted to the southern end of the thrust mass. East of Stockdale, a tuff with rhyolite and andesite fragments up to an inch long is found between pyroxene-andesites. The beds, which are vertical and strike to the south-west, compare well with the sequence beds *k* to *m* on Binsey.

To the east of the hill 500 yd S.E. of Lowthwaite, the Borrowdale rocks are shifted to the south by a north-north-westerly fault in which lies a mineral vein; and 450 yd S.W. of the summit of Longlands Fell surface workings [2733 3510] for copper have exposed silicified andesites on the eastern wall of the vein. The junction of the Borrowdale Volcanic Series and the Skiddaw Slates can be traced eastwards across Uldale Fells, but there is no section showing the actual contact of these divisions. It is inferred, however, that the thrust which separates them to the west of the mineralized fault does the same to the east of it. Nearby exposures below the thrust are referred to the Slates and Sandstones group of the Skiddaw Slates. The lowest bed in the Binsey Group above the thrust is a tuff, in which there are many large fragments of slate and quartzite, recalling bed *d* on Latrigg. To the south, the structures within the Borrow-dale outcrop are probably complicated, but exposures are few as far as the west-ward flowing stream that rises ¼ mile S. of Longlands Fell. In this stream a series of vesicular andesites crop out, and at a place [2754 3512], 300 yd S. by W. of the summit of Longlands Fell, appears to be suc-ceeded by Skiddaw Slates dipping east-wards at 40°. The slates are regarded as lying above a thrust plane, having been thrust over Borrowdale volcanic rocks

from the south. The outcrop of Skiddaw Slates on the sole of the thrust plane is small; much of the overthrust mass on Longlands Fell consists of Borrowdale rocks and in consequence the precise posi-tion of the thrust plane is difficult to deter-mine, but it is regarded as being approxi-mately horizontal.

Good exposures are seen in the northward flowing stream (Charleton Gill of the 6-in map) that separates Longland and Brae Fells. Here the Middle Eycott Lavas at the base of the High Ireby Group dip steeply northwards from a point 1100 yd S. of Norman to occupy the stream course for a distance of 230 yd. There are three and possibly four flows displaying the charac-teristic large labradorite phenocrysts. They are interbedded with fine-grained pink and pale green keratophyres, and a keratophyre immediately overlies the Middle Eycott Lavas. Downstream higher lavas of the High Ireby Group are reddened, heavily brecciated and in places silicified. They appear to lie along a zone or belt of shatter-ing that trends obliquely across the stream to the north-north-east. F.M.T.

Brae Fell to High Pike. The northerly sloping upland surface from Longlands Fell to beyond High Pike is composed of lavas and tuffs of the Binsey and High Ireby groups. In the south-west the outcrop of these is limited by the thrust which underlies the Skiddaw slates and grits centred about Great Sca Fell. In the south from the head of Roughton Gill[1] to the col south of High Pike the volcanic rocks are faulted against the Carrock complex along the line of the great mineralized dislocations of Roughton Gill.

Throughout this region there has been extensive mineralization along fractures of varying trend and widespread pneumatolytic hydrothermal decomposition of the country rock. In the streams, exposures are generally continuous but the faulting, paucity of reliable dips and the absence of good index horizons other than the Middle Eycott Lavas make the detailed structure obscure. In general it is thought that there is an upward succession northwards.

The southernmost exposures in the Dale Beck drainage occur in the western arm of

---

[1]The upper part of "Dale Beck" of the One-inch map.

the gill (Thief Gill of 6-in map) $\frac{1}{2}$ mile E. of Great Sca Fell where metamorphosed pyroxene-andesites injected by granophyric veins form the roof of the gabbro of the Carrock complex between the North and South veins of Roughton Gill. To the north of the North Vein several hundred feet of greenish tuffs crop out at the head of the gill (Silver Gill of 6-in map) $\frac{1}{2}$ mile E. of Great Sca Fell, where they are capped by the overthrust mass of Skiddaw Slates well seen on the west side of the valley head. At the contact, a rock resembling a slate-bearing tuff is probably a crush breccia. The tuffs of Silver Gill are medium- to fine-grained andesitic rocks with here and there fine banding dipping N. 10° W. at 40° to 60°. Numerous fractures carry strings of carbonate (? ankerite-dolomite) up to 1 ft thick. Quartz veins up to 2 ft are also present. The common trend is north-easterly with a north-westerly hade parallel to the Roughton Gill veins. Dip joints hading E. 10° N. at 30° affect some of the N.E.–S.W. quartz veins and may themselves carry quartz. Similar joints in the andesitic lavas to the north displace E.–W. grano-phyric veins and have here and there deter-mined the positions of basic dykes.

The tuffs of Silver Gill are succeeded by a broad belt of andesitic lavas that is typically seen on the lower slopes of the Silver Gill and Roughton Gill valleys. The absence of any metamorphic effect where these are separated from the Carrock complex by the Roughton Gill North Vein is note-worthy. The lavas of the crags of Yard Steel (the spur N.N.E. of Great Sca Fell) are massive bluish green to pale grey, non-porphyritic and sparingly porphyritic. Their lie is uncertain but east of the Dale Beck valley similar lavas on the crag [304 348] 200 yd N.E. of the Roughton Gill Mine buildings, include a band of fine tuff dip-ping N. 10° W. at 60°. Heavy jointing on the crags of Yard Steel follows regional trends and the easterly trend (roughly aligned with the Drygill Vein) is that favoured by mineralizing solutions, the fissures in such cases being nearly vertical. Granophyre and composite granophyre-dolerite dykes in the lower part of the crags also take this direction. Small veins with ankeritic calcite, umber, pink and white baryte and china clay have been noted in this area.

In the gill (Swinburn Gill of 6-in map) north of Great Sca Fell, and its tributaries from the west (Red Gill, Wet Smale Gill and Dry Smale Gill) a complex of mineralized fractures and the capping of overthrust Skiddaw Slates at the head, make the deciphering of the structure difficult. Heavily sheared andesites appear from beneath the overthrust at about 1750 ft O.D. in Swin-burn Gill and are succeeded downstream by medium-grained tuffs apparently dipping north. These are cut off by the W. by N. trending Wet Smale Gill Vein, $\frac{1}{2}$ mile E. of Brae Fell. A N.–S. vein in tuffs is well exposed $\frac{1}{2}$ mile up Swinburn Gill. In Red Gill a flat-lying lenticular andesitic mass about 20 ft thick occurs at about the horizon of the plane of the overthrust. It has a lower chilled margin welded to a thin layer of slate which is underlain by crush breccia of slate representing the sole of the thrust. The igneous rock thus appears to be intrusive but the occurrence of marginal breccias of igneous rock and slate suggests that the intrusion took place along the thrust plane before movement had ceased.

North of Red Gill the precise outcrop of the thrust is uncertain but medium to coarse tuffs with pyroxene-andesites capping Brae Fell and its western spur down to 1500 ft O.D. are not recognizable in Charleton Gill to the west, and so may be part of the overthrust mass.

North of Wet Smale Gill bluish green andesites in the upper part of the Binsey Group form a belt several hundred yards wide. A noteworthy type in the upper part is an andesite with abundant small stout glassy prisms of feldspar that is traceable from Brae Fell Mine [298 357] $\frac{3}{4}$ mile E.N.E. of Brae Fell, eastwards across Dale Beck towards High Pike.

Exposures are poor and there is extensive hydrothermal alteration at the head of Long Grain but a pre-mineralization phase of thermal metamorphism of the lavas which is recognizable eastwards into the Carrock Beck drainage may be noted.

The Middle Eycott Lavas are traceable from Charleton Gill by the gill (Ramps Gill of 6-in map) $\frac{1}{2}$ mile S.E. of Hazelhurst into the gill (Hay Gill of 6-in map) north-west of High Pike, where they are well exposed, and thence on to the northern slopes of High Pike. They are interbedded with acid andesitic or dacitic types, in the southern branch of Hay Gill. In Hay Gill there are many dolerite dykes trending E.S.E. parallel to the valley and to the strike of the lavas. North of the Middle Eycott Lavas, andesitic lavas with subordinate dacitic and felsitic types higher in the High Ireby Group form a belt half a mile wide. They are best seen in the upper part of Potts Gill, $\frac{1}{2}$ to $\frac{3}{4}$ mile S. of Potts Gill (Farm). They have been examined in cross-cuts between and beyond the Potts Gill barytes veins and along several hundred yards of a drift driven south from an adit [3189 3662] in the valley floor 750 yd S. of Potts Gill (Farm). In this drift pale grey siliceous rock was prominent between 200 and 300 yd from the mouth of the adit.

Bluish black splintery fluidal lavas lie above these lavas $\frac{1}{2}$ mile S. of Potts Gill (Farm) and seem to increase in importance eastwards towards the Caldew valley. The highest beds are a broad belt of poorly exposed tuffs, in part pale grey and possibly rhyolitic in type, but in places with moderately coarse andesitic material.

High Pike to Carrock Beck. The Middle Eycott Lavas are displaced southwards on the south-east side of the Low Pike Vein, but have not been seen east of the Driggith-Sandbeds Vein (the continuation of the Roughton Gill South Vein) until the lower part of Carrock Beck is reached on the east side of the supposed continuation of the Carrock End Fault. Debris of Eycott type seen just north of the Drygill Vein south-east of High Pike is probably *in situ* and would imply a shift of the outcrop of several hundred yards north-eastwards on the north-western side of Driggith Vein. This throw is similar to that in the Carrock complex to the south-west (Fig. 10), and would make the thick series of coarse tuffs in the wedge between the Driggith and Grove Gill (1500 yd E. of High Pike) faults lie high in the High Ireby Group and possibly be the equivalent of those south of Potts Gill. Porphyritic andesites and tuffs below these coarse tuffs are well exposed in Driggith Beck 5 furlongs E. of High Pike where they show definite evidence of thermal metamorphism (p. 127).

East of High Pike the Driggith Vein is flanked by a belt of hydrothermally rotted country rock penetrated by veins of felsite

and quartz. The soft crumbly rock is readily eroded where the cover of vegetation is broken as is illustrated by the deep gashes in the hillside hereabouts.

A distinctive black porphyritic acid lava on the southern slope of West Fell appears to be identical with one lying above the Upper Eycott Lavas in the Caldew sequence $\frac{1}{2}$ mile N. 60° E. of Line-wath. This correlation would place the outcrop of the Middle Eycott Lavas beneath the broad belt of drift in the Carrock Beck valley in the area west of the Carrock End Fault.

A suite of dolerite dykes trending E.S.E. occurs on the southern slope of West Fell and, from scattered debris, is probably represented in the poorly exposed area of massive greenish and dark fluidal banded andesites on the northern slope.

The widespread drift cover north of West Fell is broken by the stream (How Beck) $\frac{1}{2}$ to $\frac{3}{4}$ mile S.S.W. of Woodhall, revealing fine-grained greenish and purplish grey andesites with tuffs coming in at the northernmost exposure. These tuffs possibly correspond with the highest beds south of Potts Gill.

East of the Carrock End Fault, Middle Eycott Lavas probably continuous with those in the Caldew valley are exposed along Carrock Beck for 300 yd. They include a 10-ft bed of tuff and are penetrated by dolerite dykes resembling those in Hay Gill and on West Fell.

Linewath and the Caldew Valley. The broad silted-up basin east of Carrock Fell is closed to the north by higher ground composed of drift-veneered lavas through which the River Caldew has cut a gorge east of Linewath. Craggy hillocks projecting through the drift reveal a good sequence that is continued along the Caldew farther north. The dip is S. to S. by W. at 60° to 90°, but the sequence and the internal evidence of the flows indicate that here, as elsewhere on the northern crop, there is an upward succession north-wards and the beds are overturned.

The Middle Eycott Lavas are the lowest beds exposed. They aggregate 1000 ft in thickness and include a 200-ft flow of massive pyroxene-andesite. The lowest Eycott lavas seen crop out a few yards below the ford (now a bridge) 100 yd E. of Linewath. Here the rock blasted from the river bed to lower and widen it yields many excellent specimens of typical coarsely porphyritic Eycott lava. This flow has a thick rubbly and vesicular upper part and in a crag 300 yd N.E. of Linewath is succeeded by a 6-in band of tuff. Tabular rafts of this tuff have been incorporated in the vesicular basal part of the overlying flow of massive pyroxene-andesite. The massive central part of the latter is a bluish green lava with conspicuous stout pyroxenes up to 0·6 cm across. Its upper vesicular portion also carries inclusions of tuff and of the coarsely porphyritic Eycott lavas.

Some 300 yd N.N.E. of Linewath the overlying Eycott lavas include at least two flows. The massive character of the upper flow and the abundance of large feldspar phenocrysts in it contrast with the rubbly vesicular character of the lower flow and the wide spacing of the much smaller phenocrysts.

The lava with conspicuous pyroxene mentioned above is also exposed between flows of Eycott type north-east of Linewath bridge where belts of vesicular and flow-brecciated lava alternating with massive beds indicate at least three flows. Here the lacy network of the matrix of the flow breccias is well brought out by weathering.

A gap of 150 yd which separates these lavas from the black porphyritic acid flow (referred to on p. 69) next seen to the north, may be partially occupied by fine-grained, greenish and bluish black, fluidal lavas exposed at Norman Crag, east of a N.–S. fault which throws the Eycott lavas 150 yd south on its eastern side.

Above the acid lava there is a gap of about 150 yd followed to the north by fine-grained, blue-black, fluidal banded lavas with small scattered phenocrysts of feldspar. The dip is S. by W. at 60° to 80°, and from exposures 100 to 400 yd S.S.W. of Townend some 600 to 800 ft of beds are present.

Farther north, and presumably still higher in the sequence, are bluish grey andesites exposed along the Caldew gorge 200 to 400 yd N.E. of Townend. Some 500 yd N.N.E. of that farm still more dark, fluidal-banded, rather splintery lavas are interbedded with greenish vesicular flows.

The total thickness of the High Ireby Group along the Caldew probably amounts to 4000 ft. Isolated exposures of porphyritic andesites and keratophyric lavas in fields south of Low Row may belong to still higher beds.

Murrah and Eycott Hill. An isolated outcrop of Borrowdale Volcanic rocks is found south of Murrah, extending through Eycott Hill into the Keswick (29) Sheet (see Fig. 8). The outcrop may be regarded as lying in a gentle synclinal fold, with easterly pitch, to the north of the major fold in Skiddaw Slates which intervenes between this and the main outcrop of Borrowdale Volcanics to the south.

This synclinal structure is accentuated by dip faults (see Fig. 9). The strike changes from N.–S. in the north to N.N.W.–S.S.E. in the south with dip generally E. to E.N.E. at 35°–40°.

In the following summary, given in downward succession, more flows are enumerated than in the original account by Ward, whose reference numbers are given in brackets.

		ft
z	(17) Fine-grained bluish fluidal banded andesite; seen in centre of syncline only 700 yd E. by N. of Eycott Hill	50
xy	(17) Two flows of porphyritic pyroxene-andesite with well marked vesicular tops ..	250
w	(?16) Blue-black, fine-grained fluidal andesite; forming triple tier of crags 550 yd N.E. of Eycott Hill	150
v	(16) Massive dark bluish-grey pyroxene-andesite with pyroxene and feldspar up to 0·5 cm freely developed; a massive blocky lava the outcrop of which is largely beneath peat on account of extensive ice-plucking ..	200
u	(15) Blue-black, fine-grained fluidal banded lava similar to w with well-marked vesicular upper part; forming a long dip slope. This flow decreases in thickness southward and probably dies out south of the latitude of Eycott Hill .. up to	100

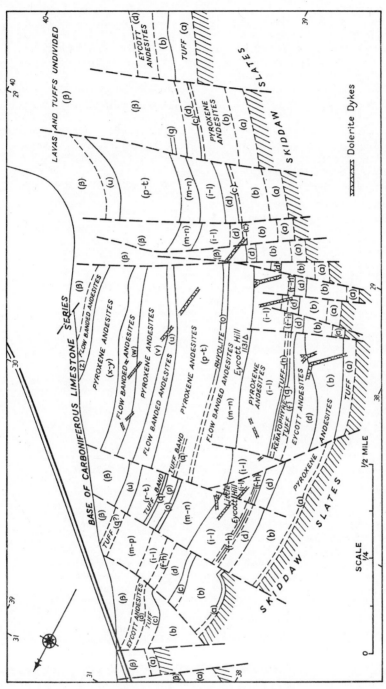

FIG. 9. *Sketch map of Borrowdale Volcanic Series on Eycott Hill*

r, s, t (14) Porphyritic pyroxene-andesites with vesicular tops. The central flow is an exceptionally massive reddish to purplish-grey rock, weathering in very large blocks (e.g. 200 yd E. of Eycott Hill) and with a much ice-plucked outcrop like lava *v*. These lavas decrease in aggregate thickness northwards and may be absent in the Caldew section 250

q (13) Andesite tuff, locally well bedded; visible 350 yd E.N.E. of Little Eycott Hill; possibly dies out southwards 20

p (13) Bluish, porphyritic pyroxene-andesite, richer in pyroxene than lavas *r-t* 70

o (12) Dark reddish grey to black, flinty rhyolite with abundant small (2 mm) stout prisms of feldspar; seen 200 yd S.S.E. of Eycott Hill 40

m, n (10, 11) Massive to platy-weathering dark, fluidal banded andesites resembling lavas *u*, *w* and *z*. Two or more flows with much highly vesicular rock. These form the summit ridge of Little Eycott Hill and the terraced crags of Eycott Hill; they appear to thin somewhat in the extreme south 250

i, j, k, l (6, 7, 8, 9) Dark bluish porphyritic pyroxene-andesites forming the main scarp of Little Eycott Hill and Eycott Hill. These flows can be distinguished from each other by the size and proportions of the phenocrysts of feldspar and pyroxene. The former range up to 0·9 cm and the latter to 0·5 cm in length. A feature of the lava *l* is the presence of masses of finely banded tuff in the upper 15 to 20 ft of the flow (e.g. west of Little Eycott Hill). In some cases these appear to represent infilling of crevices from above, but in others the high inclination of the bedding and isola-

tion of the patches suggest movement subsequent to incorporation. Many good examples of flow-brecciation are observable west of Eycott Hill. These flows decrease considerably in thickness to the south-east of Eycott Hill .. 350

f, g, h (?5) Medium- to fine-grained bedded andesitic tuff; *f* and *h* are separated by a thin flow of pale reddish porphyritic lava (*g*) of keratophyric affinities and up to 20 ft thick. These beds are exposed near the foot of the main scarp, 300 yd W.N.W. of Eycott Hill 60

e A thin flow of dark, flow-brecciated, fine-grained andesite, visible west of Little Eycott Hill and possibly not persistent 10

d (4) Middle Eycott Lavas; basic pyroxene-andesites with feldspar phenocrysts up to 4 cm in length. At least two flows, with rubbly vesicular upper portions. Good exposures 500 yd W.N.W. and 800 yd S.S.E. of Eycott Hill. Feldspars are smaller and the pyroxene more abundant in the lower flow .. 250

c (3) Greenish andesitic tuff; well developed east and north of Fairy Knott 10–50

b (2) Massive bluish green andesite with inconspicuous small feldspar phenocrysts and specks of chloritized pyroxene. This flow forms a big feature ¼ mile west of Eycott Hill 300

a (1) Purplish green, medium-grained andesitic tuff which is the lowest member of the Volcanic Series hereabouts. It is best developed on crags west of Greenahcrag, 1500 yd S.S.E. of Eycott Hill, where it is a coarse tuff with scattered fragments of pink rhyolite 50

The relations of the Borrowdale rocks of the Eycott Hill area to the Skiddaw Slates are visible only in the stream south of Fairy Knott where a thin bed of tuffaceous material intervenes between Skiddaw Slates and a thick andesite flow which is correlated with lava *b* above. The section in the stream is as follows:

	ft	in
Bluish andesite with vesicular base and included fragments of coarse tuff	2	0
Greenish, fine-grained, granular tuff ..	5	0
Fine tuffaceous shale	0	1
Bluish-grey, tuffaceous sandstone ..	3	0
Grey shale	0	2
Hard bluish sandstone	2	0
Greenish grey shale	0	4
Gap to greenish grey slates ..6 to	10	0

The Greystoke Park Inlier. In this outcrop, 3 miles N.E. of Mungrisdale, the dip is generally north-north-easterly at about 70°. The beds exposed are comparable with the Binsey Group of the Caldew valley and Eycott Hill, and they indicate the eastward continuation of the Caldew valley strike, but without the inversion of the beds found there.

A noteworthy feature is the development of the thick Calfhow Head Rhyolite ¼ mile E. by S. of Scale, probably at the horizon of the thin flow *o* of the Eycott Hill succession. Also of interest is the Tippy Hills dyke swarm, 1¼ miles E. by N. of Scale. The general succession is as follows:

		ft
g	Black fine-grained, flinty, fluidal banded andesite, several flows with highly vesicular upper portions	1000
f	Dark bluish porphyritic pyroxene-andesites	600
e	Medium to coarse-grained tuff; possibly the tuff *q* of Eycott Hill	200
d	Bluish grey porphyritic pyroxene-andesite (feldspars up to 0·6 cm); possibly the equivalent to *p* of Eycott Hill	200
c	Dark reddish grey flinty, flow-banded and nodular rhyolite ..	300
b	Black, fine-grained, non-porphyritic andesite, strongly flow-brecciated, possibly equivalent to lavas *m* and *n* of Eycott Hill	60
a	Bluish grey, porphyritic pyroxene-andesite; possibly the equivalent in part of lavas *i* to *l* of Eycott Hill	over 200

An imperfect cleavage, approximately co-planar with the general dip, is recognizable in the less massive vesicular portions of the flow on Tippy Hills. s.e.h.

REFERENCES

ALLING, H. L. 1921. The mineralography of the feldspars. *J. Geol.*, **29**, 193–294.

BAILEY, E. B., CLOUGH, C. T., WRIGHT, W. B., RICHEY, J. E. and WILSON, G. V. 1924. Tertiary and Post-Tertiary geology of Mull, Loch Aline and Oban. *Mem. Geol. Surv. Gt Br.*

BONNEY, T. G. 1885. On the occurrence of a mineral allied to enstatite in the ancient lavas of Eycott Hill, Cumberland. *Geol. Mag.*, **22**, 76–80.

BOWEN, N. L. 1913. The melting phenomena of the plagioclase feldspars. *Am. J. Sci.*, **35**, 577–99.

EASTWOOD, T. 1928. The Cockermouth Lavas, Cumberland—a Carboniferous volcanic episode. *Summ. Prog. Geol. Surv. Gt Br.* for 1927, pt. 2, 15–22.

EYLES, V. A. and SIMPSON, J. B. 1921. Silica percentages of igneous rocks. *Geol. Mag.* **58**, 436–40.

GREEN, J. F. N. 1917. The age of the chief intrusions of the Lake District. *Proc. Geol. Ass.*, **28**, 1–30.

———— 1919. The vulcanicity of the Lake District. *Proc. Geol. Ass.*, **30**, 153–82.

GUPPY, EILEEN M. 1956. (Compiler) Chemical analyses of igneous rocks, metamorphic rocks and minerals, 1931–54. *Mem. Geol. Surv. Gt Br.*

HADFIELD, G. S. and WHITESIDE, H. C. M. 1936. The Borrowdale Volcanic Series of High Rigg and the adjoining Low Rigg microgranite. *Proc. Geol. Ass.*, **47**, 42–64.

HARKER, A. 1891. Petrological notes on rocks from the Cross Fell Inlier. *Quart. Jl geol. Soc. Lond.*, **47**, 512–25.

HARTLEY, J. J. 1925. The succession and structure of the Borrowdale Volcanic Series as developed in the area lying between the lakes of Grasmere, Windermere, and Coniston. *Proc. Geol. Ass.* **36**, 203–26.

HOLLINGWORTH, S. E., TROTTER, F. M., ROSE, W. C. C. and EASTWOOD, T. 1937. Gosforth District. *Mem. Geol. Surv. Gt Br.*

KENNEDY, W. Q. 1931. On composite lava flows. *Geol. Mag.*, **68**, 166–81.

MACGREGOR, A. G. 1938. The volcanic history and petrology of Montserrat, with observations on Mt. Pelé, in Martinique. *Phil. Trans. R. Soc.* (B) **229**, 1–90.

MARR, J. E. 1916. *The Geology of the Lake District and the scenery as influenced by geological structure.* Cambridge.

MITCHELL, G. H. 1929. The succession and structure of the Borrowdale Volcanic Series of Troutbeck, Kentmere, and the western part of Long Sleddale. *Quart. Jl geol. Soc. Lond.*, **85**, 9–44.

———— 1930. Notes on the petrography of the Borrowdale Volcanic Series of Kentmere (Westmoreland). *Quart. Jl geol. Soc. Lond.*, **86**, 1–8.

———— 1934. The Borrowdale Volcanic Series and associated rocks of the country between Long Sleddale and Shap. *Quart. Jl geol. Soc. Lond.*, **90**, 418–44.

———— 1940. The Borrowdale Volcanic Series of Coniston, Lancashire. *Quart. Jl geol. Soc. Lond.*, **96**, 301–19.

———— 1956. The Borrowdale Volcanic Series of the Dunnerdale Fells, Lancashire. *Lpool Manchr geol. J.*, **1**, 428–49.

MOSELEY, F. 1960. The succession and structure of the Borrowdale Volcanic rocks south-east of Ullswater. *Quart. Jl geol. Soc. Lond.*, **116**, 55–84.

TEALL, J. J. H. 1888. *British Petrography; with special reference to the igneous rocks.* London.

WARD, J. C. 1877. On the Lower Silurian Lavas of Eycott Hill, Cumberland. *Mon. micr. J.*, 239–46.

WENTWORTH, C. K. and WILLIAMS, H. 1932. The classification and terminology of the pyroclastic rocks. *Bull. natn. Res. Coun., Wash.*, No. 89, 19.

Chapter V

ORDOVICIAN: DRYGILL SHALES

THE DRYGILL SHALES occupy an easterly-trending outcrop half to three-quarters of a mile long and 200 to 300 yd wide, a quarter of a mile south-east of High Pike. They are flanked by Borrowdale Volcanic Series on the north and by the Carrock complex on the south. These calcareous mudstones and shales, now known to be of Upper Ordovician age, have long presented problems of interest. They were assigned to the Skiddaw Slates by Ward (1876, pp. 17, 24). Although Nicholson and Marr (1877) recognized their affinity with the Dufton Shales, they first considered them on fossil evidence to belong to the Llandeilo Series. In 1892 (p. 105) Marr assigned them to the Coniston Limestone Series, and subsequently Elles and Wood (1895, pp. 246–9) endorsed this view, correlated them with the Sleddale Beds of the Coniston Limestone Series, and divided them on their fauna into a lower and an upper group.

In 1900 Marr (fig. 3, p. 468) accounted for the anomalous position of these high Ordovician beds by assuming they formed a 'window' beneath a great thrust plane, whereas Green (1917, pp. 23–4) considered that they represented part of a synclinal core of Bala rocks resting unconformably on older rocks and faulted in between flanking walls of the latter.

The igneous rocks, with which the calcareous mudstones and shales are associated, appear to have been regarded as interbedded lavas by Ward. Nicholson and Marr recognized the basic rocks as intrusive and the acid as contemporaneous breccias and lavas—a view which has been generally accepted.

The Drygill Shales, in their unaltered condition, are grey to black calcareous mudstones and shales which vary but little throughout their outcrop. The general dip is a few degrees east of south at 50° to 70° except in the head of the northernmost gully where northerly dips up to 40° are present, thus suggesting an anticlinal axis in this vicinity. Several hundred feet of strata are probably present on the southern limb of the anticline. That on this limb there is an upward succession southwards was suggested by Elles and Wood on faunal evidence.

The shales have been considerably altered over much of the present outcrop. Alteration generally takes the form of bleaching which may affect the whole rock or be developed outwards to a variable extent from joints. It is most intense in close proximity to the intrusive felsitic masses, which penetrate the shales in strings and small bosses, and to the felsite—the continuation of the Harestones Felsite—which borders the Drygill Shales on the south. Where alteration is greatest, as at the head of Long Grain [315 345], the shales and mudstones are converted to a soft, white rock resembling china clay; there is also some local silicification of the shales.

STRUCTURAL RELATIONS

Since all the contacts of the Drygill Shales with adjacent rocks are either faults or intrusive junctions there is no definite field evidence of the stratigraphical relations between these beds and the Borrowdale Volcanic Series. In the nearest outcrops of Upper Ordovician strata to the south there is a pronounced unconformity between the Caradoc rocks and the underlying Borrowdale Volcanic Series (Aveline 1872, p. 441). Green (1917) considered that this unconformity extended into the northern part of the Lake District, and it would simplify the interpretation of the present occurrence of the Drygill Shales if the original thickness of Borrowdale rocks in the area now occupied by the Drygill Shales had been considerably reduced by erosion before the deposition of the latter.

The northern boundary of the outcrop, as has been generally recognized, is a fault now occupied by a mineralized quartz vein dipping north at 70° to 80°. This stands out prominently as a wall-like mass on the northern side of the valley. The southern boundary is not clearly visible anywhere, but trenches dug in the easternmost branch of Drygills, in a tributary gully a few yards to the west and in a gully 300 yd farther west, all showed bleached hydrothermally altered shales in contact with felsite to the south. The general characters of the rocks on both sides of the contact are identical with those exhibited at various places within the shale outcrop where felsite is clearly intrusive; and contrary to previous opinion the southern boundary of the Drygill Shales is considered to be essentially unfaulted.

The Drygill Shales are not known to be in contact with any other rocks except the intrusive doleritic masses, and the quartz veins on the north. It would seem therefore that we must turn to the structural relations of the felsitic intrusions for some clue to those of the Drygill Shales. Further discussion of the problem is therefore dealt with on p. 111, where it is inferred that the shales were injected by doleritic magma during a relatively early stage in the emplacement of the Carrock Fell complex when they lay far above their present position, into which they were lowered at the time of the intrusion of the Harestones Felsite.

FAUNA AND AGE

During the resurvey collections were made by Messrs. Hester and Dewar from a number of localities. The fossils occur in considerably sheared and crushed mudstones and are principally internal and external moulds of brachiopods and trilobites. The best-preserved material (De 2660–2706) is from near the head of the northern fork of Drygills and includes *Broeggerolithus nicholsoni* (Reed) and *Brongniartella bisulcata* (McCoy); these two species occur in the Longvillian of the Caradoc Series in the Cross Fell Inlier (Dean 1959) and (together with *Kloucekia apiculata* McCoy sp. mentioned below) in the Longvillian of other areas. *Broeggerolithus nicholsoni* occurs also in Drygill proper 150 yd above its junction with the south fork, and neither here nor elsewhere can any horizon distinctly different from the principal one mentioned above be recognized. Dean (1963) has revised the names of the fossils from the Drygill Shales now in the Sedgwick Museum, Cambridge. The list includes *Kloucekia apiculata*, *Lonchodomas sp.* and *Flexicalymene* cf. *caractaci* (Salter). It is noteworthy that the identification of high forms originally listed by Elles and Wood (1895, p. 247) as restricted to the south fork exposure, particularly *Trinucleus seticornis* Hisinger, has not been confirmed in this revision. Since, moreover, *B. nicholsoni* is now recorded from both the northern and southern parts of the outcrop (Dean 1963, localities 1, 3, 6, 9), there seems to be no confirmation of the division into a lower (northern) and an upper (southern) portion; and the possibility of the occurrence of Ashgillian strata (Marr 1916, p. 42) can be eliminated.   S.E.H.

REFERENCES

AVELINE, W. T. 1872. On the continuity and breaks between the various divisions of the Silurian strata in the Lake District. *Geol. Mag.*, **9**, 441–2.

DEAN, W. T. 1959. The stratigraphy of the Caradoc Series in the Cross Fell Inlier. *Proc. Yorks. geol. Soc.*, **32**, 185–228.

———— 1963. The Stile End Beds and Drygill Shales (Ordovician) in the east and north of the English Lake District. *Bull. Br. Mus. nat. Hist. Geol.*, **9**, 49–65, pls. 1–5.

ELLES, GERTRUDE L. and WOOD, ETHEL M. R. 1895. Supplementary notes on the Drygill Shales. *Geol. Mag.*, (4), **2**, 246–9.

GREEN, J. F. N. 1917. The age of the chief intrusions of the Lake District. *Proc. Geol. Ass.*, **28**, 1–30.

MARR, J. E. 1892. The Coniston Limestone Series. *Geol. Mag.*, (3), **9**, 97–110.

———— 1916. *The Geology of the Lake District and the scenery as influenced by geological structure.* Cambridge.

———— 1900. Notes on the geology of the English Lake District. *Proc. Geol. Ass.*, **16**, 449–83.

NICHOLSON, H. A. and MARR, J. E. 1887. On the occurrence of a new fossiliferous horizon in the Ordovician Series of the Lake District. *Geol. Mag.*, (3), **4**, 339–44.

WARD, J. C. 1876. On the granitic, granitoid and associated metamorphic rocks of the Lake District. Parts III–V. *Quart. Jl geol. Soc. Lond.*, **32**, 1–34.

Chapter VI

THE CARROCK FELL COMPLEX

INTRODUCTION

THE PLUTONIC COMPLEX OF CARROCK FELL (Fig. 10) occupies an area one mile broad and four miles long, its long axis trending about W. 10° N. Its eastern part forms the watershed between the Caldew on the south and the Carrock Beck on the north. The varieties of basic and acid igneous rocks constituting this mass were grouped by Ward (1876) as hypersthenite, ?diorite and spherulitic felsite. From the general parallelism of the strike and dip and of the internal structures of the mass with the strike and dip of the adjacent stratified rocks, and the presence of large xenolithic masses of lavas of the Borrowdale Volcanic Series, Ward considered that the complex had resulted from metamorphism of the Borrowdale lavas. In his classic study of the complex, Harker (1894b, 1895) described the rocks under the major headings gabbro, diabase and granophyre. He attributed the variation in the rocks to magmatic differentiation at two periods; the first deep-seated and followed by the intrusion of gabbro, granophyre and diabase in that order, the second differentiation in place, whereby the variation in the main gabbro mass was produced. To account for the latter variation, an application of Soret's principle was advocated, whereby the earlier-separating crystals, particularly ilmenite, were concentrated in the cooler parts of the magma adjacent to the margins of the body.

The intrusion has been assigned to various periods; post-Silurian by Ward, possibly Tertiary by Harker (1902) on petrological affinities, and Ordovician by Green (1917) on the supposed Bala age of the Skiddavian grits of Great Sca Fell.

The complex may be divided into an eastern part, much of which is well exposed, and a larger western part where exposures are separated by wide areas of obscure ground. Conclusions as to the form and mutual relations of the rocks are here based on observations in the eastern part and these are described first, but it is probable that they are also applicable to the western part.

The rocks of the complex comprise a series of gabbroic types without olivine, but with few exceptions containing quartz, ranging from ilmenite-rich melagabbro through intermediate types to leucogabbro rich in feldspars (included lavas are represented by pyroxene-granulites); acid rocks, which are largely granophyric types, ranging from hedenbergite-granophyre to albite-granophyre; quartz-felsite which is probably of somewhat later date than the gabbros and granophyres. There is also a variety of minor intrusions including porphyrites, quartz-dolerites and granophyres, occurring as dykes or steeply dipping sheets within the complex and in the adjacent country rocks.

Within the complex, the constituent rocks for the most part seem to be narrow steeply inclined sheets lying parallel to the general strike of the long axis of the complex.

Field Relations of the Principal Rock-types

THE GABBROS

In the gabbros the variations, as seen in the cliffs to the south and west of Carrock Fell, reveal a rough symmetry about a longitudinal axis. The central mass of leucogabbro (the 'quartz-gabbro' of Harker and of the One-inch geological sheet) is separated from belts of melagabbro at the southern and northern margins by intermediate types in which banding and fluxion texture are displayed. This distribution, noted by Harker (1894b), was attributed by him to differentiation in place by the marginal concentration of the early crystallizing constituents. The resurvey has shown, however, that the several distinct types within the gabbro maintain their identities over considerable distances and have fairly rapid transitional contacts with one another, and this is opposed to their interpretation as a gradational series produced in place. In general, subdivision of the gabbro is possible only in the area lying south of Carrock Fell.

The melagabbros. The southern belt of melagabbro contains a variety of types so intimately associated that they have not been mapped separately. It includes ilmenite-rich gabbros, black gabbros containing much hornblende, and some more feldspathic types, commonly with an irregular, clotty and vein-like distribution of the feldspathic portions. Banded varieties are found in this belt, and here and there coarse pegmatitic veins and patches occur. Biotite, visible to the naked eye, is not uncommon in the gabbros here. These varieties are well developed in a strip up to 100 yd wide, extending westwards from Mosedale to half a mile north of Swineside. Farther west, similar ilmenite-rich and banded rocks are present on the northern side of Grainsgill and are visible in the tributary streams of Arm o' Grain and Brandy Gill. Here, however, less mafic types also occur, and it is doubtful whether any general separation, in an areal sense, of the varieties is present. Included masses of Borrowdale lavas are present throughout this belt, but reach their maximum development on or beyond its northern margin.

The southernmost marginal rock has a welded vertical contact with Skiddaw Slate on the hillside above Mosedale. It is not ilmenite-rich, but generally resembles the medium-grained gabbro forming the matrix in the main belt of lava xenoliths around Snailshell Crag. The slates are bleached and hornfelsed, and the gabbro has produced contact-metamorphic effects which differ in some important respects from those due to the Skiddaw granite. Evidence of a fault along the southern margin of the complex, such as Ward and Harker mapped, has not been found. In Poddy Gill, quarter of a mile north of the Grainsgill–Caldew junction, hornfelsed slates belonging to the aureole of the Skiddaw granite are faulted against fine-grained doleritic rock presumed to belong to the Carrock complex. Here the inclination of the contact and subsidiary fractures are suggestive of an upthrust of slate against igneous rock.

In the northern belt of melagabbro there is a wider development of ilmenite-rich rocks. These have been divided on the map (Fig. 10) into three main types. The northernmost belt contains ilmenite-rich gabbro mixed with varieties in which that mineral is not abundant. To the south are belts of banded gabbro and foliated or fluxion gabbro, both ilmenite-bearing, forming fairly well-defined strips that are traceable up the crags at the eastern end of Carrock Fell and westwards as far as Iron Crags, two-thirds of a mile north of Swineside,

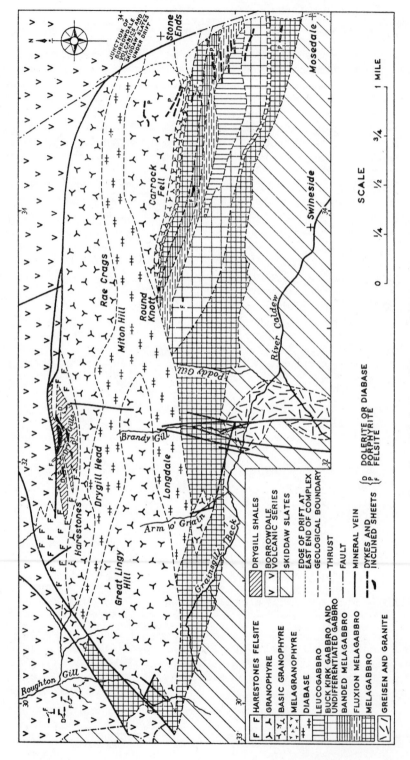

FIG. 10. *Sketch map of Carrock Fell complex*

a distance of $1\frac{1}{2}$ miles. The melagabbro belt has a northern marginal development of very coarsely crystalline rather feldspathic gabbro, approaching pegmatite in texture, with nests of granophyric material. Immediately to the north occurs the basic modification of the hedenbergite-granophyre, which Harker (1895) attributed to the incorporation of fragments of the gabbro in the granophyre magma. Xenoliths of lava are not so abundant as in the southern belt. They occur principally near the southern margin of the northernmost strip, where a good deal of medium-grained grey gabbro, not rich in ilmenite, is present. As in the southern melagabbro belt, some of the lava inclusions are sharply angular, showing little or no sign of reaction, but others are drawn out into thin bands, as if they had been thoroughly plastic. This evidence of partial fluxing of the inclusions is associated with vague merging contacts of granulite and gabbro, and is well marked in the northern belt of xenoliths.

The banded gabbros consist of alternations of layers respectively rich in feldspathic and ferromagnesian constituents. Ilmenite is often conspicuous. The banding is usually well displayed on fluted weathered surfaces. The bands vary in thickness from about an inch to less than $\frac{1}{16}$ inch (see Plate IV, B). The strike of the banding is a few degrees north of west, parallel to the margins of the belt, but whereas the latter dips southwards, the banding dips northwards, usually at 50° to 70°.

The fluxion gabbro is usually finer-grained than the banded gabbro, with a distinct foliated texture. It carries a considerable amount of ilmenite, and on the lower part of the crags about Crag Fast, 1500 yd E.S.E. of the summit of Carrock Fell, it is noticeably biotitic.

In the Roughton Gill area, to the west, melagabbro occupies much of the region between the North and South veins. An ilmenite-rich variety predominates but there is a widespread though variable development of pink granophyric material permeating the gabbros as patches and as irregular veins (see Plate IV, A). In the uppermost part of Thief Gills [297 338], the andesite roof of the intrusion is exposed. Near it the rock is medium-grained gabbro, and as the contact is approached granophyric material is common in the gabbro as veinlets and stringers which also extend into the hornfelsed roof rock.

The Buck Kirk Gabbro and the Snailshell Crag xenolithic belt. The term Buck Kirk Gabbro is applied to the medium-grained quartz-gabbro which occupies a vertical belt about 200 yd wide on the crags about Buck Kirk [355 328], 500 to 600 yd north of Mosedale. It is uniform in appearance and has an even grey colour. To the north, the Buck Kirk Gabbro merges into the coarser leucogabbro by transitional varieties in a distance of 20 to 30 yd. Similar medium to coarse leucogabbro appears to replace the Buck Kirk type to an increasing degree about half a mile west of Buck Kirk, where this type ceases to be mappable. On Buck Kirk itself, the rock appears to be devoid of lava xenoliths but these come in gradually southwards within a narrow strip which seems to be transitional to the main xenolithic belt of Snailshell Crag [355 326], 300 to 400 yd north of Mosedale. The latter, however, is separated from the Buck Kirk gabbro by a vertical sheet, 40 to 50 yd wide, of fairly coarse leucogabbro which closely resembles that of White Crags, though it is in places somewhat richer in ferromagnesian constituents. This sheet is traceable up the crags, and for a mile to the west. It has well-defined rapidly merging contacts with the gabbro on either side. The Buck Kirk Gabbro characteristically contains low-angle joints, gently dipping off an east-west axis. The absence of these in the leucogabbro, and some doubtful indications of metamorphism of the Buck Kirk type near its contacts with the narrow leucogabbro sheet, may indicate a slightly later age for the latter.

The Buck Kirk type is perhaps the most widespread of the varieties of gabbro. This type commonly occurs near the southern contact of the complex; it forms the host-rock of much of the Snailshell Crag xenolithic belt, and in the Grainsgill area it is frequently associated with fine-grained granulites.

Included masses of Borrowdale lava attain their greatest development on Snailshell Crag at the eastern end of the complex, where xenoliths predominate over gabbro across a width of 100 yd and through a vertical height of several hundred feet. They form large masses up to 40 yd across, some of which are riddled with veins of gabbro, as can be seen in the quarry [3566 3256] by the roadside, 200 yd N. of Mosedale. These xenoliths were regarded by Harker as probably forming part of the country rock to the east, and although the drift-obscured ground there is now mapped as underlain by Skiddaw Slate, it may well be that the great development of lava xenoliths at Snailshell Crag indicates proximity to the original margin of the complex. On weathered surfaces on the hillside west of the crags the detailed relations may be examined. There the large masses of lava, up to 150 yd long, completely engulfed in the gabbro, have their long axes parallel to the general trend of the complex. The smaller fragments may be angular, showing little sign of corrosion or, exceptionally, may be rounded or drawn out into lenticles or bands. In the belt of basic gabbro there is a pronounced tendency for clots of feldspathic and pegmatitic gabbro to be localized adjoining the xenolithic blocks, as if by segregation. Biotite is also conspicuously developed in the gabbros within and adjacent to the xenolithic belt, as Harker has already noted (1894b, p. 333). An interesting occurrence of biotite is as rims to small, more or less globular, patches of gabbro, one to two inches in diameter, which are occasionally found within the granulitized lavas.

Xenoliths derived from the coarsely porphyritic Eycott-type andesite are abundant in the small crags ½ mile N.E. of Swineside, where their relations with the gabbro throw some light on their history. These xenoliths vary from sharp angular blocks down to strings of drawn-out material recognizable only from the persistence of the characteristic large phenocrysts, arranged parallel to the banding of the gabbro. Fine-grained basic veins occur in the blocks of Eycott-type granulite, where they are clearly intrusive and weather with a structure parallel to the sides of the veins, the whole rock being penetrated by later irregular veins of coarse pegmatitic-type gabbro. Other fine-grained bands in the xenoliths, now pyroxene-granulites of very even grain-size, probably represent original fine-grained layers in the lavas, or perhaps minor intrusions into the lavas, of earlier date than the gabbro-complex.

The White Crags Leucogabbro. This central mass of fairly coarse black-and-white spotted rock is well exposed on the eastern face of Carrock Fell and on White Crags [349 331], ½ mile S.E. by E. of the summit of Carrock Fell. The outcrop is about 300 yd wide on White Crags, but it decreases eastwards, especially down the eastern face of the fell, becoming less than 100 yd wide where it disappears beneath the scree. To the west of White Crags it develops fluxion structure and traces of banding, and gradually loses its identity in the poorly-exposed ground south-west of the summit of the fell.

The White Crags leucogabbro lacks variation in internal structure, and xenoliths are absent. Considered with the narrower belt of leucogabbro south of Buck Kirk, and with a narrow tapering tongue of identical rock in the Snailshell Crag gabbro-granulite mélange at the northern end of the roadstone quarry, this type may be regarded as possibly the latest member of the main gabbro suite. No evidence, however, of sharp intrusive contacts, or of chilled contacts has been found.

THE DIABASE

It is convenient to retain Harker's (1894b) appellation of diabase for the suite of medium- to fine-grained basic rocks essentially composed of pyroxenes, hornblende and highly altered plagioclase, mapped by him to the north of Carrock Fell and Great Lingy Hill. His boundaries have been considerably modified by tracing them eastwards into the northern end of the crags flanking the fell on the east, and westwards as a narrow strip north of Great Lingy Hill. A narrow strip of basic rock south of the granophyre of Great Lingy Hill includes types characteristic of the diabase and this has therefore been separated from the main gabbros.

Typically, the diabase is characterized by small automorphic prisms of pyroxene, scattered throughout a white feldspathic matrix. Additionally, there are medium-grained grey gabbroic rocks, not unlike the Buck Kirk type of gabbro. Black rocks, rich in hornblende, also occur, and in places, for example on the north-east of Carrock Fell, these are interbanded with the speckled white type. Banding in the diabase is also well shown on weathered surfaces on Round Knott, $\frac{1}{2}$ mile W. of the summit of Carrock Fell, where rapid alternations of feldspathic and ferromagnesian bands dip southwards at 55°. Nearby the bands roll about north-easterly trending axes, and they are also disposed in small flat-lying, almost isoclinal folds.

Harker (1894b) contrasted the general absence of veining of the diabase by granophyre with the presence of such veins in the gabbros, and suggested that this favoured a younger age for the diabase. A plausible interpretation of the distribution of diabase and granophyre (Fig. 10) would be that the intrusion of the diabase had divided a once-continuous outcrop of granophyre into four parts, at the same time truncating the subdivisions of the main gabbro west by south of Carrock Fell. The critical parts of the latter area are, however, concealed by hill-peat and hill-wash; but the suggestion that the diabase is younger than the main gabbro is not opposed by any known facts. The age-difference, if any, is however probably slight. As shown below, there are some significant petrographical differences between the gabbros and the diabase.

The relations between the diabase and the granophyres require description. In the extreme east, the diabase forms a sheet 400 yd thick, lying at 45° between the granophyre masses of Carrock Fell and Rae Crags [335 342]. No actual contacts are visible here, but it is interesting to notice that both granophyres adjacent to the diabase show a variety rich in pseudomorphs after acicular hedenbergite, a type regarded by Harker as a marginal modification (1895, p. 127). There is nevertheless little veining of the diabase by granophyre. Dark veins in the granophyre prove to be of chlorite and biotite, not of the minerals of the diabase. On the south-eastern side of the crag called Round Knott, $\frac{1}{2}$ mile W. of the summit of the fell, a narrow layer of felsite separates the granophyre from the diabase. The granophyre probably is the later intrusion, as indicated by a one-inch vein of felsite cutting the diabase in a north-south direction on the north-eastern corner of the crag.

THE GRANOPHYRES AND THE FELSITE

The three major outcrops centred about Carrock Fell, Great Lingy Hill and Rae Crags respectively are separated from one another by diabase. These individual masses appear to be steep-sided bodies, elongated in conformity with the complex as a whole.

The Carrock Granophyre. This has a westerly-tapering wedge-shaped outcrop, and is best exposed on the 1000-ft crags of Scurth [348 337] at the eastern end of Carrock Fell. It varies in colour from reddish brown to reddish grey in the main central part, with a pale grey variety on the southern margin, next to a belt of basic granophyre which is further discussed below (p. 85). Small xenoliths occur marginally and also in the centre of the crags at 1500 ft O.D., east of Carrock Fell summit (Harker 1895, p. 137); the host-rock has a blotchy appearance, and the xenoliths look partially digested. Major joints in the granophyre dip S. 20° W. at 45° to 70° and W. 10° N. at 60° to 80°. The former direction is followed by a group of dykes at the south end of Scurth, while the latter joint-trend is prominent throughout the eastern end of the complex.

The Great Lingy Granophyre. This has an easterly-tapering wedge-shaped outcrop, not well exposed except on the crags near the outcrops of the Roughton Gill veins. Here it is a pale pinkish to reddish brown rock, much altered by hydrothermal activity in connection with the veins and with smaller parallel fractures. A grey type with acicular ferromagnesian pseudomorphs is also found, for example where Dale Beck crosses the Roughton Gill veins. Dark constituents are, however, uncommon in the granophyre blocks lying about Great Lingy itself.

The Rae Crags Granophyre. Lying to the north of the outcrop of the diabase, this has been mapped as a narrow strip extending the full length of the complex, although the boundaries are somewhat obscure. The rock is pale pinkish to reddish grey, poorly exposed except on Rae Crags, ½ mile W. by N. of Carrock Fell summit. Its relations with the Harestones Felsite are discussed on p. 86.

The Arm o' Grain Microgranite. A small area of acid rock, not generally granophyric in character, occupies some 200 yd of the lower part of the Arm o' Grain valley, a north bank tributary of the Grainsgill Beck. It is succeeded upstream by variable rocks of the diabase suite, and downstream by gabbro with granulite xenoliths, in contact with hornfelsed slates of the Skiddaw granite aureole. About 250 yd upstream from the outfall of Arm o' Grain, the microgranite has an unchilled contact against banded gabbro, and a few yards higher up it encloses what appear to be partially digested masses of basic rock. There are no exposures of the microgranite outside the valley, so that the shape of the outcrop is conjectured. Loose blocks probably nearly *in situ* on the hillside to the east are interesting as showing a network of acid veins in brecciated gabbro.

The granophyre-gabbro contact-belt of Furthergill Sike. Contacts between granophyre and gabbro are not well exposed except in the neighbourhood of Furthergill Sike, south-east of Stone Ends. Harker (1895, p. 133, fig. 1) described an important section [3518 3338] in the lowest exposures. Within a few yards there is a striking increase in the content of ferromagnesian minerals in the granophyre towards the gabbro. He noted especially the sharp contact of the most basic granophyre with gabbro, and the marginal modification of gabbro by the introduction of granophyric material.

On the north side of the sike, crags also show good contacts of gabbro with dark, medium-grained, diorite-like rock which passes northwards into brown basic granophyre. The most important exposures are on a vertical crag [350 334] at 1500 ft O.D., 570 yd W. of the point where the sike passes beneath the track from Stone Ends to Mosedale. The crag, which is readily accessible by means of a ledge at its foot, reveals the following succession of more or less vertical sheets of rock from south to north:

a   Ilmenite-bearing melagabbro (exposed in the north bank of the sike) passing northward into a coarse, pegmatite-like rock, enclosing here and there patches of diorite-like material, similar to b.

b   Dark, medium-grained rock with abundant ferromagnesian minerals and a suggestion of automorphism in the plagioclases, forming a belt about 15 yd wide. Its southern margin against the pegmatite appears sharp, but over several yards of crag, it varies from horizontal to vertical, as if following rough jointing in the pegmatite.

Northwards this type passes in a few yards into:

c   Reddish brown granophyre fairly rich in ferromagnesian minerals, with macroscopic quartz. This forms a narrow strip a few yards wide that passes gradually into:

d   Pale reddish-tinted granophyre resembling much of that on Scurth. This strip of normal granophyre is also recognisable on the crags 400 ft below, where it comes between b, c and e types. It passes northwards into:

e   Reddish brown granophyre with abundant clots of greenish ferromagnesian minerals, giving the rock a mottled appearance. This rock forms a belt 15 yd wide on the crags. Downhill it seems to be pinched out for a short distance but then widens rapidly to about 80 yd as seen in isolated exposures projecting through scree. In the 1500 ft O.D. crag, there is a knife-edge junction against:

f   A fine-grained, perhaps chilled variety of normal granophyre, which passes into normal granophyre in a distance of 10 to 20 yd. The sharp junction with the basic granophyre can readily be followed up the face of the crag.

Lower on the hillside, a distinct belt, 15 to 20 yd wide, of greyish white granophyre, rather fine-grained and poor in ferromagnesian constituents, is present as a marginal facies of the normal granophyre, against the more mafic types. The melagranophyres described under b and e above can be seen at intervals along the whole of the southern margin of the Carrock granophyre, notably immediately south of the summit of the fell. Other critical points bearing on the origin of these immediate types include the sharpness of the contacts between type a and type b, and between types e and f; and the presence of 'normal' granophyre between two belts of melagranophyre. Enrichment in ferromagnesian constituents apparently occurs at other contacts between granophyre and gabbro or diabase, though in no case is a facies developed strictly comparable with the Furthergill Sike melagranophyres. Thus the available field evidence appears opposed to interpreting the Furthergill Sike belt as being due to simple reaction between basic rocks and acid magma *in situ*. Rather does it suggest the existence of the melagranophyres *b* and *c* as entities that had developed prior to actual emplacement in their present situation.

The Harestones Felsite. The mass of felsite lying principally on the northern slope of Hare Stones, ½ mile S.W. of High Pike, is a pale greyish semi-translucent rock with small phenocrysts of nearly white feldspar and automorphic quartz, varying with gradations to a streaky, flow-banded and strongly brecciated rock, the brecciation apparently having been contemporaneous with the injection of the felsite magma. Films of black material are widespread along streaky flow lines. The principal exposures are on the northern slopes of Hare Stones, but good fresh rock can be obtained from the dump of an old level at the head of Long Grain, 530 yd W. 35° S. of High Pike. Smaller outcrops of the felsite are found within the Drygill Shales as narrow, steeply-inclined strings and stout lenticular masses. Felsite appears to border the Drygill Shales as seen in gullies on the south side of Drygill Beck, and to occur along the line of the Drygill Vein, for example 800 yd E. 30° S. of High Pike.

S.E.H.

PETROGRAPHY

The rocks of the Carrock Fell complex were among the earliest to be investigated by microscopical methods. Ward (1876, pp. 20–1) classified them as spherulitic felsites, ?diorites and hypersthenites or altered dolerites, and was impressed with the metamorphic appearance of some of the rocks. Trechmann (1882) re-examined Ward's hypersthenite and pointed out that the dominant pyroxene is diallage, not hypersthene. Teall (1888, p. 178) recognized that the 'felsite' has all the characteristics of granophyre as defined by Rosenbusch, and advanced the view that it passes by gradations into quartz-gabbro. Groom (1889) noticed the occurrence of thin veins which he classified as tachylite; he also supported Teall's opinion as to the relations between the granophyre and the gabbros. The only chemical investigation up to this time was due to Ward, who gave analyses of the 'felsite' of Carrock summit and the 'hypersthenite' of White Crags. In both, the alkali figures, especially those for soda, are very high when compared with more recent analyses.

The well-known papers by Harker (1894a, b; 1895) contain a petrographical description of the area so comprehensive that up to the time of the resurvey little further work had been done. Harker considered that an orderly, gradual variation existed within the main gabbro mass, from basic iron-ore gabbros round the margins, to quartz-gabbro in the centre. This view he supported by determinations of specific gravity showing a variation from a maximum of 3·265 at the northern margin to 2·679 in the central quartz-gabbro. A corresponding series of silica-determinations showed a range from 32·5 per cent to 59·7 per cent. Harker demonstrated the later age of the granophyres and advanced the view that the granophyre magma was hybridized by incorporation of material from the gabbros near the margins of the granophyre masses. He recognized the essential difference, which is now confirmed, between the augite of the gabbros and the iron-rich pyroxene ("a diopside approaching hedenbergite", 1895, p. 130) of the granophyres. He noted as a point requiring further study the proper determination of the nature of the opaque minerals

(1894b, p. 318). To the diabase he gave only scant attention. His account includes three chemical analyses by George Barrow; these are reproduced in Tables 5 and 7 below.

The only contribution during the present century has been a description of albite-granophyre and quartz-porphyry from Brandy Gill, by Holmes (1917).

The present account is based upon microscopic examination of 194 thin slices of rock collected mainly by S. E. Hollingworth. Harker's slices, now in the collection of the Department of Mineralogy and Petrology at Cambridge have also been examined through the courtesy of Professor C. E. Tilley.

HORNFELS OF THE CONTACT-ZONE

Altered slates of the Carrock Fell contact-zone. Along the southern margin of the complex a narrow belt, in places not more than 30 yd wide, reveals a distinctive type of metamorphism in the Skiddaw Slates, clearly associated with the intrusion of the gabbro. Between Poddy Gill and Arm o' Grain, contact metamorphism due to the Skiddaw Granite is superimposed on that due to the gabbro. Outside this area, however, the slates near the gabbro have been converted into hornfelses of a noticeably paler colour than the normal slates, and decidedly paler than the hornfelses associated with the granite. Shades of pale buff, brown, or pale greenish grey predominate, and in some, though not in all, of the rocks porphyroblasts of pink garnet and of sodic plagioclase are visible to the naked eye. Garnet is very rare in the Skiddaw Granite aureole, and feldspar porphyroblasts are not found except where they are associated with the gabbro.

Under the microscope it is found that a variable degree of recrystallization has taken place. Quartz may be partially or wholly recrystallized to form a granoblastic aggregate, in some instances showing the outlines of the original small grains marked by films of micaceous material within larger, optically-continuous quartz crystals (E 23502, E 23507).[1] At first sight the texture so produced bears some resemblance to micropegmatite, and it seems probable that this is the rock described by Green (1918, p. 131) as granophyre with phenocrysts of feldspar and biotite. That the rock was originally slate is, however, clear from the even dissemination through it of granules of opaque minerals, noted above as a characteristic feature of the slates, and from transitions to slate exhibited by many specimens (e.g. E 23499, E 23510). Other minerals showing from their coarser grain-size that they have been recrystallized include muscovite (E 23502), and chlorite with tourmaline and apatite in very small amounts (E 23496).

The commonest porphyroblasts in the gabbro contact-zone are ragged-ended chlorites, commonly reaching 2·5 mm long. It seems likely that these are pseudomorphs after biotite, for a few specimens contain biotite under identical conditions (E 23500). The plagioclase porphyroblasts reach as much as 4 mm across (E 17401–2), enclosing small inclusions of quartz and micaceous material as well as opaque granules. In composition they vary between albite and andesine; normally they are not zoned but a few examples (e.g. E 23515) show some zoning. Anorthoclase, showing fine quadrille twinning, takes the place of the plagioclase in a few specimens (e.g. E 23507). The presence of

---

[1]Numbers in brackets preceded by the letter E refer to sliced rocks in the English sliced rock collection of the Geological Survey and Museum.

sodic feldspars as phenocrysts in the contact-zone is taken to indicate mild soda-metasomatism of the adinole type, evidence for which is further discussed below (p. 105). The garnets vary up to 3 mm in diameter, rarely showing perfect crystal outlines. In some cases they are surrounded with a halo of quartz, free from chlorite and muscovite (E 23493). Usually they display sieve texture. Partial analyses of separated garnets from three localities have been carried out, with the results stated in Table IV. The partial analysis by Tilley (1926, p. 49), also quoted in the table, is of a garnet from a metamorphosed grit in Grainsgill, probably also from the gabbro contact-zone.

TABLE IV

Partial Analyses of Garnets

	1	2	3	4	5
FeO	30·3	29·1	31·8	30·16	27·48
MgO	2·3	2·5	2·1		3·28
CaO	1·1	1·2	1·2		1·42
MnO	5·3	6·9	4·4	6·02	3·84
Proximate compositions					
Almandine	70·1	67·1	73·2		
Spessartite	12·2	16·0	7·3		
Pyrope	7·9	6·8	6·7		
Grossularite	3·0	3·2	3·2		
Refractive index					
n_D	1·815	1·818	1·822		
Specific gravity					
(air dried)	4·00	4·10	4·08		

1. From quartz-chlorite-garnet hornfels, 600 yd N. 33° W. of Mosedale Bridge [3540 3246], Slice No. E 23493, Lab. No. 1566, Analyst, W. F. Waters.

2. From garnet-oligoclase-chlorite hornfels, 1130 yd N. 55° W. of Mosedale Bridge [3486 3259], Slice No. E 23496, Lab. No. 1567, Analyst, W. F. Waters.

3. From garnet-biotite hornfels, 750 yd W. of Grainsgill–Arm o' Grain junction [3107 3308], Slice No. E 23521, Lab. No. 1568, Analyst, W. F. Waters.

4. From metamorphosed grit, Grainsgill; Tilley (1926, p. 49).

5. From basic andesite, Riggindale, on slope of Kidsty Pike; Analyst, G. T. Holloway, *in* Green (1915, p. 210).

The analyses show the presence of significant amounts of the spessartite molecule in the garnets. Whether the occurrence of garnet in the contact-zone, admittedly a sporadic occurrence, is related to local concentration of manganese in the original sediment is not easy to decide. The analyses of Skiddaw Slates quoted in Chapter III show only very small amounts (0·07 to 0·54 per cent) of MnO. Moreover, if this were the controlling factor, it would be difficult to explain the abundance of garnets in the gabbro contact-zone and their paucity in the Skiddaw aureole, for the same beds appear to be involved in both.

Where the aureole of the gabbro has been affected by the higher-intensity metamorphism due to the later Skiddaw granite, the gabbro hornfelses continue to carry oligoclase porphyroblasts; biotite is far more abundant; garnet is rare or absent; and cordierite makes its appearance (E 23515).

Where the stream cuts the gabbro-slate junction [3531 3339] at the head of Grainsgill Beck, there are scattered about on the south bank of the stream blocks of a remarkable rock, not yet found *in situ*, which may represent a more advanced type of soda-metasomatism. The most abundant constituent is myrmekite (intergrown oligoclase and quartz) forming spheruliths 1·0 to 1·5 mm in diameter. Phenocrysts of oligoclase up to 1·5 mm across also occur. The base consists of quartz, chlorite and fine-grained biotite, with sporadic zircons, some worn-looking, others sharp (E 23519). It is unfortunate that lack of exposure prevents more adequate study of this rock, the only one in the district suggesting a link between the metamorphosed sediments and the granophyres.

Hornfelsed andesites of the roof. The andesites which form the roof of the gabbro west of the junction of the branches of Thief Gills contain phenocrysts of oligoclase up to 0·6 mm long in a matrix of oligoclase laths, chlorite, and magnetite and 'leucoxene' granules. Metamorphism has given rise to biotite, in ragged crystals normally 0·05–0·1 mm long, but exceptionally reaching 0·25 mm, the larger crystals being associated with nests of quartz which may represent former vesicles. Adjacent to the gabbro, micropegmatite has been introduced (E 14996–7). Much of the biotite has been converted into very pale green chlorite with inclusions of titanium minerals. The rocks have been severely sheared after metamorphism, low birefringence chlorite having $\gamma = $ 1·611, and calcite being introduced at this stage (E 23529). Some quartz also appears to have been introduced (E 23512).

Skiddaw Slates above the thrust plane. The Skiddaw Slates thrust over the andesites of the gabbro roof in Thief Gills consist of severely sheared grey-brown mudstones enclosing fragments of chloritic siltstone. The chlorite of the siltstone has been partially converted into biotite, while the mudstone contains lenticular ovoid spots up to 0·3 mm long of fine-grained white mica, probably 'pinite', after cordierite (E 23532). The chlorite in a quartz-chlorite veinlet crossing the rock has been partially converted into biotite. Thus there is some petrographic evidence in favour of the view that the intrusion of the Carrock Fell complex took place after thrusting and folding of the adjacent rocks. The evidence of hydrothermal activity subsequent to the metamorphism of the andesites in no way contradicts this view.

THE GABBROS

Southern melagabbro belt. Considerable variation is displayed by the gabbros within this belt. Ilmenite-rich gabbros occur, but it would not be correct to describe the belt as ilmenite-gabbro, for it also contains areas where the rocks owe their relatively high density (which Harker found to vary from 2·95 to 3·11) to the abundant development of late hornblende. Some rocks of this type contain as little as 2·5 per cent by weight of opaque minerals.

Specimens showing gabbro in contact with biotite-garnet-plagioclase-quartz-hornfels (E 15285) and with biotite-plagioclase-hornfels (E 17404) were obtained from the crags above Mosedale, at the southern margin of the gabbro. In the latter specimen, there is a narrow band of chlorite along the contact, and the hornfels is fringed with sericite. The gabbro contains xenomorphic

TABLE V

Chemical analyses and norms of Carrock Fell Gabbros

	I Ilmenite- melagabbro E[1]16180 940	A Ilmenite- melagabbro C[1]1866	II Leuco- gabbro E16181 941	B Quartz- gabbro C2045	III Diabase E16182 942
Slice No. Lab. No.					
Analyses					
SiO_2	41·38	32·53	52·25	53·50	48·51
Al_2O_3	14·04	—	18·71	22·20	16·83
Fe_2O_3	3·14	8·44	0·90	3·60	1·85
FeO	15·90	17·10	7·86	2·64	7·39
MgO	5·63	7·92	2·84	2·00	6·78
CaO	9·73	—	9·52	9·45	10·84
Na_2O	1·56	—	2·90	4·26	2·36
K_2O	0·72	—	1·18	0·61	1·25
$H_2O > 105°C$ ..	1·88	—	1·15	—	2·27
$H_2O < 105°C$ ..	0·18	—	0·16	—	0·19
TiO_2	5·05	5·30	2·18	0·45	1·20
P_2O_5	0·14	—	0·30	—	0·18
MnO	0·37	—	0·17	0·35	0·15
FeS_2	0·22	—	0·02	—	0·05
Cr_2O_3	—	—	—	—	0·04
Ignition loss ..	—	—	—	1·50	—
	99·94		100·14	100·59	99·89
Norms					
Q	—		4·5	4·0	—
or	3·9		7·2	3·3	8·9
ab	13·1		24·6	36·2	19·9
an	29·2		34·2	39·8	30·9
di	15·4		9·6	6·0	18·1
wo ..		7·7	4·8	3·0	9·3
en ..		3·3	2·0	1·3	5·5
fs ..		4·4	2·8	1·7	3·3
hy	10·7		12·6	3·7	4·5
en		4·6	5·1	3·7	2·8
fs ..		6·1	7·5	—	1·7
ol	10·8		—	—	10·1
fo ..		4·3			6·0
fa ..		6·5			4·1
mt	4·4		1·4	5·3	2·6
il	9·7		4·1	0·9	2·3
ap	0·3		0·7		0·3
cr	—		—	—	0·1
Normative plagioclase, An	69		58	53	61

[1]The prefix E before the slice number in this table and in Tables VI and VII indicates slices in the English sliced rock collection of the Geological Survey and Museum; the prefix C to slices in the collection of the Department of Mineralogy and Petrology, Cambridge.

plagioclase of composition An_{33},[1] and the composition of the porphyroblasts in the hornfels is the same. Chloritized hornblende, ilmenite, biotite and interstitial micropegmatite complete the assemblage in the gabbro. At a distance of 1 ft from the contact (E 17405), the plagioclase has the composition An_{50}, while elsewhere along the contact plagioclase up to An_{60} has been noted. It appears, however, that there is a tendency for the plagioclase to be less calcic along the southern margin than elsewhere in the gabbro. Ilmenite-rich gabbro has not been found near the contact, but here the gabbros are commonly rich in late hornblende or chlorite. Relics of augite may occur.

The ilmenite-melagabbro (E 16180) is a hypautomorphic-granular aggregate of plagioclase (labradorite, An_{64}), pale brown augite showing closely-spaced cleavage, ilmenite, ilmenomagnetite, hornblende and biotite. An analysis of the rock is given in Table V and a mode in Table VI. The pyroxene has $\beta = 1.702$[2] and $2V = 52°$, suggesting a composition $Ca_{41} Mg_{33} Fe_{26}$, and thus lies in the augite field of the clinopyroxene classifications proposed by Benson (1944) and Poldervaart (1947). The augite appears to mantle the labradorite and this texture is general among the gabbros. Green hornblende with $\gamma = 1.680$ and $Z : c = 12°$ has partially replaced the augite, which it penetrates in a very intimate and irregular manner. The composition of the amphibole is probably variable. It is quite clear that it originated after the crystallization of the rock, for the main hornblende regions are linked by tiny veinlets which traverse the labradorite.

The opaque minerals were studied by means of polished sections, examined under the microscope in reflected light. It was established that the ilmenite-melagabbro contains both large xenomorphic single crystals or aggregates of a few crystals of ilmenite, and also separate crystals of magnetite with plates of ilmenite segregated along crystallographic directions to make a pattern of Widmanstetten type. The ilmenite is appreciably anisotropic, with reflectivity

---

[1]All the plagioclase determinations given in the present account are based upon measurements of the minimum refractive index by the immersion method, using fragments of known orientation where possible. The maximum error by this method may be estimated at 5 per cent An.

[2]The pyroxene determinations are based upon the method advocated by H. H. Hess, 1949, p. 627; the measurements of optic axial angles quoted are direct measurements from one axis to the other unless otherwise stated.

Localities of specimens in Table V

I   Ilmenite-melagabbro, 600 yd N. 28° W. of bridge over River Caldew at Mosedale [3544 3248]. Analyst, B. E. Dixon, (*in* Guppy 1956, p. 25) (Southern melagabbro belt).

A   "Iron-ore gabbro", upper part of Furthergill Sike. Analyst, G. Barrow, quoted from Harker (1894b, p. 323) (Northern melagabbro belt).

II   Leucogabbro, 920 yd N. 39° W. of bridge over River Caldew at Mosedale [3517 3264] Analyst, B. E. Dixon, (*in* Guppy 1956, p. 20) (Southern narrow belt of leucogabbro).

B   "Quartz-gabbro", by roadside, 150 yd N.N.W. of Chapel Stone. Analyst, G. Barrow, quoted from Harker (1894b, p. 323) (Probably from central belt of leucogabbro).

III   Diabase, 720 yd N. 57° E. of spot-height 2174 on summit of Carrock Fell [3467 3397]. Analyst, B. E. Dixon (*in* Guppy 1956, p. 29).

of 20·5, measured by the photoelectric cell method of Moses.[1] The mineral appears quite homogeneous. The magnetite crystals with ilmenite plates tend to occur peripherally to the large ilmenite crystals, thus appearing to have crystallized later than the ilmenite. On the nomenclature of Orcel (*in* Termier and others 1948) they would be classified as ilmenomagnetites. As would be expected, the ilmenite has a decidedly lower magnetic susceptibility than the ilmenomagnetite, and in a selective magnetic separation it was found that the homogeneous ilmenite came out in the same fraction as hornblende. Magnetic separation of ilmenite from these rocks for economic use would clearly be difficult.

In the westernmost outcrops of the main gabbro, in the vicinity of the Roughton Gill lead veins, some of the gabbros, prior to the extensive hydrothermal alteration which has affected them (p. 109), seem to have been melagabbros rich in ilmenite and magnetite. The magnetite has remained unaffected by the alteration, but ilmenite has been converted into white-reflecting 'leucoxene' (anatase), and some of the titanium has been exported beyond the margins of the original grains to form small crystals of sphene. The 'leucoxene' crystals are of interest because they show the presence of very thin plates of unaltered magnetite along the cleavages. Here, then, it appears that the original mineral was not homogeneous ilmenite, as in the eastern melagabbros, but magnetoilmenite (in Orcel's sense of the term). The magnetoilmenite and magnetite aggregates are generally not in contact with one another in the rock (E 23524). Coarse apatite occurs in some of the western melagabbros (E 23528), and pegmatite patches, similar to those to be described below from the northern belt of melagabbro, contain crystals of purplish augite up to 4 cm long (E 16189). Micropegmatite occurs in all the gabbros in this area.

Orthoclase was not found in the analysed melagabbro and it is probable that the small potash figure in the analysis is to be attributed to biotite, which fringes some of the opaque grains, and to micaceous alteration products. Small amounts of biotite are present in nearly all the rocks of the southern melagabbro belt (e.g. E 15249, E 16191, E 17262, E 17389), and the association of this mineral with ilmenite is a general feature. It also occurs intergrown with quartz and orthoclase interstitially between the plagioclase crystals (E 15249).

Apatite is generally present, there being some indication of a tendency for this mineral to be more abundant in rocks very rich in late hornblende (e.g. E 16188). A similar tendency is noticeable in the northern melagabbro belt.

The modes of the melagabbros cited in Table VI indicate that the use of the term is consistent with the usage proposed by Johannsen (1937).

Granulite xenoliths in the gabbros. Inclusions derived from the Skiddaw Slates appear to be restricted to the few inches of gabbro immediately adjacent to the southern margin of the complex; here, fragments of microscopic dimensions which are enclosed in the gabbro show characters similar to the adjacent hornfels with, in one case, some evidence of attack by hornblende (E 15285) and chlorite. Xenoliths derived from the Borrowdale lavas are, on the other hand, of common occurrence, especially in the melagabbro and Buck Kirk type gabbro belts. These are now in the condition of pyroxene- and hornblende-granulites. Those most readily recognised in the field as being originally lavas are of the porphyritic Eycott types, derived from basic andesites. These contain automorphic and hypautomorphic plagioclase phenocrysts up to 20

---

[1] *in* Short, M. N. 1940, p. 89. Moses obtained the figure 20·1 for ilmenite.

mm long of composition An_{65}, showing marginal zoning to andesine. There is no reason to think that any change of composition has taken place in the phenocrysts during metamorphism, their composition having been close to that of the normal plagioclase of the andesites before metamorphism (see p. 58). The groundmass, on the other hand, has been completely recrystallized, and may have suffered metasomatic changes. The unaltered Eycott andesites have a hyalo-ophitic groundmass of plagioclase laths, skeletal and altered pyroxenes, and opaque minerals enclosed in devitrified glass. In the granulites, the groundmass is an even granoblastic aggregate of plagioclase and drop-like pyroxenes, with opaque minerals but no glass. The grain-size is normally decidedly finer than in the adjacent gabbro. Stringers and pockets of micro-pegmatite are conspicuous in some examples (E 23494) but entirely wanting in others (E 15261). The pyroxene, where fresh, appears to be similar in com-position to that of the adjacent gabbro; a typical example proved to contain augite with $\beta = 1\cdot703$ (E 15261). In only one instance was the presence of orthopyroxene established in a granulite; this was from low down on the crags [3513 3327], 580 yd S. 50° W. of Stone Ends, where hypersthene, appreciably pleochroic in shades of pink and green, and enclosing rods and runic inclusions of clinopyroxene, occurs. Here the adjacent gabbro also contains hypersthene. Possibly this comes from near the locality mentioned by Harker (1895, p. 125, footnote) as yielding orthopyroxene.

Other granulites contain no phenocrysts, but are similar to the groundmass of the metamorphosed Eycott type in texture (E 15259, E 17264, E 23506, E 17377). In many of the granulites, the pyroxene has been partially or wholly replaced by hornblende, the drop-like shape of the granules being, however, preserved. Tiny veinlets of amphibole link up the granules, indicating that the alteration took place after recrystallization of the rock.

At least part of the banding found in the gabbros is due to the inclusion of thin parallel sheets of granulite between layers of 'normal' gabbro, and to the presence of thin layers of non-porphyritic granulite between layers of Eycott type (E 15255, E 15256, E 17261, E 23503–4). On a microscopic scale, banding results from the alteration of layers rich in hornblende with layers poor in this mineral (E 15263); a texture such as this may perhaps be inherited from the flow-banded portion of a lava, for both layers rich and poor in ferromagnesian constituents have granulitic texture.

Adjacent to some of the Eycott type xenoliths, the process of metamorphism may be followed a step farther, for labradorite phenocrysts, similar in size and composition to those in the xenolith, but somewhat more rounded, are found embedded in a matrix, not of fine-grained granulite, but of gabbro indis-tinguishable from the Buck Kirk type (E 23494–6, E 23503, E 23505). Thus it appears highly probable that gabbro may be produced by recrystallization of lava. The scope and implications of this conclusion are further considered below (p. 106).

As already noted (p. 82), some of the inclusions merge vaguely into the surrounding gabbro, while others are sharply defined. Blebs of gabbro may also occur within obvious granulites (E 15262).

Southern leucogabbro belt. The narrow belt of leucogabbro extending west-ward from the north side of Snailshell Crag is composed of coarse, mottled white and green rock which contrasts markedly with the grey and black gabbros to the south. The analysed rock (E 16181) is composed of labradorite, zoned from An_{62} to An_{54}, in interlocked hypautomorphic crystals reaching 3·0 mm long. In thin section, considerable areas are free from ferromagnesian minerals, but clots of augite occur, their margins mantling the adjacent feldspars. The augite is pale purplish brown, exhibiting closely-spaced cleavage and 'herring-bone' structure. The composition differs little from that of the augite in the melagabbro to the south; here the optical constants are $\beta = 1·703$, $2V = 46°$, suggesting a proximate composition with the ratios $Ca_{36} Mg_{35} Fe_{29}$. Pale green hornblende has attacked and partially replaced the pyroxene. The attack appears to have proceeded mainly along cleavages, leaving rod-like relics of pyroxene within the amphibole. The feldspar in the rock has automorphic terminations towards pools of quartz and (sericitized) orthoclase. Examined in polished section, the rock proves to contain large homogeneous xenomorphic ilmenite grains, and also areas of ilmenite plates oriented in Widmanstetten fashion, but in a matrix of hornblende. Such a texture is a remarkable feature of this and other Carrock Fell gabbros; it can only indicate some such sequence of events as the following: (i) crystallization of titanomagnetite (ii) exsolution of ilmenite plates (iii) replacement of magnetite by hornblende, leaving the ilmenite plates unaffected.

A series of five specimens taken 10 yd apart across the northern margin of the leucogabbro with the Buck Kirk type gabbro to the north (E 17380–4) are indicative of gradational merging rather than intrusive relations, with a suggestion of a reduction of grain-size northward, concurrent with increasing abundance of ferromagnesian constituents.

Buck Kirk Gabbro. The grey gabbro characterizing the belt running westward from Buck Kirk differs from the leucogabbro mainly in having a greater content of hornblende (at least in part derived from augite) and in being finer-grained. The rock may be classified as quartz-hornblende-gabbro. Labradorite (An_{55-60}) forms hypautomorphic crystals averaging about 2 mm long; hornblende, pleochroic in shades of green and having $\gamma = 1·680$, forms large plates some of which enclose runic relics of pyroxene. Biotite, with $\gamma = 1·640$, may occur intergrown with the amphibole, or forming fringes round ilmenite grains. Interstitial quartz and perthitic orthoclase are present (E 15256, E 17263) and a small amount of apatite.

Among the highly-altered gabbros at the western end of the complex, some were probably of the Buck Kirk type before hydrothermal alteration connected with the Roughton Gill lead veins affected them (E 14638, E 15050, E 15244). Replacement of the plagioclases with clay minerals emphasises the fact that many of the feldspar crystals have narrow rims of quartz round them (E 14638).

Central leucogabbro belt. In the belt running through White Crags, and forming the central part of the main gabbro, white, green-speckled leucogabbro—the quartz-gabbro of Harker and of the solid edition of the One-inch Geological Sheet—is uniformly present. Plagioclase is more abundant here than in the southern leucogabbro belt; the crystals average about 3·0 mm long and have the composition An_{56-60}. Clots of pale brown pyroxene occur, containing parallel rod-like diallagic inclusions. The optical properties of the pyroxene differ very little from those of the clinopyroxenes already described: $\beta = 1·703$, $2V = 49°$, $X : c = 41°$. Partial replacement of pyroxene by oriented crystals of hornblende has occurred. Interstitial quartz, orthoclase, and micrographic intergrowths of these two minerals, probably with some albite, are present (E 15242). Ilmenite, accompanied by a little biotite, occurs only sparingly. Harker's analysed specimen (Cambridge No. 2045; Harker 1894b, p. 323) shows labradorite mantled with large clinopyroxenes and with hornblendes which contain rod-like relics of augite; micropegmatite occurs in interspaces and in tiny veinlets between the plagioclase crystals.

Fluxion and banded melagabbros. An abrupt change in the gabbro occurs to the north of the central leucogabbro belt. Dark gabbros, richer in ferromagnesian and opaque constituents, and characterized by foliated texture, make their appearance. The foliated appearance (which is also developed within the leucogabbro near its northern margin) is due to the orientation of the plagioclase crystals in the direction of strike of the complex. A similar alignment of feldspars is found in granulite xenoliths which reappear in this belt (E 15261). The plagioclase of the fluxion gabbros ranges from An_{70} down to An_{52} (E 17390, E 16192, E 15247, E 23545–6), while optical measurements on a representative clinopyroxene gave $\beta = 1·696$, $2V = 46°$ (Ca_{37} Mg_{40} Fe_{23}). Partial alteration of clinopyroxene to hornblende is displayed. The ferromagnesian minerals show little evidence of preferred orientation in the rocks, but ilmenite shows a tendency to occur in elongate, somewhat rounded plates, parallel to the foliation.

There is a marked increase in quantity of opaque constituents in the fluxion and banded gabbros, as compared with the leucogabbro. In the former, normal types carry up to 21·3 per cent by weight of ilmenite + ilmenomagnetite (E 17390) while an unusual segregation proved to contain 60 per cent by weight of opaque minerals (E 15248) in a measured section. The bulk of the opaque mineral in the segregation proved to be chromite, with discontinuous rims of ilmenite round the grains, presumably the result of exsolution. This was the only example of such a segregation found during the resurvey.

Not all the gabbro within the fluxion and banded belt can be classed strictly as melagabbro. As shown in Table VI (p. 98), some of the fluxion gabbros contain a proportion of light-coloured minerals substantially exceeding that of dark constituents. One such rock (E 23546) consisting predominantly of labradorite (An_{65}), with discontinuous bands of ilmenite crystals, and bands containing chlorite, epidote and calcite, has been hydrothermally altered.

In certain cases the banding displayed in this belt is, without doubt, the result of partial incorporation of narrow granulite xenoliths, but the greater part of the banding is caused by alternating layers of the light and dark minerals of the gabbro.

Northern melagabbro and gabbro-pegmatite belt. Some of the best examples of ilmenite-melagabbros come from the northernmost strip in the main gabbro, particularly around the head of Furthergill Sike, the locality of Harker's analysed specimen of 'iron-ore gabbro' (Cambridge No. 1866; Harker 1894b, p. 323). There is still little change in the compositions of the primary minerals; the plagioclase is labradorite, An_{60-65}; the diallagic clinopyroxene has $\beta = 1·695$, $2V = 48°$ (E 23541). The opaque grains are large, homogeneous ilmenite, up to 1·25 mm in diameter; a little pyrite also occurs. Partial replacement of clinopyroxene by pale brown hornblende with $\gamma = 1·685$ has taken place. Green biotite, associated with secondary magnetite and quartz, is a late mineral.

Towards the contact with the dark granophyre to the north, the grain-sizes of the minerals in the gabbro greatly increase, giving rise to a belt which may be described as gabbro pegmatite. Partly hornblendized clinopyroxenes several inches long may be collected here. Near the ordinary melagabbro, the minerals in the pegmatite have similar compositions to their counterparts in the mela-gabbro (E 23542–3), but as the granophyre is approached, the coarse plagioclase becomes less calcic and there is an increase in the iron-content of the clinopyroxene; for example in the pegmatite adjacent to the dark granophyre exposed in the crag 500 yd S. 58° W. of Stone Ends (E 23547) the plagioclase is andesine-labradorite (An_{50}), while the pyroxene has the following properties: $\beta = 1 \cdot 710$, $2V = 54°$ suggesting a proximate metal ratio $Ca_{43}Mg_{25}Fe_{32}$. In the crag at the 1500-ft contour (p. 85) the pegmatite next to the melagranophyre contains albite and hedenbergite, with coarse prehnite having $\alpha = 1 \cdot 619$, $\gamma = 1 \cdot 641$. Apatite is more than usually abundant in the pegmatite; a micrometric estimate on one section gave $4 \cdot 1$ per cent by weight (E 23547). Hornblende and green biotite are locally abundant.

At the extreme northern margin of the main gabbro there is thus evidence of coarse crystallization and fluxing, with a transition towards the composition of the granophyre indicated by enrichment of the clinopyroxene in iron, and of the plagioclase in soda.

THE DIABASE

The diabase has two characteristics which serve to distinguish it petrographically from the gabbros. The first is the persistently automorphic character of the clinopyroxenes, which contrasts markedly with their xenomorphic, enveloping disposition in the main gabbros. There is also some tendency for the plagioclases to exhibit crystal faces. The second characteristic is the extensive sericitization shown by the feldspars. Although this kind of alteration is not absent in the main gabbros, it never reaches the advanced stage seen in the diabase. This alteration, and the extensive development of hornblende from the pyroxene, justifies the continued use of the term diabase, originally applied by Harker, in the accepted British sense of the term.

The analysed rock (Table V, p. 90) differs chemically from the gabbros in its higher magnesia-content, and in containing more combined water. The plagioclases are heavily altered to sericite, chlorite and perhaps epidote. Augite forms crystals up to $1 \cdot 5$ mm long, intimately penetrated by green hornblende. Ilmenite granules have haloes of 'leucoxene' (anatase) round them. Quartz and micropegmatite occur interstitially, filling up the spaces between the main constituents.

The clinopyroxene of the diabase (E 17375) is an augite with $\beta = 1 \cdot 705$, $2V = 50°$, suggesting a proximate composition corresponding to $Ca_{38} Mg_{31} Fe_{31}$, which differs very little from the pyroxene of the main gabbro mass. Where the rock has not been heavily hornblendized it has an easily-recognisable appearance in hand specimen, for the tiny eight-sided augites can be seen as spots scattered through a matrix of white feldspar and quartz (E 15250, E 17258, E 23534). Where sufficient plagioclase remains unaltered to make determination possible, a range between An_{47} and An_{60} is found. A polished section (E 23534) showed only round-ended platy crystals of homogeneous ilmenite, with a little pyrite, the latter mineral occurring as veinlets in the silicates.

In the heavy, dark, rather fine-grained rock well-represented on Miton Hills the amount of hornblende is considerable. An amphibole pleochroic in shades of brown here has the appearance of a primary mineral: this is not an oxyhornblende, for the maximum refractive index is less than 1·690. Green amphibole, probably of later age, is also present; apatite crystals which enclose amphibole are also believed to be of later origin (E 15252). The green amphibole penetrates and to some extent replaces plagioclase (E 17259, E 17260).

Relation to the granophyres. Contact-specimens between diabase and granophyre have been secured from two localities, Round Knott (as already mentioned) and from 500 yd N. 65° W. of Stone Ends. Both sets of specimens are disappointing in that they fail to provide unambiguous evidence of the age-relations of the two rocks. The diabase at the latter locality (E 23536) contains its characteristic automorphic pyroxenes, but the plagioclase has the composition An_{20} and may thus have been albitized. Between this and the granophyre occurs a vein-rock, containing quartz, epidote and hornblende. The granophyre is heavily altered, and now consists of epidote pseudomorphs after the typical equant sodic plagioclases and quartz. At Round Knott (E 15273, E 23557, E 23708) the plagioclase of the diabase is not more calcic than oligoclase near the contact, again suggesting albitization. Between the diabase and the granophyre, a narrow band of dark grey felsite occurs, evidently emplaced later than either of the adjacent rocks, for it carries inclusions of minerals derived from the diabase, and it cuts sharply across the granophyre, sending branch veinlets into the latter carrying with them fragments of material from the diabase. The adjacent variety of granophyre contains acicular pseudomorphs after hedenbergite, and is of marginal type (p. 83). All that can be established from these suites of specimens is that there has been hydrothermal or felsitic veining along the contact.

However, at the locality north-west of Stone Ends, a narrow veinlet containing albite, micropegmatite and epidote was found cutting diabase (E 23535). Having regard also to the fact that the plagioclase of the diabase is probably albitized near the granophyre, while the granophyre is enriched in hedenbergite, it appears probable that the diabase was emplaced before the granophyre.

THE GRANOPHYRES AND THE FELSITE

Marginal melagranophyre. At the northern margin of the main gabbro mass, coarse pegmatitic gabbro grades northward into pegmatite with sodic plagioclase, hedenbergite and coarse micropegmatite. This is succeeded to the north by a belt of grey mottled rock (E 15271, E 15258, E 17368, E 17385–8, E 23550) which might be described as granophyric diorite or markfieldite. To emphasise the fact that this is a marginal modification of granophyre, the term melagranophyre is here employed. The analysed rock (E 16183) is composed of stout hypautomorphic plagioclase crystals reaching 3·0 mm long but averaging about 1·0 mm, zoned outward from An_{30} to An_{10}; pale green clinopyroxene having $\gamma = 1·736$, $2V = 56°$ (hedenbergite of proximate composition Ca_{41} Mg_4 Fe_{55}); coarse micropegmatite; opaque minerals and a little late biotite. The other specimens are essentially similar. A few zircon crystals occur (E 17387) and a little apatite is present. Pyroxene-granulite xenoliths, though not common, are occasionally found enclosed in the melagranophyre

TABLE VI

Modes of Carrock Fell Rocks

(Weight–Percentages)

Slice No.	Name	Plagioclase	Pyroxene	Hornblende + Chlorite	Biotite	Quartz + Orthoclase + Micropegmatite	Ilmenite + Magnetite	Apatite
(Assumed specific gravity:-		2·7	Augite 3·3 Hedenbergite 3·6	3·0	3·0	2·6	5·0	3·2)
E 17405	Marginal melagabbro, S. belt	45	—	40	2	5	7	1
E 16180[a]	Ilmenite-melagabbro, do.	41	10	34	1	—	14	x
E 17389	Melagabbro, do.	41	7	25	5	5	17	x
E 16188	Melagabbro, do.	15	3	75	1	—	6	x
E 15261	Pyroxene-granulite	60	12	11	—	—	7	
E 16181[a]	Leucogabbro, S. belt	60	11	13½	½	8	7	x
E 15246	Buck Kirk type gabbro	63	2	26	1	4	4	
E 15242	Leucogabbro, Central belt	71	11	8	—	5	5	
C 2045[a]	"Quartz-gabbro" (Harker)	73	8	8	—	10	1	
E 23545	Fluxion gabbro	60	9	18	1	4	9	x
E 16192	Fluxion gabbro	50	24	14	1	1	10	x
E 23548	Ilmenite-melagabbro, N. belt	35	20	24	1	1½	17	2½
E 23550	Melagranophyre	34	23	17	—	18	8	x
E 16183[a]	Melagranophyre	51	12	11	—	18	8	
E 16184[a]	Granophyre	13	3	3		78	3	
C 2051[a]	"Augite-granophyre" (Harker)	9	3	3		85	x	
E 16182[a]	Diabase	43	17	24		13	3	x

[a]Chemically analysed rock

(E 16187, E 23551). These were presumably derived from basic lavas; the constituent minerals are hedenbergite and plagioclase, apparently identical in composition with the minerals of the enclosing host-rock.

The melagranophyre is confined to the strip along the junction between the main gabbro mass and the Carrock Fell granophyre (p. 85), save that a small area of similar rock occurs adjacent to the diabase, about ¼ mile north-northwest of the summit of Carrock Fell (E 15269).

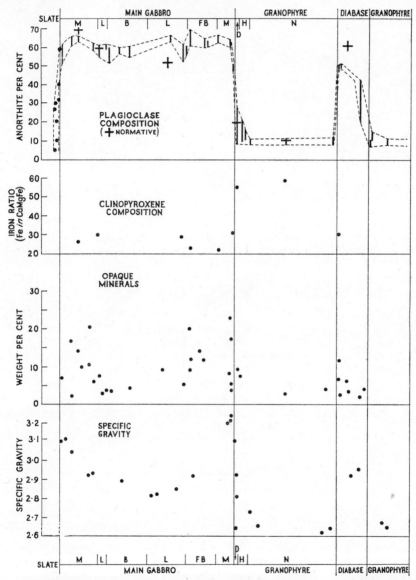

FIG. 11. *Mineral variation diagram for a cross section at the eastern end of the Carrock Fell complex. M = melagabbro, L = leucogabbro, B = Buck Kirk gabbro, FB = fluxion-banded gabbro, D = melagranophyre, H = intermediate granophyre, N = normal granophyre*

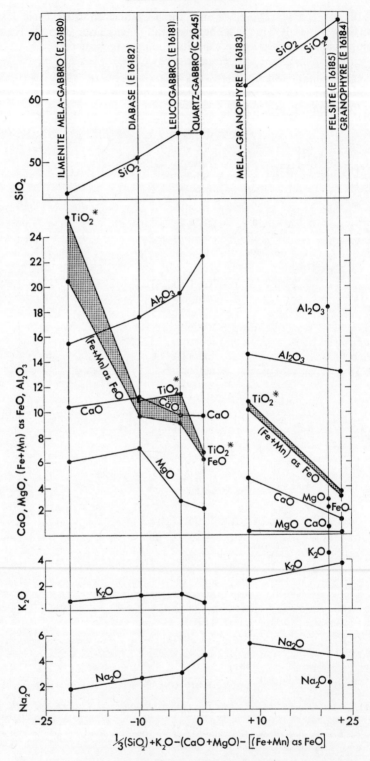

FIG. 12. *Chemical variation diagram for the Carrock Fell complex*

Between the melagranophyre and the normal granophyre there occurs an intermediate type which contains more micropegmatite than the melagrano- phyre, but more hedenbergite (and its alteration products) than the ordinary granophyre. The belt north of the melagranophyre in which this type occurs has been distinguished on the sketch map (Fig. 10). Similar rock, however, is also found near the margins of the diabase, in both the Carrock and Rae Crags granophyres. The long acicular crystals of pyroxene are plainly visible in hand- specimen (E 15268, E 17368, E 23552, E 23554, E 23559), but in many cases they have been converted by hydrothermal action into amphibole or chlorite, or by weathering into limonite. In the crag at 1500 ft O.D., east of the fell summit, the belt of marginal granophyre of this type is split by a zone of normal granophyre (E 23553), while to the north there is a sharp contact between marginal and normal granophyre (E 16186, E 23555), though without satisfactory evidence of chilling. Fragments of melagranophyre have also been found enclosed in normal granophyre (E 15257, E 17388). Thus the marginal granophyre and melagranophyre appear to have been partially or wholly crystallized before the consolidation of the normal granophyre; but no sub- stantial time-break is indicated.

Normal granophyre. The analysed rock (E 16184) is a pinkish grey heden- bergite-bearing granophyre, composed of automorphic albite-oligoclase crystals (An_{10}), zoned to albite, engulfed in abundant fine-grained micro- pegmatite, in places showing crudely spherulitic growth. It will be evident from a comparison of the mode given in Table VI with the norm in Table VII, that the amount of sodic plagioclase actually present far exceeds that con- tained in the albite-oligoclase phenocrysts. As Harker (1895, p. 130) tentatively suggested, plagioclase components must enter extensively into the alkali feldspar of the micropegmatite, and in many instances it can be proved that the feldspar continues with no break from the margins of the phenocrysts into the surrounding micropegmatite. The pyroxene, which occurs in scattered crystals, is hedenbergite with $\beta = 1 \cdot 740$, $2V = 56°$. Sporadic crystals of mag- netite and apatite are present, and some late amphibole and chlorite.

In small amounts, hedenbergite has been present throughout the Carrock granophyre area, and in the exposed part of the Rae Crags granophyre to the north. The poorly-exposed Great Lingy granophyre, however, appears to contain substantial areas without dark minerals (E 14632, E 16195, E 23553). The leucocratic variety described by Holmes (1917) from Brandy Gill, which contains 12 per cent sericite but no orthoclase, owes its character at least in part to hydrothermal alteration. Zircon is occasionally found as a minor constituent of the granophyres; its form may be automorphic (E 17369–70) or rounded (E 15270). In the headwaters of Drygill Beck the Rae Crags grano- phyre is conspicuously brecciated (E 15762), with distortion of albite pheno- crysts as seen in thin section (E 15764). Quartz and chlorite (E 15763) or calcite (E 17373) have been introduced along the fractures. Near Rae Crags the granophyre is traversed by dark grey streaks which prove to consist of green biotite and chlorite (E 23481).

Inclusions in the granophyres are uncommon, but one example of quartz- gabbro, resembling the Buck Kirk type, was found as a xenolith (E 15724). Fine flakes of biotite have been abundantly developed in it, replacing horn- blende in both the larger masses and the tiny veinlets which traverse the feld- spar. This suggests that the hornblendization of the gabbro preceded the

TABLE VII

Chemical analyses and norms of Carrock Fell Granophyres and Felsite

		I	II	A	B	III
		Mela-granophyre	Normal Granophyre	'Augite-Granophyre'	'Albite-Granophyre'	Felsite
Slice No.		E 16183	E 16184	C 2051	—	E 16185
Lab. No.		943	944			945
Analyses						
SiO_2		61·89	73·17	71·60	80·12	67·37
Al_2O_3		14·38	12·95	13·60	10·68	17·94
Fe_2O_3		1·67	1·45	2·40	0·06	0·56
FeO		8·12	2·06	—	0·41	1·86
MgO		0·20	0·08	0·21	0·63	2·55
CaO		4·54	1·30	2·30	1·01	0·73
Na_2O		5·16	4·37	5·55	3·44	2·14
K_2O		2·30	3·67	3·53	1·42	4·39
$H_2O > 105°C$ ..		0·84	0·43	—	0·80	2·15
$H_2O < 105°C$ ..		0·30	0·14	—	0·28	0·15
TiO_2		0·64	0·39	—	0·09	0·07
P_2O_5		0·14	0·07	—	tr	0·07
MnO		0·33	0·11	—	0·05	0·03
CO_2		tr	0·10	—	1·20	0·10
FeS_2		0·07	n.d.	—	0·17	0·08
BaO		—	—	—	0·01	—
ZrO_2		—	—	—	0·03	—
Ignition loss ..		—	—	0·70	—	—
		100·58	100·29		100·40	100·19
Norms						
Q		11·0	30·7		54·1	31·6
or		12·2	21·7		8·3	26·1
ab		43·5	36·7		28·8	18·3
an		10·0	4·7		—	2·5
C		—	—		3·6	8·6
di		10·4	0·6		—	—
wo ..		4·9	0·2			
en		0·2	0·1			
fs ..		5·3	0·3			
hy		8·1	1·9		1·1	9·5
en		0·3	0·1		0·5	6·3
fs		7·8	1·8		0·6	3·2
mt		2·3	2·1		0·1	0·7
il		1·2	0·8		0·1	0·2
ap		0·3	0·2		—	0·2
py		0·1	—		0·2	0·2
cc		—	0·2		2·4*	0·2
Normative plagioclase An ..		19	11	9	0	12

*including dolomite.

metamorphism due to the granophyre. Xenoliths of Borrowdale lava are also occasionally found. The metamorphism shown by these is markedly different from that produced in lava xenoliths by the gabbro. A porphyritic type, perhaps formerly an Eycott andesite, shows the plagioclase phenocrysts thoroughly replaced by sericite, and biotite and pale green hornblende abundantly developed in the groundmass which is not, however, in the least granulitized.

In 1963 Mr. R. Garrett of the Royal School of Mines undertook trace-element determinations on a sample of the normal granophyre (Geological Survey Lab. No. 944), and he obtained the results shown in Table VIII.

TABLE VIII

Trace-elements in granophyre

Ba	390 p.p.m.
Sr	95 „
Pb	10 „
Ag	—
Cu	10 „
Sn	—
Mn	1200 „
Zr	410 „
Rb	150 „
Yt	80 „
Nb	—

Locality: 600 yd E. of trigonometrical height 2174, Carrock Fell, Cumberland. E 16184 A, Geological Survey Lab. No. 944, Imperial College Geochemistry Department No. 7705.

Mr. Garrett states that the Sr, Zr, Rb, Yt and Nb were determined by X-ray spectrography and a standard deviation of $\pm$ 20 per cent achieved; the detection limit of all these elements was 40 p.p.m. All the remaining elements were determined by optical spectrography. The analyses for Ba, Pb, Cu and Mn have a standard deviation of $\pm$ 20 per cent, and the Ag of $\pm$ 30 per cent.

Arm o' Grain Microgranite. The small area of acid rock apparently surrounded by gabbro revealed by Arm o' Grain probably differs little in composition from the granophyres, but texturally it is microgranite, carrying little or no micro-pegmatite (E 15266, E 23517). The constituents are albite (An_8), orthoclase,

---

Localities of specimens in Table VII

I   Melagranophyre, 690 yd W. 21° S. of Stone Ends, about 1 mile N. of Mosedale [3503 3342]. Analyst, B. E. Dixon, *in* Guppy (1956, p. 14).

II   Normal granophyre, 600 yd E. of spot-height 2174 on summit of Carrock Fell [3467 3365]. Analyst, B. E. Dixon, *in* Guppy (1956, p. 3).

A   'Augite-granophyre', 100 yd E. of summit of Carrock Fell. Analyst, G. Barrow, quoted from Harker (1895, p. 129).

B   '*Albite-granophyre', near head of Brandy Gill, west of Carrock Fell. Analyst, H. F. Harwood, quoted from Holmes (1917, p. 406).

III   Felsite, dump from old level at head of Long Grain, 550 yd W. 34° S. of spot-height 2157 on High Pike [3148 3472]. Analyst, B. E. Dixon, *in* Guppy (1956, p. 7).

quartz, a little fibrous amphibole and chlorite, scattered magnetite granules and traces of sphene.

Harestones Felsite. The analysed rock (E 16185) is a light grey quartz-feldspar-porphyry, with phenocrysts of quartz up to 1·5 mm across, in part automorphic, in part deeply corroded. Phenocrysts of perthitic orthoclase or anorthoclase (some sections show fine quadrille twinning) are of similar size. The groundmass is microfelsite, extensively sericitized and crossed by veinlets of fine white mica. Some carbonate and kaolin are present, and a little pyrite. In other nearby rocks, albite phenocrysts occur (E 14647). Silicification is also displayed (E 15761).

THE DYKES

Acid intrusions in gabbro. Small injections of granophyre in the main gabbros are better described as veins than dykes. A typical example contains albite crystals embedded in a mass of micropegmatite. Chlorite pseudomorphs after an acicular mineral, probably hedenbergite, are present, and some epidote and magnetite (E 17395). Of similar composition but different texture are narrow dykes of albite-porphyry which also cut the gabbro (E 15280); these contain albite phenocrysts in a microfelsitic groundmass, with acicular hornblende crystals.

Intermediate types. The wider dykes which are conspicuous features of the eastern cliffs of Carrock Fell are mostly quartz-porphyrites. A specimen from the centre of a dyke, 30 ft wide [3478 3374], 700 yd E. 15° N. of the summit of Carrock Fell, contains automorphic augites up to 0·3 mm across, with β near 1·700, occasional 'bastite' pseudomorphs, probably after orthopyroxene, oligoclase laths, interstitial quartz, and orthoclase and 'leucoxenized' ilmenite (E 15276). The other dykes examined were found to be similar except that augite was lacking (E 17396, E 17269, E 15278).

In gabbro at the margin of a porphyrite dyke (E 17266) the feldspars were found to have suffered albitization, and to be no more calcic than An_{20}. Granophyre adjacent to another dyke (E 15278) carried biotite and epidote, probably as a result of local metamorphism, while fragments of granophyre enclosed in a porphyrite dyke were found to have narrow selvedges of glass (E 15279).

An interesting porphyrite dyke [3495 3349], 930 yd E. 11° S. of the summit of the fell contains inclusions which appear to have been derived from olivine-gabbro. Pale chlorite forms serpentine-type aggregates with the crystal outlines of olivine; pale green augite with $\beta = 1·702$, $2V = 50°$, similar in composition to the augites of the Carrock gabbros; coarse labradorite (An_{64}) and ilmenite are present among the fragments. There are also quite separate quartz xenocrysts in the dyke, rimmed in the usual way with tiny pyroxenes (E 15281).   K.C.D.

DISCUSSION AND CONCLUSIONS

METAMORPHISM

As historically the earliest hypothesis of origin of the complex postulated that it was produced by metamorphism of Borrowdale lavas (Ward 1876), it is appropriate to consider first the evidence of metamorphism in the surrounding and enclosed country rocks.

Skiddaw Slates. Along the southern margin of the complex a narrow zone of bleached hornfelses, containing porphyroblasts of biotite, sodic plagioclase, anorthoclase and spessartine-bearing almandine has been produced from arenaceous and argillaceous regionally-metamorphosed Skiddaw Slates. Alkali-determinations on three typical hornfelses from this zone are compared in Table IX with figures for unaltered Skiddaw Slates.

TABLE IX

Alkali-contents of Skiddaw Slate and Hornfels

Slice No.	Rock	Na$_2$O	K$_2$O	Normative albite
E 23496	Garnet-oligoclase-chlorite-hornfels	1·29	4·12	11·0
E 23508	Quartz-albite-chlorite-hornfels	2·06	2·98	17·3
E 23515	Biotite-oligoclase-sericite-quartz-hornfels	1·04	3·97	8·9
E 17555	Unaltered Skiddaw Slate	0·68	2·50	
E 17553	Unaltered Skiddaw Slate	0·98	3·02	

Localities

E 23496—1130 yd N. 55° W. of Mosedale Bridge [3486 3259]   ⎫ Analyst, K. L. H.
E 23508— 600 yd N. 10° W. of Swineside [3383 3289]   ⎬ Murray, G.S.M.
E 23515— 50 yd N. of outfall of Arm o' Grain [3176 3313]   ⎰ Lab. Nos. 1569–71,
                                                               ⎭ 1949
E 17555—1470 yd W. 43° S. of Mungrisdale Church [3040 2953], full analysis p. 125.
E 17553— 200 yd S. 16° W. of Barkbeth [2408 3109], full analysis p. 22.

Two of the three analyses of hornfels indicate an unmistakable rise in soda above what is normal in the Skiddaw Slates (see also analyses of Skiddaw Granite hornfelses, p. 125). Some increase in potash also appears to be indicated. Mild soda-metasomatism, such as accompanies basic hypabyssal intrusions elsewhere (for example, the Whin Sill and the Cornish 'greenstones') has evidently occurred. Introduction of potash, which may be fixed in biotite, muscovite or anorthoclase, may also have taken place. As already noted, some uncertainty is felt as to whether the formation of the garnet is to be ascribed to thermal effects in beds in the slate richer in manganese than normal, or to actual migration of manganese, but there are few precedents for the latter suggestion. If it is concluded, however, that development of garnet is merely a thermal metamorphic effect, it is necessary to concede that conditions were generally unsuitable for the formation of garnet in the same beds where they become involved in the Skiddaw Granite aureole. Tilley (1926) has pointed out that in many contact-aureoles in pelitic sediments, almandine is absent, while in others there is evidence that garnet produced by regional metamorphism has been destroyed by contact metamorphism. In the present case, it is possible that garnet produced by the gabbro metamorphism has been destroyed by the granite metamorphism where this is most intense.

It is clear that gabbro has not been generated by metamorphism of Skiddaw Slate here, and this suggestion has never been advanced. The curious spherulitic myrmekitic rock from the headwaters of Grainsgill (p. 89) does, however, suggest a possible, though not proven, link between slate and granophyre. Somewhat similar spherulitic albite-rocks occur among the Cornish adinoles (Harker 1939, p. 129).

Borrowdale Lavas. The andesites in the roof of the gabbro in Thief Gills are normal biotite-hornfelses locally with metasomatic micropegmatite. The included lava masses in the gabbro, and the occasional xenoliths in the granophyre, show more advanced metamorphism. Harker (1894b, p. 333) in describing the Eycott-type lava inclusions in the gabbro, concludes that "the gabbro-magma has to some extent corroded away and incorporated in itself the glassy base of the lava, and even in places some of its minerals, in the immediate neighbourhood of the junction". This effect we have fully confirmed, for groundmass converted into pyroxene- or hornblende-granulite can be traced into groundmass identical with the Buck Kirk type of gabbro, the large labradorite phenocrysts persisting throughout, though becoming more rounded and corroded in the gabbro groundmass (p. 93). In Table X alkali-determinations on unmetamorphosed Eycott andesite, Eycott-type granulite, gabbro with Eycott-type phenocrysts and adjacent non-porphyritic gabbro are compared with figures for the analysed melagabbro and leucogabbro.

TABLE X

Alkali-contents of Eycott Andesite, Granulite and Gabbro

Slice No.	Rock	Na_2O	K_2O	Normative ab	cr
E 16233	Eycott-type basic andesite	2·46	1·45	21·0	8·9
E 23494	Granulitized Eycott andesite, in gabbro	3·53	1·45	28·9	8·9
E 23494A	Gabbro with Eycott phenocrysts	3·83	1·41	32·5	8·4
E 23495	Apparently normal gabbro, 1 ft from xenolith	3·13	1·38	26·7	8·3
E 16181	Leucogabbro	2·90	1·18	24·6	7·2
E 16180	Melagabbro	1·56	0·72	13·1	3·9

Localities

E 16233—850 yd S. 30° W. of High Ireby Grange [2275 3639], full analysis, p. 58.

E 23494 ⎫
E 23494A ⎬ 770 yd N. 36° W. of Mosedale Bridge [3528 3257], Analyst, K. L. H.
E 23495 ⎭ Murray, G.S.M. Lab. Nos. 1558–1560, 1949. (see Guppy 1956, p. 40).

E 16181—920 yd N. 39° W. of Mosedale Bridge [3517 3264], full analysis, p. 90.

E 16180—600 yd N. 28° W. of Mosedale Bridge [3544 3248], full analysis, p. 90.

While these figures indicate little significant change in potash, there appears to be a definite enrichment in soda, both as compared with the original lava and with the ordinary gabbros of the adjacent belts. From the data given in Dr. Phemister's account of the Eycott basic andesite (see Chap. IV), it appears that some desilicification of the lava must take place also; for whereas the glassy base of the unaltered lava carried occult quartz to the amount of 11·6 per cent (normative) in the example studied by him, the granulites are generally notably lacking in quartz, though here and there a little is found intergrown with orthoclase or albite in micropegmatite veinlets.

It is a striking fact that the composition of the clinopyroxene in the granulites is brought into harmony with that in the enclosing rocks, be they gabbro or granophyre. In the former host, the granulites carry augite of similar optical properties; in the latter, hedenbergite. Only a single occurrence of ortho-pyroxene in granulite and adjacent gabbro was found.

From these facts the conclusion is drawn that recrystallization of the lava xenoliths was accompanied by local metasomatism, and that the process could go so far as to produce rock indistinguishable from gabbro. The Buck Kirk and the banded types of gabbro clearly derived at least part of their substance from the Borrowdale lavas. On the other hand, in the leucogabbros there is no evidence of any such contribution by the lavas, though the compositions of the plagioclase and pyroxene in them do not differ from the counterparts in the other gabbros.

Harker's contention that biotite is found in the gabbros only near their junctions with the lava inclusions has not been confirmed but it is certainly exceptionally abundant at some junctions. In small amounts the mineral is widespread in the gabbros. There is a tendency for it to occur round the margins of magnetite and ilmenite crystals, similar to that noticed by Read (1921) in the contaminated gabbro at Easter Saphook, Aberdeen, but what significance is here to be attributed to this is not clear.   K.C.D.

CRYSTALLIZATION FROM MAGMA

The Gabbros. The resurvey confirms that the gabbro has more ilmenite and ferromagnesian minerals, and less quartz and feldspar, in belts near the northern and southern margins than in the central belt, as Harker (1894b) maintained. Although his bold extension of Soret's principle, calling for a greater concentration of early-formed constituents (those which ultimately produced apatite, ilmenite, magnetite) in the cooler marginal parts of a magma-chamber, has frequently been quoted, with Carrock Fell as the example, the principle cannot be said to have recommended itself widely to petrologists. Our re-examination reveals many difficulties in detail. The arrangement of broad, comparatively uniform colour-belts in the gabbro, with rapid transitions between the belts is unfavourable to this hypothesis, as already noted. Further, the distribution of ilmenite and magnetite in the melagabbros is very uneven, and many of them owe their melanocratic characters to abundance of hornblende, demonstrably a late-stage, and not an early-crystallizing mineral. Moreover, if diffusion of Ti, Fe^{11} and Fe^{111} towards the cooler parts of a magma-chamber be admitted, in this case a series of substantial screens of included lava must have occurred between the central part of the chamber and the marginal belts; yet no concentration of opaque minerals is found round them; on the contrary they are engulfed in intermediate, 'Buck Kirk type' gabbro. It is not considered, therefore, that it can be argued from the distribution of iron-titanium oxides that the whole body of the gabbro was at one time fluid in its present position.

Nevertheless the uniformity of composition of the plagioclase and clino-pyroxene both in the gabbros and in the granophyres, illustrated by the numerous determinations used in constructing Fig. 11, appears to provide evidence that a liquid phase was important at some stage in the evolution of each body. Metasomatism, for example in the gabbro contact-zone, and in the development of late hornblende in the gabbros, produced minerals of far more variable composition, the range of plagioclase in the contact hornfelses being An_5 to An_{60} and of refractive indices of the hornblendes in the gabbros being between $\gamma = 1 \cdot 640$ and $1 \cdot 690$. The uniform compositions of the primary minerals of the gabbros away from the marginal zone would, it is suggested, be most readily achieved if they crystallized from a liquid of reasonably uniform composition; this did not necessarily occur wholly *in situ*.

The texture of the fluxion gabbros suggests flowage of a medium already rich in separated crystals of plagioclase and ilmenite, though not of clinopyroxene, quartz and orthoclase. These rocks may thus be of cumulate origin, at least in part. A search for graded bedding or other evidence of igneous sedimentation[1] such as has been found in the gabbros of Skaergaard (Wager and Deer, 1939) or Belhelvie (Stewart, 1947) failed to reveal any such effect here. Nevertheless the possibility of local settling of ilmenite and magnetite, and accumulation of labradorite under gravity, prior to the intrusion of a mush of crystals, is one that cannot be dismissed. Fragments incorporated in a porphyrite dyke (p. 104) suggest the presence of olivine-gabbro at greater depth below the complex.

The transitional contacts between the major types of gabbro, and the total lack of chilling or of cross-cutting relationships between them, seem to preclude successive injections of magma separated by long intervals of time. It remains, however, possible that a stratified mush was injected, and that crystallization of the inter-crystal liquid was well advanced when one or more later waves of magma (with crystals) arrived, the whole complex still being hot. Such a mechanism might account for the leucogabbro bands.

There are thus two hypotheses of origin of the gabbros: (1) that they were produced by recrystallization and metasomatism of lavas, either *in situ* or with limited movement; (2) that they resulted from the completion of crystallization of a mush of crystals and liquid—that is, a magma in the original sense of the term—in which some layering of minerals had already been produced before intrusion. Neither is entirely satisfactory and a combination of the two seems nearest to the truth in the present state of knowledge.

The Granophyres. Here there is plain evidence, in the pegmatitic belt between the northern melagabbro and the melagranophyre, of recrystallization of gabbro, and mingling with granophyre. Harker's (1895) view of the belt as a hybrid zone seems amply justified. Whether the melagranophyre likewise derived part of its substance from the gabbro is less certain; here, early concentration of the automorphic, acicular hedenbergite would be sufficient to explain the facts.

The granophyres offer no evidence of relict textures from which some clue to their ultimate origin might be obtained, and no case could be made for transformation of rhyolitic lava *in situ*. We consider that the granophyres were intrusive at their present levels. Occasionally a worn-looking crystal of zircon may be found in them, perhaps derived from a parent rock, though most of the crystals of this mineral are automorphic and thus probably of primary origin. Whatever source the granophyres may have had, it was unusual in that Na_2O was more abundant than K_2O in it. The evidence of metamorphism of Borrowdale lava inclusions in granophyre (p. 103) shows that these rocks were formed at substantially lower temperatures than the gabbros.

In Fig. 12 the compositions of the analysed granophyres and gabbros are compared by means of a variation diagram, constructed according to the

---
[1]The help of Professor F. H. Stewart in this work is gratefully acknowledged.

method proposed by Larsen (1938), using as its basis $1/3$ (SiO_2) $+$ K_2O $-$ $(CaO + MgO)$ $-$ $[(Fe + Mn)$ expressed as $FeO]$. This emphasises the sharp break in trend between the gabbros and the granophyres and may be interpreted as indicating that the granophyres are not direct differentiates of the gabbro magma, or of gabbro magma that has assimilated acid rock. The association of granophyre with gabbro is a very common one, the most satisfactory explanation for which is that the heat of the basic magma at depth was sufficient to bring about partial fusion of sialic material. The basic magma reached high levels in the crust first, but was soon followed by granophyre, which represents the low-melting fraction of the partly fused crustal rocks. Such an hypothesis could well explain the gabbro–granophyre association here, and might also be invoked to cover the abundant late quartz and micro-pegmatite in some of the gabbros. We cannot, however, claim that the reinvestigation of the Carrock Fell complex has provided sufficient new facts to establish the hypothesis.   K.C.D., S.E.H.

LATE HYDROTHERMAL EFFECTS

In the northern and southern melagabbro belts, and to a less extent elsewhere, extensive development of hornblende has occurred, for the most part after the consolidation of the rocks. The amphibole replaces pyroxene to form partial or complete pseudomorphs; it also replaces feldspar, and penetrates feldspar, quartz, micropegmatite and opaque minerals in tiny veinlets. A wholesale permeation of the gabbros by hot, late-stage solutions must be postulated. In the melagabbros, the amount of hornblende in many cases considerably exceeds the amount of pyroxene previously present, and migration of Fe and Mg must therefore be envisaged. It is again emphasized that the high specific gravity of some of the melagabbros is due to hornblendization, and not to abundance of iron-titanium oxides. The possibility that magnetite and ilmenite were introduced during the late mineralization was considered, but no critical evidence was found calling for a departure from Harker's view that these minerals crystallized early. They may not, however, have been the first to separate, for in places they appear to envelop plagioclase. The only opaque minerals found in the form of veinlets are pyrite and 'leucoxene'.

In the diabase, not only was late hornblende abundantly developed, but replacement of feldspar by sericite and related clay minerals also occurred extensively. Some biotite belongs to this stage, for it is intergrown with the amphibole. It must be added that further hornblende, biotite, apatite and sericite were introduced into the gabbros in the Brandy Gill area, in the course of the Skiddaw Granite metamorphism and hydrothermal mineralization. Here it is difficult to distinguish alterations due to late liquors of the gabbro from those due to the granite. However, as noted on p. 104, there is some evidence that hornblendic veinlets had developed in the gabbro before the intrusion of the granophyre, and hence considerably before the emplacement of the Skiddaw Granite.

In the granophyre, the chief late-stage alterations are replacement of heden-bergite by amphibole or chlorite, and introduction of vein-like chains of crystals of green biotite. In the track of the Skiddaw Granite mineralization at the head of Brandy Gill, very complete sericitization of potash feldspar in the granophyre is indicated in the specimens studied by Holmes (1917). Such an alteration is consistent with the greisenization which accompanied this intrusion.   K.C.D.

AGE-RELATIONS

There is a close correspondence between the strike and the steep dips in the Skiddaw Slates to the south and the Borrowdale lavas to the north on the one hand, and the form and internal structures (contacts, banding, foliation) of the complex on the other. This gives the impression of a composite sheet generally conformable to the bedding in the country rock, that may have been tilted into its present position during folding. Harker (1895, p. 126) pointed out that "the rocks have been intruded at the junction of the Skiddaw Slates and Eycott Hill lavas since these two groups attained their present mutual relations" and he further comments that "the intrusions must be later than these (post-Silurian) crust movements".[1]

Further examination however shows that the horizons of actual intrusive contacts range from low down in the arenaceous Skiddaw Slates through the Borrowdale Volcanic Series into the Drygill Shales, and that several thousand feet of strata are missing between the rocks forming the north and south boundaries of the complex. Moreover, where the strike of the country rock has changed from the local west-by-north trend into the more general west-south-west trend, as for example at the head of Grainsgill Beck, the intrusion becomes markedly transgressive to the structures of the folded Skiddaw Slates.

The vertical and, in places, transgressive intrusive contact on the south, the more or less horizontal roof of lavas in Thief Gills to the west, and the great marginal mass of included lavas at Snailshell Crag in the east, are all most simply regarded as bounding a steep-sided, plug-like mass, injected after the main folding. This is supported by the swarms of dykes that trend parallel to the long axis of the intrusion, both within the complex and in the country rock to the east, west and north of it. This trend, though locally parallel to the strike and dip of the country rocks, persists into regions where there is no such parallelism, e.g. on Eycott Hill. These dykes, also, are clearly later than the main earth-movements. The dyke-swarm is pre-Carboniferous (p. 5) and so the complex itself is also at least as old as that.

The Skiddaw Granite gives off greisen dykes and mineral veins, to be described in the next chapter, which penetrate the gabbro and are clearly younger than that member of the Carrock complex. The granophyre at the head of Brandy Gill is likewise affected by hydrothermal alteration connected with the granite.

The available evidence is wholly in favour of a post-Caledonian-folding–pre-Carboniferous age for the complex.

MODE OF EMPLACEMENT AND STRUCTURAL RELATIONS OF THE COMPLEX

The outcrop of the complex as a whole has a plano-convex form, and it is situated where the general Caledonian west-south-west strike changes to west-

---

[1] The critical point in Green's (1917) argument for a pre-Bala age for the intrusion—the Bala age of the grits of Great Sca Fell—has not been confirmed (see p. 31).

by-north. In this area there may well have been relief of pressure favourable to plutonic-hypabyssal igneous activity.

From time to time almost all the boundaries of the complex have been regarded as faults of considerable magnitude, the northern and southern margins in particular having been variously interpreted (e.g. Marr 1916, p. 105; Green 1921, p. 125). Except in the west, however, where it is crossed by the Roughton Gill veins, the complex is, in our view, nowhere broken by any considerable faults. It does not seem necessary, on the interpretation offered below, to consider that the faults which have been mapped as bounding it on the north and east (well marked in places by mineral veins, but with their supposed courses much obscured by drift) are more than adjustment fractures between the rigid igneous mass and its less rigid surroundings. In the south there is clearly no fault of importance (p. 79).

In the area adjacent to the complex there is a general upward succession northwards, in relation to which the stratified rocks within the complex (the Snailshell Crag xenoliths and the Drygill Shales) and to a less extent the Thief Gills lava-roof are in highly anomalous positions. Thus the Eycott Lavas north of Swineside, probably those at the base of the High Ireby Group, are adjacent to arenaceous slates low down in the Skiddaw Slates. The Drygill Shales lie to the south of the lavas of the Binsey Group, and so apparently stratigraphically below, instead of above, several thousand feet of lavas and tuffs. In the west, the lavas of Thief Gills are found west of the Roughton Gill South Vein only, and their relations to the adjacent rocks outside the limits of the complex are obscured by the overthrust mass of grits and slate of Great Sca Fell. Nevertheless, they lie well to the south of a line drawn across the complex to connect the undisturbed Skiddaw–Borrowdale junctions to the east and west of it.

To the east of the complex the recognition of black Skiddaw Slates and their mineralized equivalents (slice E 23560) near the foot of the crags 250 yd S. of Stone Ends necessitates alteration of the mapping of a considerable drift-covered area previously regarded as underlain by Borrowdale Volcanic Series. It also provides a link which suggests that there is a normal upward succession between the low arenaceous Skiddaw Slate about Mosedale and the Eycott and succeeding lavas of the High Ireby Group about Linewath. This is important, for if the Borrowdale rocks of Snailshell Crag are the country rock into which the gabbro was injected, they also have suffered an apparent southward displacement of one to two miles relative to the present outcrop.

Thus all the rocks intimately related to the complex lie well to the south of their normal outcrop positions while the surrounding strata are relatively undisturbed. On the northerly limb of an anticlinorium, such displacement is most readily explicable in terms of downfaulting or subsidence of the area concerned. Downfaulting subsequent to the intrusion is ruled out by the welded contact of the gabbro with the Skiddaw Slate to the south. There remains the alternative that the subsidence was associated with the intrusion complex. Drygill Shales and Borrowdale lavas may safely be assumed to have been present some thousands of feet above the present exposed surface. Their preservation within the complex is ascribed to general subsidence of the roof during emplacement of the complex. The narrow, sheet-like form of the granulitized lava xenoliths within the main gabbros may be regarded as implying north-south tension during intrusion. As has already been suggested, intrusion of the gabbros as a mush of crystals and liquid—that is, as a magma in the original sense of the term—seems the best hypothesis to explain both the petrographical and structural facts. Vigorous recrystallization of the lava xenoliths accompanied the process. Consolidation of the gabbros, and of the contemporaneous or slightly later diabase, was already far advanced before the granophyre was emplaced, from the evidence of veins of granophyre in gabbro and diabase, and the inclusion of gabbro in granophyre.

Possibly the form of the main outcrops of granophyre—two inward-pointing wedges and a long, lens-like mass—might be explained as due to relative lateral northward movement of the rocks to the west of the complex, such as is implied by the tear-fractures which became the Roughton Gill veins (p. 239). These fractures may well have been initiated before the intrusion of the Hare-stones Felsite, for felsitic stringers and dykes parallel to these fractures are extensively developed in the valley heads around High Pike. A movement such as has been suggested would provide a favourable locus for the intrusion of the Harestones Felsite in the lee of the northward-directed pressure on the north side of the rigid igneous mass of Carrock Fell. Some brecciation of the granophyre has occurred, possibly at the time of the intrusion of the felsite (p. 101). It remains, however, uncertain whether the felsite properly belongs to the Carrock Fell suite or to the Skiddaw Granite, with which it is more closely allied chemically.   S.E.H.

REFERENCES

BENSON, W. N. 1944. The basic igneous rocks of Eastern Otago and their tectonic environment. Pt. IV Section B: Petrology, with special reference to the crystallisation of pyroxene. *Trans. Roy. Soc. New Zealand*, **74**, 71–123.

GREEN, J. F. N. 1915. The Garnets and streaky rocks of the English Lake District. *Miner. Mag.*, **17**, 207–17.

———— 1917. The age of the chief intrusions of the Lake District. *Proc. Geol. Assoc.*, **28**, 1–30.

———— 1918. The Skiddaw Granite: a structural study. *Proc. Geol. Assoc.*, **29**, 126–36.

———— 1921. Long excursions to the Lake District. *Proc. Geol. Assoc.*, **32**, 123–38.

GROOM, T. T. 1889. On a Tachylyte associated with the Gabbro of Carrock Fell in the Lake District. *Quart. Jl geol. Soc. Lond.*, **45**, 298–304.

GUPPY, EILEEN M. 1956 (Compiler). Chemical analyses of igneous rocks, metamorphic rocks and minerals 1931–54. *Mem. Geol. Surv. Gt Br.*

HARKER, A. 1894a. On some variolitic rocks on Carrock Fell. *Geol. Mag.*, **1**, 551–3.

———— 1894b. Carrock Fell: a Study in the variation of igneous rock-masses. Pt. I. The Gabbro. *Quart. Jl geol. Soc. Lond.*, **50**, 311–37.

———— 1895. ibid. Pt. II. The Carrock Fell Granophyre. Pt. III. The Grainsgill Greisen. *Quart. Jl geol. Soc. Lond.*, **51**, 125–48.

———— 1902. Notes on the igneous rocks of the English Lake District. *Proc. Yorks. geol. polytech. Soc.*, **14**, 487–93.

———— 1939. *Metamorphism*. 2nd edit. London.

HESS, H. H. 1949. Chemical composition and optical properties of common clino-pyroxenes. Pt. I. *Am. Miner.*, **34**, 621–66.

HOLMES, A. 1917. Albite-granophyre and quartz-porphyry from Brandy Gill, Carrock Fell. *Geol. Mag.*, (6), **4**, 403–7.

JOHANNSEN, A. 1937. *A descriptive petrography of the igneous rocks. 3. The Intermediate Rocks*. Chicago.

LARSEN, E. S. 1938. Some new variation diagrams for groups of igneous rocks. *J. Geol.*, **46**, 505–20.

MARR, J. E. 1916. *The Geology of the Lake District*. Cambridge.

POLDERVAART, A. 1947. Subcalcic ferroaugite from Mount Arthur, East Griqualand. *Mineralog. Mag.*, **28**, 159–63.

READ, H. H. 1921. The Contaminated Gabbro of Easter Saphook near Old Meldrum in Aberdeenshire. *Geol. Mag.*, **58**, 177–83.

SHORT, M. N. 1940. The microscopic determination of the ore-minerals. *Bull. U.S. geol. Surv.* 914.

STEWART, F. H. 1947. The gabbroic complex of Belhelvie in Aberdeenshire. *Quart. Jl geol. Soc. Lond.*, **102**, 465–98.

TEALL, J. J. H. 1888. *British Petrography*. London.

TERMIER, H., TERMIER, G., and JOURAVSKY, C. 1948. Une roche volcanique à gros grain de la famille des Ijolites: La Talzastite. *Ext. des notes et mémoires. Division des mines et de la géologie Maroc*. No. 71, 81–120.

TILLEY, C. E. 1926. On garnet in pelitic contact-zones. *Mineralog. Mag.*, **21**, 47–50.

TRECHMANN, C. O. 1882. Note on the so-called 'Hypersthenite' of Carrock Fell, Cumberland. *Geol. Mag.* (2), **9**, 210–2.

WAGER, L. R. and DEER, W. A. 1939. Geological investigations in East Greenland. Pt. III. The Petrology of the Skaergaard Intrusion, Kangerdlugssuag, East Greenland. *Medd. om Grønland*, Bd. 105, Nr. 4.

WARD, J. C. 1876. On the quartz-felsite, syenitic and associated metamorphic rocks of the Lake District. *Quart. Jl geol. Soc. Lond.*, **32**, 11–27.

Chapter VII

THE SKIDDAW GRANITE AND ASSOCIATED METAMORPHISM AND MINERALIZATION

THE GRANITE

FIELD RELATIONS

THE TERM Skiddaw Granite is applied collectively to three distinct outcrops of white or grey biotite-granite that lie within a region of thermally altered Skiddaw Slates. It is generally agreed that these belong to one granite mass and are connected at no great depth below the surface. The largest area is spoken of as the central or Caldew outcrop; the northern one, though partly in the Caldew valley, as the Grainsgill outcrop; and the third and smallest outcrop as the Sinen Gill outcrop. The last-mentioned, lying in a tributary to the Glenderaterra, is in the Keswick (29) Sheet and will be referred to only incidentally.

Apart from the earlier brief accounts by Sedgwick, Nicholson and Ward, the principal developments of our knowledge of this mass are due to Rastall (1910) who, following the pioneer microscopic work of Ward, made a detailed study of the metamorphism, and to Hitchen (1934), who paid particular attention to the modifications of the granite and its connexion with the metalliferous veins.

The central outcrop. This inlier of granite forms the lower slopes and floor of the Caldew valley and its tributaries, 3 to 4 miles west of Mungrisdale. The outcrop is much hidden by peat and boulder clay and little solid rock is visible outside the stream courses. The upper surface of the granite appears to be a gentle dome, the highest part of the outcrop, in contact with the country rock, being situated about half a mile south of the outfall of Blackhazel Beck. From this region the surface of the granite appears to fall gently westwards, north-wards and north-eastwards, as indicated by the relation of the junction to the topography. In most of the exposures the rock is a grey medium-grained biotite-granite. In the east, marginal variations, described by Hitchen, show that the granite is there mixed with some aplitic material that was introduced at a late stage, prior to complete consolidation. Aplitic veins trending east-by-north to west-by-south are present in the granite near its margin in White Gill, 100 yd S. of Blackhazel Beck outfall, where they are associated with a peg-matitic variety of the granite in which feldspar and quartz crystals, partly in coarse graphic intergrowth, attain breadths of more than an inch. Aplitic dykes also occur in the hornfels 200 yd farther south. Blocks of micacized aplite and muscovite-rich hornfels together with specimens showing contacts of these types are abundant in the river cliff 80 yd N. of the outfall of Blackhazel Beck. They are probably of local derivation from the nearby roof-rocks of the granite. A tourmaline-bearing pegmatite vein in aplite was noticed among the blocks hereabouts, while on the hillside to the south-west, granite blocks with xenoliths of granitized cordierite-hornfels are present. Thus both here and in White Gill an intimate association of aplitic and pegmatitic phases is displayed.

Variation in the proportion of biotite is a noteworthy feature of the central outcrop. For example in the River Caldew, 450 yd above the outfall of Black-hazel Beck, occurs a biotite-rich type, while towards the northern end of the central outcrop biotite decreases and the proportion of silica in the granite increases. This variation has been studied in detail by Hitchen, who attributes it to assimilation of shaly material and simultaneous differentiation by removal of biotite. Taking the outcrops of the granite as a whole, there is a progressive decrease in biotite-content and increase in silica from Sinen Gill in the south, through the central outcrop to the Grainsgill outcrop in the north.[1]

The northern or Grainsgill outcrop. This appears from its irregular form to be a rather steep-sided elongated dome, with its long axis trending north–south. Hitchen has shown that, in the workings along the Emmerson Vein, the slate overlying the granite dips northwards in the top level, but southwards in the lower level.

This outcrop is of particular interest because of the beautiful greisen (muscovite-quartz) rock developed in it. Harker (1895) recognized that the granite at its southern end was more acid and had more muscovite than in the central outcrop and that the feldspars were secondarily micacized. Northwards there is a progressive increase in white mica at the expense of feldspar, finally giving a yellowish muscovite-quartz rock in which quartz commonly appears as large automorphic phenocrysts. Harker, while recognizing that the mica was largely the result of metasomatism, considered that the greisen was in part due to the squeezing-out of a fraction from the crystallizing granite by northerly-directed pressure. The later work of Hitchen, however, indicates that the change from granite to greisen is essentially due to metasomatism in place. In a general way, the concentration of late fluids in the granite may nevertheless be attributable to uprise due to squeezing against the earlier Carrock Fell mass to the north.

Mineral Veins. The greisenized granite together with the adjacent 'mica-schist' and gabbro to the north are crossed by a series of north-south mineral veins carrying quartz, apatite, wolfram, arsenopyrite and other minerals including uraninite (Dawson and Harrison 1966, p. 91). From field evidence and from microscopic examination of the ores Hitchen has confirmed and amplified the conclusions of Finlayson (1910) that the introduction of ore-minerals is related to the greisen. The following sequence of events in the veins is recognised by Hitchen: (1) injection of barren quartz, feldspar-quartz and

---

[1] In the Grainsgill outcrop this is largely due to greisenization but the variation in biotite-content may nevertheless be an original character of the intrusion. The richness in biotite of the Sinen Gill outcrop is attributed by Hitchen to derivation, as an apophysis, from a deeper portion of the granite than is exposed elsewhere. There appears, however, to be no difference in the degree of metamorphism adjacent to this outcrop and that shown near the southern part of the central outcrop. The porphyritic character of the Sinen Gill granite is one that it shares with a large number of boulders found in the drift on the southern part of the central outcrop. These boulders are associated with Borrowdale rocks of southern provenance, and it is possible that a concealed outcrop of porphyritic granite occurs beneath the broad peat- and drift-covered area between the Sinen Gill and central outcrops. The apophysal character of the Sinen Gill granite does not, therefore, appear well-established.

apatite-quartz veins; (2) injection of wolfram-quartz veins; (3) introduction of bismuthinite—and tetradymite-quartz stringers and molybdenite; (4) conversion of wolfram into scheelite and deposition of arsenopyrite and pyrite; local replacement of the sulphides by sphalerite; fracturing and deposition of chalcopyrite and quartz; (5) introduction of carbonates.   s.e.h.

PETROGRAPHY

Central outcrop. Typical biotite-granite from the exposures in the River Caldew is composed of hypautomorphic oligoclase crystals up to 1·5 mm long, enveloped by or enclosed in perthitic orthoclase crystals up to 5 mm across, with streaks of albite. Blebs of quartz occur in both kinds of feldspar, and interstitial pools of quartz reach 5 mm across. Brown biotite having $\gamma = 1·642–1·649$ encloses tiny zircon inclusions, and has been partially converted into chlorite + sphene. A little smoky apatite and magnetite may be present (E 15735–7). Granite from the former Cumberland Water Board's boreholes near the northern tip of the central outcrop (E 23655–8, E 23660–5) contains less biotite, though in small amount the mineral is generally present. In a core from Borehole No. 13 at 107 ft depth (E 23658) oligoclase An_{14} is zoned outward to albite An_8; some zones show albite-law twinning, others fail to do so. In this rock the biotite has refractive index $\gamma = 1·621$, presumably indicating a lower iron-content than farther south.

The pegmatitic variety from White Gill (E 15741) contains quartz, albite-oligoclase and perthitic orthoclase, coarsely intergrown; the feldspars have been partially replaced by a mineral with maximum refractive index between 1·524 and 1·532, and birefringence at least 0·02, tentatively identified as montmorillonite; a Carlsbad-law twin of feldspar is pseudomorphed in this mineral. Aplites cutting the slate (E 15739) and granite (E 15740, E 23653) are mosaics of fine-grained quartz, orthoclase and oligoclase, with a little brown and white mica.

Greisen occurs in the central outcrop, though not, as far as is known, on any substantial scale. It was found in Water Board Borehole No. 11 (E 23654) and also in a dyke cutting Skiddaw Slate in the Caldew (E 15743).

From the Blackhazel Beck outcrop, a series of specimens (E 15741–4) show the country rock and granite immediately adjacent to the contact. The country rock, a quartz-biotite-chlorite-hornfels with, in places, andalusite, has been converted into granulite with muscovite, oligoclase and orthoclase in addition to the minerals listed. The laminated texture is preserved, as are the evenly-scattered opaque granules so characteristic of the slate (see p. 122). This effect is confined to the inch adjacent to the contact, and there is no reason to think that this example of incipient granitization has any wider significance here. The andalusite has been attacked by muscovite (E 15733). Specimens collected from loose blocks show feldspathization of biotite-hornfels fragments enclosed in granite (E 16211–2). The granite immediately adjacent to these specimens shows no relic textures (e.g. lamination or scattered opaque granules) and is considered to have been intruded into its present position.

In view of the very complete chemical study of the granite and greisen carried out by Hitchen (1934) no further analyses of the granite have been considered necessary. His account includes an analysis of biotite from Sinen Gill, five full analyses of granite and four of greisen, and calculated mineral compositions of the granites using the composition of biotite obtained. In Sinen Gill the normative albite (27·0) is a little less than normative orthoclase (29·8) but, after recalculation for biotite, the orthoclase is reduced (18·6) to a figure below that for albite + anorthite. This rock might, therefore, be described as biotite-granodiorite. In the central outcrop, however, calculated orthoclase exceeds plagioclase in amount except in the southernmost specimen, and biotite decreases from 6·2 per cent in the south to 1·4 at the north-eastern margin, where the rock is a leucogranite.

TABLE XI

Comparison of Skiddaw Granite and Carrock Fell Acid Rocks

		K_2O	Na_2O	K_2O/Na_2O	FeO
Skiddaw Granite					
Hitchen's locality	2	4·78	3·12	1·54	1·25
do	3	7·47	2·18	3·57	0·76
do	4	4·66	3·42	1·36	0·38
do	5	4·86	3·39	1·44	0·43
Carrock Fell					
Melagranophyre		2·30	5·16	0·45	8·12
Granophyre		3·67	4·37	0·33	2·06
Granophyre (Harker)		3·53	5·55	0·63	
Granophyre (Holmes)		1·42	3·44	0·41	0·41
Felsite		4·39	2·14	2·0	1·86

(Reference: Hitchen, 1934, p. 172; full analyses of Carrock rocks on p. 102).

The comparison between the Skiddaw Granite of the central outcrop, and the acid rocks of Carrock Fell shows that while the ratio K_2O/Na_2O in the granite exceeds 1, it is less than 1 in the Carrock granophyres. On the other hand, the Harestones Felsite seems to be allied to the granite in this and other respects. The ferrous-iron content of the granophyres, which carry hedenbergite, is substantially higher than that of the granite except in the case of the leucocratic altered granophyre at the head of Brandy Gill described by Holmes (1917). It seems a fair conclusion that the granophyres and granite are on different lines of descent.

Grainsgill outcrop. The granite as seen in that part of the northern outcrop traversed by the River Caldew is a white, black-speckled rock, composed of oligoclase, orthoclase (both partly replaced by white mica), quartz and intergrowths of chlorite and muscovite (E 15744). The onset of greisenization is marked by the appearance of abundant small flakes, up to 0·1 mm long, of muscovite within the feldspars. These may be more or less oriented in crystallographic directions in the feldspar, or may develop as small rosettes (E 17406–8). At a more advanced stage, the feldspars are wholly replaced by mica, but their outlines can still be distinguished (E 15747). It is evident, however, that migration of the quartz-muscovite mixture could take place and in the greisen dykes, a coarse aggregate of mica flakes up to 2·5 mm across with quartz averaging 0·5 mm shows little or no evidence that feldspar was ever present (E 15745). Apatite, zircon, tourmaline, rutile and arsenopyrite occur in the greisen (E 23564–5). The refractive index γ of the muscovite was found to vary only within very narrow limits, the observed range being $1\cdot593$ to $1\cdot601$. A specimen of coarse yellowish muscovite from Harding Vein, lower level, was analysed after separation of very small amounts of impurities, with the results in Table XII.

TABLE XII

Analysis of Muscovite, Harding Vein, Grainsgill

SiO_2	47·74
Al_2O_3	34·19
Fe_2O_3	0·95
FeO	0·22
MgO	0·63
CaO	0·04
Na_2O	0·34
K_2O	11·27
$H_2O > 105°C$	4·37
$H_2O < 105°C$	0·18
TiO_2	0·11
P_2O_5	0·04
MnO	0·04
B_2O_3	0·2*
F	0·24
S	0·01
Cr_2O_3	not detected
BaO	0·05
Li_2O	not detected
	100·62
Less O for F	0·10
	100·52

Analysts, W. F. Waters and K. L. H. Murray, G.S.M. Lab. No. 1561, 1950. Fluorine estimation by Miss A. Shollick. (see Guppy 1956, p. 63).

*Spectrographic determination by J. A. C. McClelland.

The optical data for this muscovite are as follows: biaxial negative, $\gamma = 1\cdot593$. The impurities remaining in small amount in the analysed powder (mainly as minute inclusions between the plates of the mica) are considered to have been apatite (accounting for the CaO and P_2O_5, though not quite enough lime is present), limonite (Fe_2O_3 and some water), pyrite and tourmaline. After applying corrections for the first three, the following formula is obtained on the basis of 20 oxygen atoms:

$$(K_{1\cdot62}Na_{0\cdot07}Ba_{0\cdot002})_{1\cdot69} (Al_{3\cdot78}Fe^{2+}_{0\cdot02}Mg_{0\cdot10}Ti_{0\cdot01})_{3\cdot91} (Si_{5\cdot32}Al_{0\cdot68})_{6\cdot00}O_{20}[(OH)_{3\cdot36}F_{0\cdot04}]_{3\cdot40}$$

As only an approximate spectrographic figure is available for boron, no attempt has been made to correct for this, but it may be noted that the amount of boron cannot be enough to justify assigning the amount of soda present to tourmaline. Chromium was not found to be present in detectable amount in this mica, and the absence of lithium is also noteworthy.

The four analyses of greisen given by Hitchen (1934, p. 173), upon recalculation for muscovite using the data above, show that the white mica-content in his analyzed samples varied from 32·5 to 36·2 per cent. Quartz must therefore vary between 56·5 and 65·6 per cent in these specimens. These data serve to place in perspective the composition of the greisen, which consists roughly of two-thirds quartz and one-third muscovite, with very small amounts of apatite, tourmaline, arsenopyrite, pyrite and zircon. In the metasomatism of granite to form greisen, much of the potash is presumably derived from orthoclase, some from biotite, but probably a little is removed. The addition of some silica, water and fluorine is indicated, and removal of soda (as Hitchen 1934, p. 182, notes), possibly with some lime and iron.   K.C.D.

THE METAMORPHIC AUREOLE

FIELD RELATIONS

The metamorphic aureole of the Skiddaw Granite (Fig. 13) lies partly in the Cockermouth (23) district and partly in the Keswick (29) district to the south. As previously recognized, it was thought to lie wholly within Skiddaw Slates, forming an oval outcrop about 6 miles by 3½ miles with its longer axis trending W. 30° S.–E. 30° N., approximately parallel to the general trend of the Caledonian folds hereabouts. There are, however, thermally altered rocks in the Carrock Fell complex, and in the Drygill Shales and Borrowdale Volcanic rocks to the north that for reasons given below are here considered to have been metamorphosed by an underground extension of the granite to the north, or by some related intrusion.

Within the Skiddaw Slates the relation of the outer limit of metamorphism and of certain inner zones to the topography clearly indicate that the outer limit of the aureole forms a broad, flat-topped dome. The gentle inclination of this surface is best seen in the deeply dissected eastern portion of the area, west of Mungrisdale. The steeply plunging sides of the dome are revealed by the comparatively slight changes in direction of the outcrop when crossing the steep-sided valleys of the Caldew, Glenderaterra, Glenderamackin and Wash becks.

In the field the early stages of metamorphism of the Skiddaw Slates are indicated by the development of spotting and of porphyroblasts of chiastolite. With increasing metamorphism there is a progressive hardening of the rock to a massive hornfels, the spots become clearly-defined crystals of cordierite, the chiastolite changes to clear, translucent andalusite and biotite becomes a visible constituent of the base. The general inward change is thus one of increasing recrystallization of the hornfels, and of increasing definition of characters that appear first in the low-grade type of metamorphism; there is little that can be described as zonal appearance of metamorphic minerals.

On Fig. 13 an attempt has been made to construct, from field observations, surfaces of equal metamorphism which approximately delimit three zones of metamorphism of equal thickness. These are: (1) an outer zone of chiastolite and spotting, with a limited amount of hardening of the rock; (2) an intermediate zone of fairly massive hornfelsed slate or mudstone, considerably hardened, with spots of cordierite well defined but dull black on a fresh surface; (3) an inner zone of tough, well-crystallized hornfels with cordierite as black spots with a pitchy lustre, and andalusite as clear, translucent porphyroblasts. The arenaceous rocks are subordinate in amount, and do not seriously complicate this scheme.

The degree of dissection of the aureole is ideal for a study of the distribution of these zones in relation to the topography and it is clear that the total thickness of the three zones amounts to about 2500 ft.

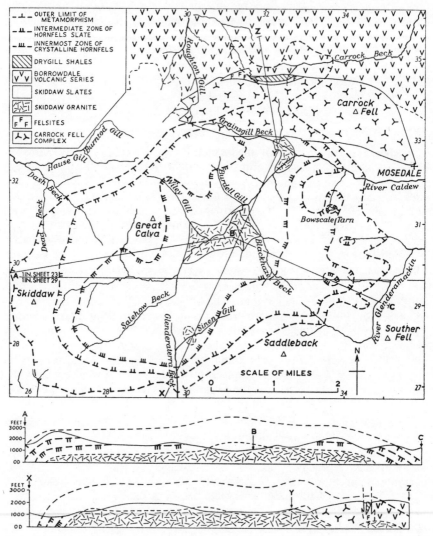

FIG. 13.   *Sketch map and sections showing metamorphic aureole of Skiddaw Granite*

It has also been possible to reconstruct a contoured surface, representing the outer limit of metamorphism. This emphasises the fact, implicit in Fig. 13, that the aureole as a whole can be resolved into a W.S.W.–E.N.E. oval with its long axis trending from Skiddaw to east of Bowscale Fell, and a northern extension with the north-south dome of the Grainsgill granite outcrop as its core. The axis of the larger oval passes somewhat south of the southern margin of the central granite outcrop, where the granite reaches its highest exposed position. The extent of the inner zone amply confirms views of previous workers of the existence of a great granitic mass at small depth below the surface.

The northern projection points in the direction of the metamorphosed volcanic rocks about High Pike.

There has been considerable confusion about the relative order in which the early indications of metamorphism—spotting and chiastolite—appear. Ward (1876) recognized faint spotting as the earliest stage, but Rosenbusch (1887) affirmed that chiastolite appeared first. Rastall (1910) attempted to clear up this discrepancy by pointing out that, as distinct from the main belt of spotting —Ward's 'spotted schist' lying within his chiastolite-slate belt—there was also an outer zone of spotting in black slates. It is clear that the misunderstanding is due to the fact that within the broad outcrops of black slates there are some types which readily develop chiastolite crystals and other types which do not. In the latter, the first sign of metamorphism is the appearance of spots which are faint at first, and recognizable only on bedding- or cleavage-planes, and not in cross-section. From a detailed examination of the aureole, particularly in Bannerdale, the spotting appears in the chiastolite-bearing types; and the belt of chiastolite-slate without spotting is about 200 ft thick, measured inwards from the first appearance of the index mineral. Rastall's (1910, p. 126) outer spotted belt, for example on Grey Crags in Sheet 29 on the west slope of Little Man, represents the outermost recognizable metamorphism in a series of beds lying not far above the Slates and Sandstones. These are of non-chiastolite-forming type, here and elsewhere represented by spotted or cordierite-hornfels, but they do not lie outside the range of chiastolite-formation.

The rocks of all three zones are normally black, but there are considerable areas, particularly in the inner zone, where they have been extensively altered to soft pale grey and greenish-grey rocks in which muscovite is conspicuous. Broadly, these rocks represent Ward's innermost zone of 'mica-schist', but their distribution is decidedly irregular. Thus normal inner-zone hornfelses reach the granite at places in the central granite outcrop, while as might be expected from the abundance of muscovite in the altered hornfelses, they have a great development adjacent to the Grainsgill greisen. The change is clearly a metasomatic one, superimposed on the thermal metamorphism at a late stage in the consolidation of the granite, and it has no true zonal significance. On Great Calva a pale bluish or bluish grey type is developed from the massive black hornfels of the intermediate zone, and similar rocks appear in the crags west-south-west of Swineside. This type appears to represent an early stage in the alteration of the hornfels by micacization; its mineralogy and distribution are not consistent with an origin by subaerial weathering.   S.E.H.

PETROGRAPHY AND PETROLOGY

The unaltered slates. A preliminary discussion of the constitution of the regionally metamorphosed slates has already been given (p. 119); it is suggested that the slates, composed of 'sericite', chlorite, quartz-silt and minor amounts of iron-titanium oxides and carbon, had already reached the grade of the Green-schist facies as a result of regional metamorphism. In Table XIII is set forth an analysis of a typical striped black slate, representing the argillaceous facies of the formation. The rock (E 17555) exhibits closely spaced laminae which differ from one another in content of carbonaceous matter, and in proportions of the main constituent minerals. The white mica has been recrystallized; it occurs as discrete flakes and partially developed rosettes up to 0·1 mm across. Recalculation of the analysis indicates that if the potash-content of the mica is that of a normal muscovite, about 22 per cent of the mineral is present in the rock. The mica is enclosed in a general matrix of very pale green chlorite, having very low birefringence, which mineral is believed to account for the magnesia and much of the ferrous iron in the rock. However, recalculation of the chlorite as aphrosiderite still leaves substantial amounts of silica and alumina in the rock not accounted for. The most probable explanation is that the potash-content of the mica is below normal, i.e. that the mica is a hydromuscovite or illite. This subject is one that deserves further investigation. Cleavage-traces, in the form of ramifying, carbon-lined fractures, run perpendicular to the bedding in this rock.

Elsewhere, alternations of argillaceous bands containing quartz-silt give rise to the 'silty-banded' type of slate, while in the neighbourhood of the head of Grainsgill, and on Great Sca Fell, impure greywacke-type sandstones, with micaceous and chloritic matrices, occur (E 14591, E 14972, E 14975). These may be conglomeratic, with fragments of quartzite, quartz-schist, rhyolite (E 14590), and chert with dolomite (E 14975).

Granules and rods of ilmenite, 'leucoxene', magnetite and iron sulphides generally occur in the slates and persist through the metamorphism, probably with some augmentation. Granules of graphite may also be present.

Metamorphosed sediments of the outer zone of the aureole. At Mosedale Farm the slate has not been affected by contact metamorphism (E 14991), but 100 yd to the north appreciable alteration is indicated by recrystallization of the chlorite and the appearance of tiny flakes of biotite at the expense of chlorite in certain bands (E 14992). On Kelt Crag and to the west, macrosopic spotting appears, the spots, about 0·15 mm in diameter, consisting of fine white mica, from which the chlorite has been cleared to the margins (E 15654, E 15700). Here the spotting only effects the argillaceous bands. This type of spotting prepares the way, it is suggested, for the development of andalusite porphyroblasts. The andalusite, when it appears in the low-grade rocks, takes the form of chiastolite, with carbonaceous inclusions not yet eliminated (E 15709).

There is, however, another kind of spotting, in which the spots when they first appear, consist of chlorite with very low birefringence, from which the mica has been cleared to the margins (E 15655, E 15699). These spots are considered to be the precursors of cordierite, which develops in ovoid masses as metamorphism progresses. These also may be clouded with carbonaceous matter when they first appear, and their outlines may be poorly defined (E 15669–70). They may reach as much as 2 mm long by 0·5 mm across, with their long axes parallel to the bedding of the rock.

As already noted in the field account, the type of spot or porphyroblast which appears first is dependent upon the local composition of the rock. The chemical changes involved may be pictured in the simplest way in the following equations:

$$H_4K_2Al_6Si_6O_{24} = 3Al_2SiO_5 + 3SiO_2 + K_2O + 2H_2O$$
(Muscovite)   (Andalusite)

$$\begin{array}{l}(H_4Mg_2Al_2SiO_9)\\(H_4Fe_2Al_2SiO_9)\end{array} + 3SiO_2 = (Mg, Fe)_2Al_4Si_5O_{18} + FeO + MgO + 4H_2O$$
(Chlorite)   (Cordierite)

The potash, ferrous iron and magnesia are used up in the formation of biotite from chlorite:

$$(H_4Mg_2Al_2SiO_9)$$
$$(H_4Fe_2Al_2SiO_9) \quad + 10SiO_2 + 2K_2O + 4MgO + 4FeO = (H_4K_2Mg_6Al_2Si_6O_{24})$$
$$\text{(Chlorite)} \qquad\qquad\qquad\qquad\qquad\qquad\qquad (H_4K_2Fe_6Al_2Si_6O_{24})$$
$$\text{(Biotite)}$$

The formation of andalusite and cordierite can proceed quite independently, but biotite is formed in both andalusite- and cordierite-hornfelses. The equations given here represent, of course, an over-simplification of the process, but they serve to emphasise that the reactions involve all the principal minerals in the slate, and that their main effect is the elimination of water.

Among the low- and intermediate-grade metamorphic rocks of the aureole, a few carry chloritoid (E 15697, E 15704, E 15717–8). In some cases the chloritoid forms rod-like crystals, but it is not possible to be certain that these are not products of the regional metamorphism. One instance of substantial spongy porphyroblasts of chloritoid was found (E 14985). The refractive index γ of the chlorite in the metamorphic rocks is in the neighbourhood of 1·640 in those cases investigated; this coupled with the optically negative character of the mineral suggests aphrosiderite composition. From this the chloritoid is readily distinguished by its much higher refractive index and oblique extinction (E 15718). Garnet has been found in only two outer-zone rocks, associated with biotite in one, with chloritoid in the other.

Metamorphosed sediments of the intermediate zone. The analyzed rock from this zone (Table XIII, analysis II, E 17442) is a black hornfels with pitchy-looking spots and visible scattered andalusite porphyroblasts. The constituents are reddish brown biotite with $\gamma = 1·649$ (presumably a ferriferous variety); cordierite in discrete xenoblastic masses up to 1·5 mm long, showing poly-synthetic twinning; and a matrix of fine white mica and chlorite. The matrix is dark with carbonaceous matter, and scattered rods of black oxide occur, and occasional pyrite masses. The andalusites show the black cross of carbon particles. Similar rocks are widespread in this zone (e.g. E 15702–3, E 15725). In one instance andalusite porphyroblasts up to 6 mm long by 1·5 mm across were found (E 15723).

Not all the rocks in this zone carry andalusite; cordierite-biotite-hornfels, presumably representing chlorite-rich slates, is also common (E 15689, E 15716, E 17414).

Some retrogressive metamorphism involving metasomatism of cordierite and andalusite by fine white mica occurs in this zone, especially in the area west of Great Calva (E 14989, E 15722).

Metamorphosed sediments of the inner zone. The rocks of the inner zone differ from those just described not in their mineralogy, but in the complete-ness of their metamorphism and in the elimination of carbon from the por-phyroblasts. The analysed cordierite-biotite-hornfels from Bannerdale (Table XIII, analysis III, E 17443) contains ovoid cordierite aggregates up to 2·5 mm long, evenly scattered biotite, and white mica which has evidently been re-crystallized, the flakes reaching 0·04 mm across. Pyrite and black oxides occur as granules.

Between the central and northern outcrops of the granite in the Caldew valley, most of the hornfelses contain porphyroblasts of andalusite, clear and glassy-looking, as well as cordierite and biotite (E 15690, E 15712–3, E 15724, E 15727–8, E 17413, E 17415). The andalusite in some of these rocks shows common orientation in large areas. Recrystallization of quartz-silt is displayed in places in this zone (E 15726).

A consideration of the analyses of unmetamorphosed slates (see also Barkbeth, p. 22) and hornfelses (Table XIII) suggests that such variations in composition as occur are probably to be attributed to original variations in the composition of the sediments. The essential character of the composition of the sediments is preserved throughout the metamorphic zones, justifying the view that the process is essentially simple thermal metamorphism. The conversion of chlorite and mica to andalusite, cordierite, biotite (and, very locally, garnet) cannot, of course, be effected without some migration of material; but no large scale metasomatism is called for.

In the second analyzed specimen from the inner zone (Table XIII, analysis IV, E 17441), a biotite-muscovite-cordierite-hornfels, muscovite is abundant and this specimen may provide a link with the metasomatized rocks to be described below. Cordierite forms a background in the layers relatively free from silt. Both biotite and muscovite flakes here reach 0·1 mm long.

Most, perhaps all, of the rocks of the inner zone show recrystallization of the white mica. In places, especially (though not invariably) near the granite outcrops, the mica becomes very abundant (E 15712, E 15719, E 17417) and has evidently continued to develop after cordierite, which it replaces. Andalusite is less readily attacked, but it, too, succumbs (E 15720). All stages may be found from hornfels in which the cordierite and andalusite are quite fresh, to rocks almost wholly consisting of quartz and muscovite, but still preserving vestiges of sedimentary structure. Thus not only is granite converted into greisen, but so are sediments. Introduction of tourmaline accompanies the more advanced manifestations of the process (E 15663, E 15691, E 17410–1, E 17418). Clearly this change is a metasomatic one, involving additions of silica, potash and water, and, in the more advanced stages, removal of iron and magnesia. Dr. Hitchen's analysis of "mica-schist" (Table XIII, analysis B) illustrates a stage in this process. Garnet occurs in some of the metasomatized hornfelses in Grainsgill, west of Brandy Gill, but these are near the gabbro, and the garnets may have been produced first in connexion with the gabbro metamorphism (e.g. E 15659). Where removal of magnesia and iron has not been complete, chlorite remains in the altered hornfelses (E 15691, E 15693, E 17419).

As already noted (p. 116), hornfels immediately adjacent to the granite in Blackhazel Beck has received feldspars by metasomatism. The absence of feldspars throughout the rest of the aureole is noteworthy.

Metamorphosed minor intrusions. Two vertical dykes near the old Bannerdale lead mine prove to have suffered metamorphism in the aureole (p. 116). One, a basic porphyrite (E 16199–16200) shows a considerable development of wisps of pale amphibole and brown biotite; the other, a dolerite with remains of augite and labradorite (E 16201–2) shows replacement of augite by hornblende and the occurrence of typical hornfels biotite.

What are probably sills intruded into the slates before folding, now exposed on Coomb Height, are in the condition of amphibolite with some biotite and a little quartz (E 15288). These are in the intermediate zone. In the outer zone, a band of amphibolite south-west of Burn Tod is composed of pale green hornblende with $\gamma = 1·660$, accompanied by chlorite and partially altered ilmenite (E 14976).

TABLE XIII

Chemical Analyses of Skiddaw Slate and Hornfelses

	I	II	III	IV	A	B
Slice No.	E 17555	E 17442	E 17443	E 17441	—	—
Lab. No.	1036	1013	1014	1012	—	—
SiO_2	58·41	56·19	55·25	63·18	53·35	54·37
Al_2O_3	20·25	22·48	22·38	19·29	23·37	22·11
Fe_2O_3	0·63*	0·58*	0·72*	0·27	1·66	2·23
FeO	8·05*	7·65*	8·59*	6·55	8·39	6·52
MgO	2·02	1·93	2·06	1·86	1·18	2·04
CaO	0·41	0·61	0·82	0·46	0·56	0·46
Na_2O	0·68	1·06	1·08	1·04	0·63	0·73
K_2O	2·50	3·34	2·70	3·81	3·58	4·94
$H_2O > 105°C$	4·87	3·37	3·49	2·12	4·19	4·42
$H_2O < 105°C$	0·46	0·44	0·50	0·19	0·21	0·15
TiO_2	1·00	1·21	1·12	0·98	0·80	1·03
P_2O_5	0·23	0·28	0·13	0·11	0·45	0·00
MnO	0·07	0·07	0·54	0·10	0·19	0·36
S	tr.	—	—	—	n.d.	n.d.
BaO	0·04	0·05	0·03	0·05	0·02	0·05
C	0·39	0·20	0·13	—	0·32	—
FeS_2	—	0·32	0·12	0·05	—	—
Fe_7S_8	—	0·24	0·54	0·03	—	—
Cr_2O_3	—	0·01	0·01	0·01	—	—
CO_2	—	0·01	0·02	0·02	0·53	0·96
	100·01	100·04	100·23	100·12	100·05	100·37

Localities

I Unaltered black striped Skiddaw Slate, 1470 yd W. 43° S. of Mungrisdale Church [3040 2953].

II Andalusite-biotite-cordierite-hornfels, middle zone, 200 yd S. of outlet of Bowscale Tarn [3359 3128].

III Andalusite-biotite-cordierite-hornfels, inner zone, 30 yd N.W. of Lead Mine Hut, Bannerdale, 1·8 miles W. 17° S. of Mungrisdale Church [3355 2955].

IV Biotite-cordierite-muscovite-hornfels, inner zone, River Caldew, 300 yd below outfall of Grainsgill Beck [3302 3260].

Analyst, Nos. I-IV, C. O. Harvey (see Guppy 1956, pp. 52-4).

A "Chiastolite slate," in contact with modified granite on the eastern fringe of the central area; quoted from Hitchen 1934, p. 172, analysis 7.

B "Mica-schist" (micacized hornfels), Grainsgill. Analyst, C. S. Hitchen, 1933. This hitherto unpublished analysis is included here by kind permission of Dr. Hitchen.

*Owing to the presence of carbonaceous matter, these figures should be regarded as approximate.

From the condition of these metamorphosed igneous rocks, and from the mineral assemblage in the slates, it would seem appropriate to refer the thermal-metamorphic rocks of the Skiddaw aureole to the Amphibolite Facies, where the slate-hornfelses would for the most part lie on the A–F line, rather than to the Pyroxene-Hornfels Facies, represented in many contact aureoles (*vide* Turner 1948, p. 78).

Metamorphosed Carrock Fell Gabbro. Brandy Gill, running northwards from the Grainsgill greisen outcrop into the gabbro, cuts across the gabbro more or less along the course of the quartz-wolfram veins associated with the greisen. In a small creek below the lower waterfall in the gill, Hitchen has recorded a dyke of greisen cutting the gabbro (1934, p. 164). The veins traverse and alter the gabbro, and the gabbro is also generally metamorphosed, so that it is certain that the granite and greisen are younger than the gabbro. The gill exposes a remarkable variety of altered gabbros. Primary variations in the gabbro are present here as elsewhere. Banded gabbro and granulite may be seen on the right bank above the waterfall (E 15356) while about half-way up the gill, good ilmenite-melagabbro occurs (E 17400). Adjacent to the southern margin of the gabbro outcrop, gabbro containing labradorite crystals (An_{60}) has been invaded by abundant biotite, which penetrates and extensively replaces the primary minerals (E 15254). This rock, with adjacent biotite-rich varieties (E 15748–50) is assumed to be the rock described by Hitchen in his account (1934, p. 183) as kersantite. We prefer to regard these biotitic rocks as thermally metamorphosed gabbros, rather than separate lamprophyre intrusions. In them, the feldspar has the composition normal for the gabbro, save in one specimen from below the waterfall, which shows silicification and albitization of the plagioclase (E 15758). Albitization is also well displayed farther north, the result of the process being to produce a diorite-like rock with plagioclase no more calcic than An_{20}. It is believed that albitization is connected with the early stages of hydrothermal mineralization produced by the Skiddaw Granite; for some of the albitized gabbros contain large apatite porphyroblasts (E 17398–400). In the gabbro wall-rocks of Harding Vein, however, where similar apatites have been introduced, the plagioclase has not been albitized (E 23561–2).

Hornblende is, generally, more abundant in the gabbros exposed in the gill than elsewhere in the Carrock complex. At 1170 yd N. 27° W. of the outfall of Grainsgill, a rock almost wholly composed of hornblende occurs; the amphibole has the following optical properties: α approximately 1·650, $\gamma = 1·672$, Z : c $= 10°$, X (slightly greenish yellow) Z (pale blue-green). A little sericite, chlorite and apatite are present. Notwithstanding the abundance of hornblende, it is difficult or impossible to distinguish amphibole related to the late fluids of the Carrock magma itself (see p. 109) from that due to fluids from the granite. It may, however, be concluded that some extra hornblende has been produced by the granite. Hydrothermal mineralization has also produced abundant chlorite in some of the rocks (e.g. E 15756, a gabbro with the feldspars almost completely chloritized).

In the vicinity of the Roughton Gill lead veins, alteration of the gabbro of a different type is to be seen. Many of the rocks show the effects of stress in the shattering and distortion of the minerals (E 15244, E 23526). Probably the gabbro had suffered extensive hornblendization before the alteration associated with the veins began; the hornblende appears to be variable in composition but one example examined in detail showed X (olive-green) less than Z (strong bluish green), with $\gamma = 1\cdot670$, this encloses remnants of coarse clinopyroxene (E 23524). The local alteration includes the following changes: (1) conversion of the labradorite to albite, locally with epidote; (2) extensive introduction of chlorite of variable composition; (3) introduction of quartz, ankerite with $\omega = 1\cdot709$, and calcite (E 23526–7). It is uncertain whether the rather coarse apatite occurring in some of the altered gabbros is original, or associated with the hydrothermal mineralization, but the mineral is not a constituent of the veins as it is at Brandy Gill and Grainsgill (E 23527–8). Ilmenite is replaced by spongy 'leucoxene' and sphene. A further stage in the alteration, which has perhaps occurred since the veins were brought by erosion into the zone of surface weathering, is represented by the conversion of the albitized feldspars into clay minerals (E 23525, E 23528), and replacement of the ferromagnesian minerals and ferriferous carbonate by red iron-oxide (E 23525).

Metamorphosed Borrowdale Volcanic rocks. On the north side of the Carrock Fell complex, contact metamorphic effects occur in the lavas and tuffs of the Borrowdale Volcanic Series for a distance of nearly three-quarters of a mile from the northern margin of the complex. The effects are so extensive in comparison with the very limited contact aureole along the south side of the Carrock gabbro, that it is considered more likely that in the north they are due to a concealed northward extension of the Skiddaw Granite, with its axis along Brandy Gill. The metamorphosed lavas are best seen around High Pike. The principal effect is the conversion of chlorite in rhyolite (E 14599, E 14642, E 14662) and in acid andesite (E 14658) into tiny scales of biotite. Another type of alteration in the lavas, not so certainly due to contact metamorphism, is the replacement of feldspar phenocrysts by epidote (E 15007).

Local metamorphism of lavas beyond the limit shown on Fig. 13 is indicated by the presence of fresh pale amphibole in amygdales of a pyroxene-andesite 1200 yd north of the summit of Brae Fell (E 14599), and by the occurrence of amphibole in cavities in tuff on Uldale Fells, S.E. of Stockdale (E 15834).

K.C.D.

AGE OF THE SKIDDAW GRANITE

Ward (1876, pp. 10, 68) considered that the metamorphism was later than the cleavage and remarked on the tendency for planes of cleavage and foliation to coincide in the metamorphosed rocks. Harker (1895, p. 144) observed that the greisen produced foliation on cleavage planes, and Rastall (1910, p. 138) also considered that the cleavage and foliation were anterior to the intrusion of the granite. A post-Silurian, pre-Carboniferous age was thus generally accepted. Opposed to this consensus of opinion was the view of Green (1918, p. 126) that the intrusion preceded the main folding and the cleavage, and was intruded in the core of the main Skiddaw Anticline at the time of its initiation during the Borrowdale Volcanic epoch. The older view is here considered to be correct for reasons that are given below.

Relation of the intrusion to the folding. The mapping of the major lithological divisions of the Skiddaw Slates, and of certain distinct types of hornfels within these, indicates that the major folds are truncated below by the intrusion. Furthermore, the steep dips in acute minor folds that follow the regional strike characterize the hornfelses almost to the granite contact. More or less vertical dykes intruded into slates having a variable dip, for example in Banner-dale (p. 140) are clearly later than the folding, but they have been meta-morphosed by the granite. The Carrock Fell complex, which is considered to be later than the main folding (p. 110), is certainly earlier than the granite.

Green (1918, p. 133) has discussed certain hornfelses in the Caldew valley which in his opinion suggest metamorphism prior to folding. The folding is of a somewhat abnormal type with steep, almost vertical pitch to the minor folds, and with much fracturing. A combination of these factors, however, is not unusual in the arenaceous type of slate to which the beds belong. By com-parison with the behaviour of massive beds such as the sandstones in the Skid-daw Slates, it seems improbable that the hornfelses have been folded into their present attitude after metamorphism. Moreover, the fractures have clearly been sealed up by the metamorphism.

When the long slender porphyroblasts of andalusite which occur in many of the hornfelses are examined, it is impossible to believe that these beds have suffered severe folding since the andalusite was formed. Most examples of such porphyroblasts are unbroken, and in some cases they have obviously grown oblique to the direction of minor folding in the rock (e.g. E 15725). The few cases where minor fractures have broken such porphyroblasts (E 15710, E 15723, E 23659) show that healing of the fractures with quartz and biotite took place, evidently during metamorphism. Folding had evidently taken place before high-temperature mineralization commenced, for a 'ptygmatic' quartz vein carrying tourmaline and biotite in Bannerdale (E 16198) is certainly oblique to the fold-lineation.

It is concluded therefore that the intrusion of the granite took place after the main folding.   S.E.H., K.C.D.

Relation of the intrusion to the cleavage. The incidence of cleavage in the unmetamorphosed slates (p. 23) is variable, and cleavage is poorly developed in some areas, where it is absent from relatively hard arenaceous beds such as flagstones, sandstones and grits. Thus its absence from much of the central part of the metamorphic aureole is negative evidence of no critical value. Critical evidence, however, is afforded at the northern end of the Skiddaw massif. Here, south-south-westwards from Dead Crags on the upland surface of Broad End, cleavage that crosses the bedding planes is present in tough chiastolite-andalusite-bearing slates, being well displayed at paper thickness on weathered surfaces. These slates do not split along the cleavage planes in the manner of normal cleaved slates, because the cleavage is sealed. They break with a blocky fracture that in part is determined by the frequency of the chiastolite–andalusite crystals which are scattered throughout the rock, with a more or less rough alignment in the direction of the bedding. The weathered-out fine cleavage of the slates is absent from the andalusite–chiastolite crystals. These field exposures clearly display sealed fine-cleavage in slates that have been subsequently metamorphosed.

It is considered, however, from a study of a large number of thin sections, that the traces of cleavage, where it has been present, can be seen as lines of carbonaceous and other impurities that pass through the cordierite xeno-blasts.[1] The long axes of the cordierites are often determined by the orientation

---

[1] Much of Mr. Green's microscopical evidence is considered capable of a different inter-pretation. Thus the "crushed crystal of andalusite" figured by him (1918, plate 12, fig. 2) appears to be an example of diablastic texture, occasionally represented in the Geological Survey slices (e.g. E 15705), and quite distinct from the normal autoblastic type of andalusite.

of original chlorite-rich laminae, thus these probably have a preference for the bedding–direction; but the chiastolite-andalusite tends to occur along the intersections of cleavage and bedding planes (e.g. E 15702, E 15713). It is therefore concluded that the intrusion is later than the cleavage.

F.M.T., S.E.H., K.C.D.

Radiometric age determinations. Recently A. J. Miller (1962) has determined the age of the Skiddaw Granite by the potassium-argon method from samples collected in Sinen Gill. Five age determinations were made, the results in millions of years being as follows: 395 ± 14; 408 ± 14; 393 ± 14; 406 ± 15; 395 ± 14; average 399 ± 6. As pointed out by Miller such an average age for the Skiddaw Granite places it within the Lower Devonian to which geological period the Shap Granite and the Eskdale Granite are also assigned by radiometric age determination. In Northern England the orogeny of this period is Caledonian.

F.M.T.

REFERENCES

DAWSON, J. and HARRISON, R. K. 1966. Uraninite in the Grainsgill Greisen, Cumberland. *Bull. Geol. Surv. Gt Br.*, No. 25, 91.

FINLAYSON, A. M. 1910. The ore-bearing pegmatites of Carrock Fell, and the genetic significance of tungsten-ores. *Geol. Mag.*, **7**, 19–28.

GREEN, J. F. N. 1918. The Skiddaw Granite: a structural study. *Proc. Geol. Ass.*, **29**, 126–36.

GUPPY, EILEEN M. 1956 (Compiler). Chemical analyses of igneous rocks, metamorphic rocks and minerals, 1931–1954. *Mem. Geol. Surv. Gt Br.*

HARKER, A. 1895. Carrock Fell: a study in the variation of igneous rock-masses. Pt. II. The Carrock Fell Granophyre. Pt III. The Grainsgill Greisen. *Quart. Jl geol. Soc. Lond.*, **51**, 125–48.

HITCHEN, C. S. 1934. The Skiddaw Granite and its residual products. *Quart. Jl geol. Soc. Lond.*, **90**, 158–200.

HOLMES, A. 1917. Albite-granophyre and quartz-porphyry from Brandy Gill, Carrock Fell. *Geol. Mag.*, **54**, 403–7.

MILLER, A. J. 1962. The postassium-argon ages of the Skiddaw and Eskdale Granites. *Geophys. J. R. Astro. Soc.*, **6**, No. 3, 391–3.

RASTALL, R. H. 1910. The Skiddaw Granite and its metamorphism. *Quart. Jl geol. Soc. Lond.*, **66**, 116–41.

ROSENBUSCH, H. H. 1887. *Die Steiger-schiefer und die Contakt-zonen an den granititen von Barr-Andlan und Hochwald.* Strassburg.

TURNER, F. J. 1948. Mineralogical and structural evolution of the metamorphic rocks. *Mem. geol. Soc. Am.*, **30**.

WARD, J. C. 1876. The Geology of the northern part of the English Lake District. *Mem. Geol. Surv. Gt Br.*

Chapter VIII

MINOR INTRUSIONS

INTRODUCTION

AN ASSORTMENT of intrusive, for the most part basic, igneous rocks is here grouped for descriptive purposes as 'Minor Intrusions'. These intrusions are of sporadic occurrence in the pre-Carboniferous rocks of the Cockermouth district, and do not lend themselves readily to genetic classification. With few exceptions they are highly inclined and they have been intruded along lines of weakness—bedding-planes, fault-planes or joints. The minor intrusions embrace dykes, sills and bosses, and also intrusions that cannot be assigned with certainty to any of these three categories. In this account they are treated as small associated groups, or exceptionally as individual intrusions.

Dyke-like intrusions related to the Carrock Fell complex are found north of the complex, in the Borrowdale Volcanic rocks and in the Drygill Shales; they constitute a natural grouping of known age, since they are the same age as, and link up with, the major intrusion; indeed they may be regarded as a dyke swarm of the Carrock Fell complex. In the following account these are considered first. Other minor intrusions, probably not all of the same age, are found in the Skiddaw Slates. They occur in three geographical areas— the western area, the central area, and the eastern area—and are described below under these headings.   F.M.T.

MINOR INTRUSIONS ASSOCIATED WITH THE MAJOR INTRUSIONS OF CARROCK AND SKIDDAW

In the Borrowdale Volcanic Series simple dykes are predominant and there is a general recurrence of rock types such as quartz-diabase, and to a less extent of granophyre, in the form of parallel intrusions which together constitute small dyke swarms. In the northern outcrop, between Longlands Fell and the River Caldew, the dykes are parallel to the strike of the Borrowdale Volcanic Series and they show a marked preference for the Middle Eycott lavas. On the other hand dykes in the Greystoke Park inlier and in the eastern outcrops of Eycott Hill (Berrier) also display other trends, which are related to the joint systems (Fig. 9).

Other minor intrusions are found in the Drygill Shales (p. 75), and these include lenticular masses and veins of felsitic rock as well as diabasic rock.

Petrological relations of certain dykes to the Carrock Fell complex, general uniformity of trend, the occurrence of a parallel series of dykes within the complex, and the frequency of dykes in the Borrowdale Volcanics to the north of the complex compared with areas to the west, all strongly support the view that they should as a whole be regarded as a dyke swarm related to the Carrock centre.

Dykes within the complex are described on p. 104; and dykes and veins of aplite and greisen associated with the Skiddaw granite are mentioned on p. 115.

Dale Beck, High Pike and Carrock Beck. A number of small easterly-trending dykes on the west side of the Dale Beck valley south-west of the old Roughton Gill Mine buildings include granophyre, diabase and composite dykes, partly of reddish rock of granophyre affinities and partly of diabase.

A series of small fine-grained, dark greenish grey to almost black dykes, mostly quartz-diabase, but including other more acid dacitic types with a brownish tint and a more flinty character, is well exposed in the outcrop of the Eycott lavas along the Short Grain–Hay Gill stream for ¾ mile N.W. of High Pike to its junction with Dale Beck. The dykes range from 1 to 10 ft in thickness and in places exhibit irregular branching form. Their general trend is a few degrees south of east with a southerly hade of about 20°.

Quite distinct from the dykes described above are a number of grey-white to pink felsite or albite-porphyrite intrusions exposed in valleys to the east and west of High Pike. They follow trends to the north-east and to the north-north-west—directions favoured by the mineralizing solutions at a later date (p. 237). Good examples are to be found at the head of Birk Gill [306 352] 1400 yd W. 10° N. of High Pike and along Driggith Beck [328 352] 1030 yd E. 12° N. of that summit.

Loose material doubtless derived from similar dykes is present on the same strike west of Dale Beck and eastwards across High Pike. Quartz-diabase dykes of similar trend are again visible on the southern slopes of West Fell, along Carrock Beck south of Calebrack, and along the Caldew valley northwards from Linewath. In Carrock Beck irregular offshoots tend to follow cross-joints trending north by east.

Berrier and Greystoke Park. In the Eycott Hill outcrop of the Borrowdale Volcanic Series, west of Berrier, there are a number of dark bluish grey dykes which, where quite fine-grained, closely resemble the non-porphyritic lavas. They fall into groups having the following trends: N. 10° E.; N. 40° E.; and N.W. In the outcrop of the Eycott lavas they are liable to be irregular in form and variable in trend and hade.

Points worthy of note are a small dyke [3894 3005], 500 yd S. of spot height 1064 on the Murrah–Berrier road, which is rich in macroscopic red garnet; and a curious weathered surface [3831 2999], 900 yd W. 40° S. of the same spot height. This shows a network of 'veins' each about quarter of an inch wide that has a tendency towards a radiate pattern. These 'veins' weather out in strong relief giving an impression of auto-injection. They are however probably due to some process of secondary alteration adjacent to joints developed during consolidation.   S.E.H.

PETROGRAPHY

The intrusions include felsites, porphyrites, granophyric sub-basic rocks, and quartz-dolerites, the latter being predominant. Deuteric alteration with production of albite, chlorite, calcite and epidote is widespread and frequently renders classification difficult. Contact alteration by the Skiddaw Granite affects certain of the quartz-dolerites strongly, and certain of the more acid rocks also show contact-effects though it is not always clear to what intrusion the effect is due.

Quartz-dolerites. These are fine-grained dolerites or basalts consisting essentially of albitized plagioclase, pale brown or colourless augite, and a turbid mesostasis composed of quartz, alkali-feldspar, skeletal plagioclase and chlorite (E 15805). Crystals of iron-titanium oxides are enclosed in the other constituents, and apatite in needles is accessory. The plagioclase is sometimes oligoclase, sometimes albite (E 17272), and usually has a turbid or watery appearance. It forms the usual diversely arranged stout prisms, but sometimes occurs in stellar groups (E 17271). Augite builds subhedral prisms, sometimes sub-ophitic to plagioclase, but in slide E 14603 it assumes a cervicorn habit (Thomas and Bailey *in* Bailey and others 1924, p. 303). In this specimen it has a reddish tinge, and the presence of orthorhombic pyroxene also is suggested by the shape of certain chloritic pseudomorphs. Quartz is present as separate grains usually in small proportion, but in the more decomposed rocks it is abundant and probably has been in part introduced (E 14632, E 15040).

Scarce tholeiitic types with labradorite feldspar are found, one south-west of Brae Fell and another near Roughton Gill, the latter being slightly contact-altered.

Sub-basic dykes, mostly of very fine grain, appear between Berrier and High Row and on the north of the Caldbeck Fells. They vary from hypo-crystalline andesitic types, with little (E 15807) or much quartz (E 15041), to more crystalline rocks composed of laths of oligoclase, granular quartz, chlorite, calcite and iron-titanium oxide and more or less interstitial alkali-feldspar. Some appear to be closely related to the preceding group, e.g. E 15038, E 15806, E 17268.

Porphyrites, granophyres, felsites. The porphyrites vary from exceedingly close-textured rocks carrying a few plagioclase phenocrysts to rocks with numerous, less automorphic, phenocrysts of feldspar in a coarser granular base. The feldspar is usually highly sericitized, and where determinable is albite or oligoclase. The groundmass always contains quartz, scarcely distinguishable in the finer grained types (E 14613), and the lathy development of oligoclase or albite in a base of anhedral quartz and alkali-feldspar (E 15046, E 15048) contrasts with the granular development of all these minerals in other specimens (E 15037, E 15804). Chlorite, hydrated iron oxide, and calcite are constantly present. The most sericitized member of this group lies well outside the aureole of the Skiddaw Granite, about $1\frac{1}{2}$ miles E.S.E. of Mungrisdale.

Fine-grained granophyres are represented by two dykes close to Roughton Gill. Stout prisms of turbid oligoclase-albite act as centres for micropeg-matitic growths (E 14629, E 14630); chlorite is abundant in ragged flakes. Transitional between the sub-basic rocks and the granophyres are two dykes cutting the lavas east of Carrock Fell. They are composed of narrow prisms of turbid oligoclase in a bed of red almost opaque material and some interstitial quartz. The red material is probably an extremely fine micropegmatitic inter-growth stained with iron-oxide. Chlorite is more abundant than in the grano-phyres and is probably replacing hornblende (E 16207). Granular epidote and iron-ores are abundant. These rocks belong petrographically to the mark-fieldite group.

The most acid dyke is a felsite (E 15047) from Caldbeck Fells, showing a granular association of quartz and reddened turbid feldspar. Much of the quartz is so full of finely divided foreign matter that it appears at first glance to be turbid feldspar. Devitrification of this rock has perhaps been hastened by contact-alteration.

Contact-alteration of an albite-porphyrite dyke (E 15009), in the stream ½ mile E.S.E. of High Pike is shown by development of tiny flakes of pale red biotite from the interstitial chloritic material. The phenocrysts of oligoclase-albite show a smoky clouding.   J.P.

MINOR INTRUSIONS INTO SKIDDAW SLATES

These rocks include bosses, as for example north-north-east of Dash and east of Mirkholme; lenticular sill-like masses as on Bassenfell and east-north-east of Embleton Station; intrusions of phacolitic character, as on Watch Hill; and numerous dykes. The intrusions tend to be elongated towards the east-north-east or east, in the general direction of the strike of the Skiddaw Slates, but not infrequently they cut across the strike of the country rock at an acute angle, and in the case of the bosses to the north of Dash their elongation is to the north-north-west almost at right angles to the strike of the Skiddaw Slates.

The rocks vary from types which have been classed as quartz-dolerites and quartz-diorites (for example the extensively worked rock east-north-east of Embleton Station known commercially as 'Embleton granite') to rocks termed picrites at Dash and at Little Knott. These minor intrusions have been considered petrographically by Dr. K. C. Dunham as belonging to one consanguineous group (see below); the petrographic descriptions of individual or associated intrusions are by Dr. J. Phemister.   F.M.T.

PETROGRAPHY

The minor intrusions of the Skiddaw Slates of this area may be broadly classified petrologically as dioritic lamprophyres. Considerable variation is shown in the composition of the rocks, however, some of the larger intrusions near Embleton having previously been regarded as sufficiently acid to be called quartz-diorites, while others near Dash were considered sufficiently basic to be classed as picrite. The present grouping of all these rocks with the lamprophyres is based on the abnormally large proportion of ferromagnesian minerals present, even in the more acid types, the marked tendency for the development of a pan-automorphic texture, and the presence of large quantities of alteration products. The Embleton rock on the one hand, and those of Dash and Barkbeth on the other, are regarded as the acid and basic extremes respectively in the composition of the suite as a whole. It should be noted, in addition, that the rocks of these two relatively large intrusions are unusually coarse when compared with the fine-grained, compact rocks of the majority of the intrusions.

In many respects a close comparison may be made with the suite of Caledonian lamprophyric dykes in the Lower Palaeozoic rocks of Kirkcudbrightshire. As in many lamprophyres the original character of these rocks is often largely obscured by the development of alteration products such as calcite, sericite, and chlorite; often the proportion of calcite is sufficient to cause the rock to effervesce with dilute acid.

Plagioclase is the dominant mineral, and biotite and hornblende provide the ferromagnesian constituents. Often the proportion of hornblende greatly exceeds that of biotite, as in the intrusions near Dash and Barkbeth, and the rock may then be more accurately classed as a spessartite. Similarly if biotite is more abundant, as in the Sale Fell rock and other small intrusions of the Sale Fell–Setmurthy area, a grouping with the minette-kersantite group is possible. A considerable amount of pyroxene is present in the Embleton rock, and also in that of Sale Fell; in one example (Slate Fell) pyroxene and plagioclase feldspar form the bulk of the rock.

The Embleton rock is grey in colour, with a characteristic speckled appearance; it is moderately coarse and of uniform grain. Decomposed, lath-shaped crystals of plagioclase feldspar, probably albite-oligoclase, with horn-blende and biotite form the bulk of the rock (E 17423, E 17204); most of the minerals show good crystal faces, and the texture is pan-automorphic. The biotite is partially altered into chlorite pseudomorphs associated with skeletal groups of ilmenite. Small automorphic crystals of augite are also present, together with interstitial quartz, pyrite, and secondary calcite. The quartz may be intergrown with feldspar as micropegmatite (E 13903). Towards the margin of the intrusion the rock becomes finer in grain (E 13905), but is similar in composition. Intrusions near Fell End, Lambfoot, Crag, and Bassenfell compare closely with that of Embleton in hand specimens and under the micro-scope (E 16229, E 17207). Rocks less rich in ferromagnesian minerals than usual are classed as non-porphyritic microdiorites (E 15677, E 15679, E 17206).

The characteristic pink and green rock of Sale Fell contains both orthoclase and plagioclase feldspar, a good deal of biotite (largely altered to chlorite), quartz, and a little augite. The pink colour is probably due to subsequent staining of the alteration products of the orthoclase feldspar.

Intrusions in the neighbourhood of Elva Hill, Watch Hill and Setmurthy are much altered, and their precise determination difficult. They appear to be of a rather acid type, and contain interstitial quartz which sometimes tends to be granophyric (E 15673, E 15679). The ferromagnesian mineral was probably originally biotite, but is now represented entirely by chlorite.

The coarse, melanocratic rocks of the Dash and Little Knott intrusions are made up of large, often automorphic crystals of hornblende, plagioclase feld-par, and a little orthoclase, quartz, and chloritized biotite (E 15818, E 16220). The margins of these intrusions (E 15821, E 16221) are finer-grained, and more typical of the lamprophyres; in the case of the Little Knott intrusion the margin appears also to be more acid than the central portion, containing a greater amount of quartz (E 16221). Smaller intrusions in this neighbourhood are similar in character, containing feldspar, hornblende, and a little quartz (E 16216–17, E 16223–28). They are much decomposed, with the production of calcite, sericite, and chlorite; occasionally pseudomorphs after original horn-blende can be recognized.

Dykes in the neighbourhood of Orthwaite are fine-grained rocks consisting of interlocking lath-shaped crystals of sericitized plagioclase feldspar (which is often zoned), with pseudomorphs after hornblende and biotite. There is a little iron-titanium oxide, quartz, and orthoclase (E 15823–25, E 16232, E 16309).   K.C.D.

WESTERN AREA: FIELD RELATIONS

Cockermouth to Bassenthwaite Lake. There are several intrusive masses into the Skiddaw Slates between Cockermouth and Bassenthwaite. All are of dioritic character, and that of Close Quarry, Embleton, may be taken as typical. Most of them appear to be sills; they vary in thickness from a foot or so to hundreds of feet.

On Slate Fell, which lies ½ mile E. of Anfield and 1½ miles E. of Cockermouth, there are three small outcrops of diorite separated at the surface by hard, pale slates but possibly forming one mass underground. Both slates and diorites have been quarried on a small scale. The southernmost outcrop [145 303] is a light blue-grey, finely crystalline rock in places vesicular, intruded more or less parallel to the strike of the slates. The other two masses [144 305, 146 305] are more irregular in form and are associated with quartz veins; in the north-western one the outcrop is terminated by a fault hading to the north-west which brings in hard, pale slate.

To the east of the above, and commencing at the second milestone from Cockermouth, there are two intrusions ranging east-north-east parallel to the strike of the associated slates which near the igneous rocks are again hard and slabby and pale grey in colour. The southernmost appears to be a sill about 12 ft thick, with a lens of shale near the middle which is not shown on the One-inch map. The other is probably 60 ft in thickness but much of the rock is rotten due to excessive jointing. One shatter-belt, trending west-north-west, and 6 ft wide in places, is veined with quartz, loughy in places, and carrying calcite, sphalerite, manganese and limonite. The last named mineral may have been derived from pyrite which is common as specks throughout the igneous rock; no hematite was noticed.

There is another large intrusion on the Golf Course, Embleton [162 308]. Farther east is the largest of these sills with an estimated thickness of about 400 ft. It is worked for road metal and sets by the Cumberland Granite Co. at Close Quarry [175 309] Embleton. At this quarry the slates are spotted and bleached in juxtaposition to this granophyric diorite.   W.C.C.R.

Watch Hill to Setmurthy. There are several intrusions on the Watch Hill ridge which appear to be associated with sharp folds in the grits. One forms the summit of Watch Hill where there is a small quarry, and there are others farther east. In that of the summit quarry [1495 3190] the weathered rock shows feldspars up to one eighth of an inch and laths of ferromagnesian mineral up to half an inch in length. The rock in the upper part of the quarry has some vesicles.

A fairly large mass of diorite emerges from the grits on Elva Hill and may be traced to a point ⅓ mile S.E. of Dunthwaite, where it is cut off by an east and west fault. Near the latter a nearly vertical face of the rock forms a *roche moutonée* surface. In an old quarry 400 yd W. of the summit of Elva Hill [1711 3199], the diorite in places fails to break through the grit cover over a sharp fold.

A quarry in a wood, 1000 yd E.S.E. of Dunthwaite [1820 3237] shows diorite resting on 4½ ft of sandstone that succeeds 20 ft of slabby shales. Some 18 ft of diorite, the lower part fine-grained, is visible in the quarry, but the full thickness must be about 50 ft. On the north, the east and west fault mentioned above also terminates this outcrop but to the south-east the intrusion dies out a short distance from the quarry.

                                                                                     T.E.

WESTERN AREA: PETROLOGY

The sheet-like intrusion at Embleton is composed of a granophyric diorite or markfieldite, grey in colour, with a characteristic speckled appearance, and of medium grain. It is composed essentially of tablets of oligoclase, anhedral interstitial grains of quartz, potash-feldspar and micropegmatite, and a number of dark minerals (E 9166, E 17201, E 17423). Outwards from the plagioclase with which they are in contact, the pools of micropegmatite may pass into entirely feldspathic or entirely quartzose portions, the individuality of the pool being preserved. The ferromagnesian minerals include colourless augite, reddish brown hornblende and reddish biotite. Augite forms idiomorphic prisms (E 17204) commonly bordered by hornblende, and in places more or less altered to green amphibole and chlorite. The reddish brown hornblende is automorphic only against quartz or potash feldspar, and biotite occurs as ragged flakes gathered around skeletal grains of ilmenite. Stout prisms of apatite are abundant. Paulopost alteration of the rock is made evident by the general turbidity of the feldspar, by the partial replacement of plagioclase by prehnite, and by the presence of calcite and prehnite among the interstitial constituents. Prehnite is especially abundant in the rock from the quarry on Seathwaite How (E 13903).

The rock from Close Quarry has been analyzed (Table XIV, analysis I). Chemically it compares well with the lamprophyric markfieldite of Newmains, Dumfriesshire (Table XIV, analysis A), which has a similar low value for alumina, but is distinguished by higher alkalies, and by the reversal of importance of ferrous iron and magnesia. An old analysis of the Markfield type of granophyric diorite is quoted for comparison (Table XIV, analysis B).

Varieties within the Embleton intrusion include a coarser more granophyric (E 13906) and a finer-grained very decomposed lamprophyric rock (E 13905), both of which come from the quarry of Seathwaite How. The ferromagnesian minerals are almost entirely replaced by chlorite.

A low degree of contact alteration is found in the slates within one foot of the under-surface of the intrusion. The altered rock (E 17203) is composed of a sericitic aggregate mottled by irregular plates of carbonate and aggregates of pale green chlorite. Biotite occurs throughout the rock in clusters of tiny reddish brown scales which are larger and more numerous in certain bands containing many small grains of iron-ore. The carbonate patches consist of calcite with a rim of darker but optically continuous carbonate.

From an old quarry near Grassmoor House (One-inch Sheet 29) comes a spessartite (E 13899) which contains patches rich in micropegmatite, quartz, and feldspar. It is petrographically allied to the Embleton rock. A similar rock (E 17207) constitutes the intrusion at Crag, Higham, but is greatly sericitized and calcitized.

The well-known Sale Fell 'minette', south of Routenbeck, is a medium-grained red rock with conspicuous plates of chloritized biotite. It is composed of idiomorphic tablets of plagioclase, stout rounded prismatic plates of a potash feldspar with perthitic appearance, interstitial quartz, large plates of biotite, and numerous partly decomposed idiomorphic crystals of colourless pyroxene (E 17477, E 17535). The plagioclase seems to have been originally a basic oligoclase but is greatly albitized and sericitized. Biotite, completely altered to chlorite and epidote, has an ophitic relation to the plagioclase and so gives sections of very irregular shape with poikiloblastic appearance. The interstitial grains of quartz frequently grade into the potash feldspar through a fringe of micropegmatite. Ilmenite and apatite are abundant accessory minerals. The rock differs from typical lamprophyres in overall granularity and in the unusual habit of the biotite. Nevertheless in both respects, as in mineral composition, it agrees with the so-called minette of Fuchsmühle, near Weinheim, Odenwald. The dominance of plagioclase relegates the Sale Fell rock to the kersantite group. A much finer-grained, highly sericitized rock from 250 yd N. of Setmurthy church probably belongs to the same group.

The intrusions on the Watch Hill–Elva Hill area are microdiorites in which the original feldspathic and ferromagnesian minerals are extensively converted to sericite, chlorite and calcite. The least-altered material (E 15679) shows a rock composed mainly of idiomorphic albite and allotriomorphic quartz in approximately equal proportions, and it is probable that the albite is due to albitization of a more basic plagioclase. Ragged flakes of incompletely chloritized biotite and irregular grains of iron-ore are abundant. The thick sill 1000 yd E.S.E. of Dunthwaite contains turbid potash feldspar intergrown with the interstitial quartz (E 15673), and near its margin contains porphyritic sericitized plagioclase (E 15674). Contact effects by these intrusions are inappreciable.

TABLE XIV

Chemical analyses of granophyric diorites

	I	A	B			I
	Analyses				Norm	Mode (Volume per cent)
SiO_2	54·24	55·17	55·7	Q	8·34	Plagioclase 43 (albitized and prehnitized)
Al_2O_3	13·25	13·90	17·5			
Fe_2O_3	0·76	1·19	5·2	or	7·23	
FeO	10·44	4·39	4·7			
MgO	3·63	8·37	2·9	ab	28·30	Pyroxene, hornblende and secondary amphibole 26
CaO	6·54	5·02	6·7			
Na_2O	3·38	4·53	2·4	an	17·24	
K_2O	1·18	2·83	2·1			
$H_2O > 105°C$	3·12	2·77	2·3	di	8·18	Biotite and chlorite 4
$H_2O < 105°C$	0·18	0·20	—			
TiO_2	2·40	1·56	—	hy	19·87	Iron ore 7
P_2O_5	0·31	0·22	—			
MnO	0·22	0·17	—	int	1·16	Quartz, micro-pegmatite and orthoclase 18
CO_2	0·57	0·00	—			
Cl	tr.	—	—	il	4·56	
FeS_2	0·14	—	—			
Fe_7S_8	0·02	—	—	ap	0·67	Interstitial calcite and prehnite 2
Cr_2O_3	tr.	—	—			
BaO	0·02	—	—		95·55	100
	100·40	100·32	99·5			Sp. Gr. (undried rock) 2·85

Localities

I   Granophyric diorite of Markfield type. Close Quarry [175 309], Embleton, 3½ miles E. of Cockermouth. (E 17423, Lab. No. 1009). Anal. C. O. Harvey (see Guppy 1956, p. 14).

A   Markfieldite. Newmains dyke, Dumfriesshire. Quoted from Kennedy and Read (1936, p. 126).

B   Granophyric diorite-porphyry, Markfield type. Anal. J. H. Player, (*in* Hatch, Wells and Wells, 1961, p. 328).

The intrusion on Slate Fell is a quartz-basalt (E 15672) in which prismatic, often glomeroporphyritic, phenocrysts of colourless augite and of decomposed feldspar are set in a base consisting mainly of plagioclase laths, chlorite, and interstitial quartz and micropegmatite. The porphyritic feldspars are replaced by sericite and calcite but the feldspars of the groundmass are determinable as labradorite zoned normally to oligoclase. The chlorite occurs both interstitially to the plagioclase and as large aggregates which occasionally possess a prismatic outline. Thin flakes of biotite are numerous throughout the groundmass and grains of iron ore altering to sphene are abundant. The rock resembles the Castle Head diabase of the adjoining sheet to the south.   J.P.

CENTRAL AREA: FIELD RELATIONS

Kilnhill and Orthwaite. Lamprophyres outcrop at several localities between North Row and Orthwaite and these have been regarded as exposures of one intrusive sheet (Postlethwaite 1893). Although they are not on the same line of strike and none of them can be traced far, they were connected by faults near Robin Hood and again near Orthwaite on the old edition of the One-inch map, so as to appear as one sill-like intrusion that has been stepped backward and forward by dip faults. The outcrop north-west of North Row, some 250 yd in length, is an undoubted sill. It is best seen in a quarry [2217 3256] 130 yd N.N.W. of that place, as a dark grey even textured rock, the crystalline character of which is readily discernible with the naked eye. Some 60 ft are exposed including the junction with the overlying slates. These, although altered to a light grey hardened slate, are heavily cleaved up to the margin of the intrusion and it would appear that the sill was intruded after the development of cleavage in the slates. The outcrop west of Little Tarn is probably also a sill but several of the other exposures, as for example that [231 331] 400 yd N.E. of Robin Hood and that [245 339] 900 yd W. by S. of Orthwaite are vertical or almost vertical sheets 10 to 15 ft wide, having all the characteristics of dykes. The slates into which they are intruded, however, are highly inclined and the intrusions lie parallel to or nearly parallel to the bedding. Nevertheless in their field relations they do not differ from other vertical intrusive sheets in the Skiddaw Slates that are mapped as dykes. Accordingly each outcrop is mapped as a separate intrusion and the faults which connected the outcrops on the old map are omitted on the present edition.

Bassenthwaite Common to Great Cockup. Sill-like intrusions that were classed by Bonney (1885) as picrites occur $\frac{1}{2}$ mile S. of Barkbeth (the Little Knott Picrite) [243 305] and $\frac{1}{4}$ mile N.E. of Dash (the White Hause Picrite)[1] [271 324] on Great Cockup near Brocklecrag. The two occurrences were considered to be part of one intrusion. The rocks are now classed as spessartites (see p. 133). Characteristically they are dark green to black coarsely crystalline rocks composed principally of hornblende crystals up to $\frac{1}{4}$ in across with a few scattered feldspars. But the rock is very variable particularly at Little Knott, and specimens may be obtained of a coarse type that appears to consist almost entirely of hornblende crystals up to $\frac{1}{2}$ an inch in length; on the other hand there are finer-grained types, the extreme in this direction being a fine-grained greenish grey and pinkish grey marginal rock in which the crystalline character is only distinguishable with the aid of a lens.

The Little Knott outcrop maps as a sill-like sheet that terminates abruptly at its western end. The White Hause outcrop also maps either as an irregular sill or as a laccolite, and it appears doubtful whether the intrusion extends across the drift-filled valley to the outcrop [268 328] near Brocklecrag. Consequently the outcrops on both sides of the valley have been mapped as separate intrusions.

At each of the three localities the spessartites have been intruded into black slate which has been baked to a hard light grey spotted rock for a distance of several feet from the intrusion. In the case of the White Hause intrusion the slates are equally cleaved within and without the belt of hardened slate, from which it would appear that the cleavage probably preceded the intrusion.   F.M.T.

CENTRAL AREA: PETROLOGY

The intrusions between Bassenthwaite and Great Cockup include hornblende-porphyrite and microdiorite, but are in the main dioritic lamprophyres and related ultrabasic rocks. In many the original minerals are entirely replaced by calcite, chlorite, quartz and iron-oxides, but in general the igneous structure is preserved.

A hornblende-porphyrite, 100 yd W. of Little Tarn shows phenocrysts of sericitized feldspar and calcite-epidote pseudomorphs after porphyritic hornblende in a base of

---

[1]See notes by T. G. Bonney in Postlethwaite (1892).

sericitized feldspar, quartz, chlorite and calcite (E 15823). Microdiorites are also greatly decomposed, but consisted originally of more or less idiomorphic plagioclase, biotite and hornblende, cemented by anhedral quartz and potash-feldspar (E 16227). Fairly fresh specimens of dioritic lamprophyres (E 15824–5, E 16309) consist of stout laths of plagioclase, chloritized laths of brown biotite and idiomorphic pseudo-morphs after hornblende, and perhaps augite (E 15825), with abundant interstitial quartz and reddened potash-feldspar. The plagioclase is normally zoned from andesine in the centre to oligoclase at the margins and the rocks include varieties transitional between the kersantite, vogesite and spessartite groups. Similar but coarser-grained rocks (E 15821) in which hornblende is the dominant dark mineral, occur as marginal facies of the very basic intrusions described below, and also constitute the smaller intrusions to the north-east and south-east of Barkbeth, but these are extensively altered to calcite, chlorite, sericite and quartz (E 16216–7).

The well-known intrusion ½ mile S. of Barkbeth—the Little Knott Picrite of Bonney (1885)—shows in hand-specimen conspicuous large (5 mm) black, lustre-mottled crystals of hornblende in a grey-green fine-grained base. Under the microscope (E 227, E 16220) the hornblende is seen to form large and small crystals idiomorphic except where they mutually interfere. The pleochroism is X = yellow, Y = Z = reddish brown, and the brown colour changes marginally to olive-green. Enclosed in the hornblende and occurring also in the base are roundish pseudomorphs of two kinds, presumably representing two different original minerals. One variety is composed of blades of pale green amphibole often recrystallized in continuity with the surrounding hornblende; the other of calcite and chlorite, or chlorite alone, within which sometimes lies a net of amphibole hairs set nearly at 90° and 45°. Bonney (1885) suggested the existence of enstatite as an original mineral, while Harker (1902) thought some of the pseudomorphs were after olivine. It is probable that both augite and olivine or enstatite were original minerals. Apatite and iron ores are abundant accessory minerals.

Very similar basic rocks form the intrusions exposed to the north and south of Hause Gill, ¼ mile N.E. and ½ mile N.N.W. of Dash. These are respectively the White Hause and Great Cockup localities for the dioritic picrite described by Bonney (in Postlethwaite 1892). The original minerals are better preserved than in the Little Knott intrusion, with which the rock from Great Cockup is identical in hand specimen, while the White Hause material is speckled with pinkish feldspathic patches and has smaller hornblende crystals. Under the microscope the latter (E 15818) shows brown hornblende forming plates which possess some good crystal faces but are ophitic to plagioclase and enclose prisms and prismatic aggregates of colourless augite partly replaced by aggregates of chlorite and calcite. Other shapeless pseudomorphs are composed of chlorite and pale green amphibole, and the chlorite contains the net of hair-like inclusions mentioned above. It seems probable that these represent the schiller inclusions arranged along the prismatic and pinacoidal cleavage planes of original enstatite. Biotite, completely chloritized, is an essential constituent forming ragged flakes on the margin of amphibole, and isolated in the feldspathic areas. The plagioclase, much sericitized and epidotized, was originally an oligoclase-andesine, and forms stout prisms mantled by alkali-feldspar. The latter also occurs as grains which form intergrowths with the interstitial quartz. Stout prisms of apatite and crystals of ilmenite, greatly altered to leucoxene, are abundant, and rosettes of chlorite form interstitial aggregates.

In the rock from Great Cockup it is certain that some of the pseudomorphs enclosed in hornblende were originally olivine since they are composed of talcose aggregates traversed by curving strings of finely divided iron-ore (E 15819). Biotite, completely chloritized, is an essential constituent but otherwise the description of the Little Knott rock is applicable. Marginally this intrusion takes the form of a hornblende-lamprophyre (E 15821) in which automorphic brown and green hornblendes and shapeless aggregates of calcite and chlorite, representing pyroxene, are set in a base of sericitized plagioclase prisms, with interstitial chlorite, quartz, and orthoclase.

These very basic rocks have been termed picrites but their affinities lie more with the appinite-cortlandtite series. Thus the intrusions of the area between Cockermouth and Great Calva correspond petrographically with the minor intrusions of Caledonian age in Scotland which show the same range of hornblende-porphyrite, microdiorite, dioritic rocks of Markfield and Spessart types, appinite and cortlandtite.   J.P.

EASTERN AREA: FIELD RELATIONS

Knott to Mungrisdale. Debris of a fine-grained, greenish igneous rock with small phenocrysts of a ferromagnesian mineral is freely scattered over the hillsides south of the summits of Knott and Coomb Height, and small lenticular dyke-like bodies are present in the Skiddaw Slates at the heads of streams hereabouts (Little Wiley Gill and Burdell Gill of 6-in map). These occurrences are represented by a continuous outcrop of 'lava' on the Old Series Geological Map. More than one rock type are probably represented, and a series of lenticular outcrops is more in accordance with the actual exposures. In common with other minor intrusions within the aureole of the Skiddaw Granite, these rocks have been hornfelsed by that intrusion and therefore pre-date it.

The distribution of small intrusive bodies in the Great Sca Fell area suggests some connexion between the location of the intrusions and the important overthrust which brings Skiddaw Slates on top of Borrowdale Volcanic rocks. Thus high up in Red Gill, ¼ mile N. of Great Sca Fell, a horizontal sheet of porphyrite is present close to the thrust-plane, where slates and grits overlie tuffs of the Borrowdale Volcanic Series; and in several of the stream valleys radiating from the overthrust capping of grits, small sill-like and irregular shaped bodies of fine-grained, dark grey igneous rock of diabasic character have been found near the observed or conjectured position of the thrust plane. It seems possible then that injection followed certain lines of weakness that were developed during the thrusting. If this were established it would follow that the thrusting here was of earlier date than the metamorphism due to the Skiddaw Granite.

Hornfelsed basic dykes trending a few degrees south of east and with a low southerly hade occur within the aureole of the Skiddaw Granite; for example there is a dyke [280 318], 4 ft wide, 1150 yd S. 10° W. of Burn Tod, and another [333 297], 30 yd wide, on Bannerdale Crags ½ mile S. of the summit of Bowscale Fell. These have the regional strike and hade common to dykes in the Carrock complex and in the Borrowdale Volcanic Series to the north of the latter. The Bannerdale dyke is discordant to, and clearly later than, the folding of the adjacent slates. It has however suffered some shearing prior to metamorphism and this may have been contemporaneous with the cleavage of the slates. There is a notable difference between the fairly coarsely spotted hornfelsed slates typical of the Skiddaw aureole at say 30–40 yd away from the dyke, and the fine spotting of the hornfels within a few feet of its margin. The latter resembles in size fine spotting developed adjacent to certain other minor intrusions, and it appears that the thermal effects of the dyke on the slate restricted the mobility of the constituents when subsequently subjected to metamorphism by the Skiddaw Granite.

The line of the Bannerdale dyke was followed at a later stage by hydrothermal solutions which deposited quartz and baryte as veins marginal to the dyke and metallic sulphides within the dyke itself.[1]

Among other minor intrusions in the eastern area may be mentioned an outcrop [354 308] about 100 yd square, 1000 yd W. by N. of Mungrisdale Church. Locally

---

[1]The trials known as the Bannerdale Lead Mine some 350 yd to the south-east, and just beyond the southern margin of Sheet 23, are also on a vein which, for part of its course at least, also follows a hornfelsed dyke.

this rock develops a platy jointing parallel to the cleavage of the adjacent slates and possibly representing that structure.

A group of three small dykes disturbed by small tear-faults is exposed in the quarry [3632 3058] 150 yd N. of Mungrisdale Church. The northern wall of the quarry shows a dyke terminated by a small reversed fault with local overturning of the normally southerly dipping slates due to movement from the north.   S.E.H.

EASTERN AREA: PETROLOGY

Contact-alteration of the basic intrusions is observable in the Roughton Gill-Burn Tod area and in Bannerdale, which lies partly on Sheet 29. The less altered rocks, in which igneous structure is fully preserved, show green fibrous amphibole replacing pyroxene or its decomposition products, while biotite replaces the chloritic material which occurs interstitially and as replacement of feldspar (E 14597). As the degree of alteration increases, the amphibole is dispersed as minute needles through the rock, though the shape of the original ferromagnesian mineral is still retained (E 16202). In the slide quoted the feldspar is labradorite-andesine and, in view of the almost universal albitization of the ordinary dykes, it is possible that the reverse change has occurred as an incident of the contact-alteration. In other rocks there is little igneous structure remaining, but it is probable that this is due in part to decomposition before contact-alteration (E 15044), since no specimen shows a high degree of recrystallization. Thus the specimens E 14976, E 16201 are composed of acicular prisms and sheaves of fibrous amphibole and flakes of biotite embedded in a sericitic base containing some small grains of quartz. In another specimen, E 16199, the base is formed mainly by ill-defined plates of andesine crowded with amphibole needles. The amphibole often includes two varieties, both monoclinic; one corresponds to actinolite in colour and refractive index, while the other is colourless and has much higher refractive indices, $\alpha = 1 \cdot 643$, $\gamma = 1 \cdot 670$, with negative sign and $Z : C = 19°$. In its mode of occurrence, habit, and optical properties with exception of the sign of the double refraction, this amphibole is comparable with the cummingtonite of hornfelsed basic igneous rocks in Cornwall (Tilley and Flett 1930). The contact-altered rocks frequently carry a dusky apatite in small stout prisms with a greenish tinge and strong absorption parallel to their prism axis. Irregular grains of iron-ore are abundant and epidote is sometimes present. The apatites are well developed in a less basic type of rock, (E 16200), where biotite is the main contact mineral, amphibole being scarce. Chlorite persists in this rock as large irregular flakes in a base of partly granulitized quartz and plagioclase. The latter retains more or less prismatic outline and is crowded with minute inclusions. A similar rock shows chlorite and amphibole but no biotite (E 15801). A dyke [302 328], 660 yd E. 20° S. of the trigonometrical point 2329 on Knott, has probably been a porphyritic basalt, the ferromagnesian phenocrysts being now replaced by flaky biotite and acicular amphibole in a finely crystalline base consisting of plagioclase laths, amphibole fibres, and iron-ore grains.   J.P.

REFERENCES

BAILEY, E. B., CLOUGH, C. T., WRIGHT, W. B., RICHEY, J. E. and WILSON, G. V. 1924. Tertiary and post-Tertiary geology of Mull, Loch Aline and Oban. *Mem. Geol. Surv. Gt Br.*

BONNEY, T. G. 1885. On the so-called diorite of Little Knott (Cumberland) with further remarks on the occurrence of picrites in Wales. *Quart. Jl geol. Soc. Lond.*, **41**, 511–22.

GUPPY, EILEEN M. 1956 (Compiler). Chemical analyses of igneous rocks, metamorphic rocks and minerals, 1931–1954. *Mem. Geol. Surv. Gt Br.*

HARKER, A. 1902. Notes on the igneous rocks of the English Lake District. *Proc. Yorks. geol. polytech. Soc.*, **14**, 487–93.

HATCH, F. H., WELLS, A. K. and WELLS, M. K. 1961. *Petrology of the igneous rocks. 12th edit.* London.

KENNEDY, W. Q. and READ, H. H. 1936. The differentiated dyke of Newmains, Dumfriesshire and its contact and contamination phenomena. *Quart. Jl geol. Soc. Lond.*, **92**, 116–45.

POSTLETHWAITE, J. 1892. The dioritic picrite of White Hause and Great Cockup. *Quart. Jl geol. Soc. Lond.*, **48**, 508–13.

————— 1893. Notes on an intrusive sheet of diabase and associated rocks at Robin Hood near Bassenthwaite. *Quart. Jl geol. Soc. Lond.*, **49**, 531–5.

TILLEY, C. E. and FLETT, J. S. 1930. Hornfelses from Kenidjack, Cornwall. *Summ. Prog. Geol. Surv. Gt Br.* for 1929. Part II 24–41.

Chapter IX

CARBONIFEROUS ROCKS: GENERAL

THE CARBONIFEROUS ROCKS of the district consist of a basal conglomerate, overlain in the west by a group of lavas, followed by a sequence dominantly of thick marine limestones, which in turn are overlain by sandstones, grits, mudstones and coal seams with a few thin bands of marine fossils. The change from marine limestones to terrigenous deposits is abrupt and dramatic and provides an obvious basis for a twofold lithological division.

The sequence has not hitherto been described in any detail; thus the classification of these rocks necessitates comparison and correlation with those found in adjoining and adjacent areas where the sequence has been long established.

The adjoining area to the south-west which includes the West Cumberland iron-orefield has been extensively explored; some 20 miles to the east of the eastern margin of the sheet lies the Alston Block which, due to its lead-zinc-copper mineralization, is equally well explored in Lower Carboniferous rocks. In both orefields stratigraphical sequences have been long established, initially on the basis of lithology, later supplemented by the aid of fossils. In the work of zoning the Lower Carboniferous rocks by means of fossils (mainly corals and brachiopods) the pioneer work of Vaughan (1905) in the South-West province and of Garwood (1913) in the North-West province, are highly important. In the Upper Carboniferous Bisat's (1924) work on goniatites and Trueman's work on non-marine lamellibranchs, summarized (1954) in text-book form, are contributions of outstanding importance. Additionally mention should be made of fossil plants as a basis of classification of the Carboniferous rocks. Kidston's work (1923–5) is pre-eminent in this field. In their several fields these authors have had co-workers, and advancements and refinements to the zonal schemes are being made continually.

CLASSIFICATION AND NOMENCLATURE

The major sub-divisions of the Carboniferous rocks of the area are given below with their European equivalents.

Local Classification	European equivalents
Upper Carboniferous	Silesian
Coal Measures	Westphalian
Millstone Grit Series	Namurian
Lower Carboniferous (Carboniferous Limestone Series)	Dinantian
Chief Limestone Group	
Cockermouth Lavas	Viséan
Basement Conglomerate Series	

Lower Carboniferous. The Basement Conglomerate Series and the Cockermouth Lavas are local developments and their classification, based on lithology, is given later (pp. 150–2).

The Chief Limestone Group of the West Cumberland iron-orefields, as proved by numerous boreholes, includes seven limestones. These are named numerically in downward succession, viz. First Limestone, Second Limestone and so on down to the Seventh Limestone. The sequence was first described by Kendall (1885) and by Smith (1919). Later, faunal assemblages of the seven limestones were given by Edmonds (1922) and Dixon (in Eastwood and others 1931) and the zonal scheme based on Garwood's work was applied to them.

This well-established West Cumberland terminology is valid in the western part of the present district, but becomes inapplicable towards the east due to the splitting of the Fourth Limestone into a number of distinct limestones each of which is separated by sandstones (or grits) and shales. The splitting takes place above the Rough Limestone (see Fig. 14), and the top of this limestone is consequently taken as the divisional line between a Lower and an Upper Chief Limestone groups. The Lower Chief Limestone group thus consists of the Seventh Limestone, Sixth Limestone, Fifth Limestone and the lower parts of the Fourth Limestone known both as the White and as the Rough limestones. All of these limestones have been mapped under their West Cumberland names throughout the district.

The expansion of the sequence towards the east caused by the incoming of sandstones and shales between bands of limestone occurs essentially in the Upper Chief Limestone group and where this group presents a Yoredale limestone facies it is essentially similar to the equivalent measures in the orefield of the Alston Block, where a sequence and a nomenclature for the limestones were set out by Westgarth Forster (1809). Thus in upward sequence the limestones in the Upper Chief Limestone group, where separated by sandstones and shales, are named in upward succession as follows: Jew, Tyne Bottom, Single Post, Cockleshell, Scar, Five Yard, Three Yard, Four Fathom and Great.

The expanded sequence of the Upper Chief Limestone group is found in the east and north-east; in the central part of the area some limestones join together, as for example the Jew and Tyne Bottom limestones, and also the Four Fathom and the Great limestones. It may be noted that where the sequence is fully expanded it corresponds precisely to the Yoredale series of Phillips (1836).

The divisional line between Upper and Lower Carboniferous. To the immediate west of the district the Hensingham Group has been included within the Carboniferous Limestone Series *i.e.* within the Lower Carboniferous. On Sheet 23, however, the Group has been placed within the Upper Carboniferous, being regarded as the equivalent of the Millstone Grit Series. The reasons for this change in classification are given below.

Viewed regionally it has been shown (Trotter 1952, table iv) that the top of the Great Limestone marks a horizon of widespread change in sedimentation. Presumably because of this facies change Phillips (1836) chose, more than 100 years ago, the top of the Main (or Great) Limestone as the base of his Millstone Grit in his type area of Wensleydale and he applied it farther north to the area now known as the Alston Block. From a local viewpoint, Phillips's historical line applies ideally to the Carboniferous rocks of Sheet 23, although this district is some way from his type area.

It has become the practice of the Geological Survey of Great Britain to equate the base of the Millstone Grit Series with the base of the Namurian, wherever this is possible. The Namurian is defined in terms of a sequence of goniatite zones with numerous species subzones, and within a goniatite-bearing sequence the base of the Namurian proposed by the Fourth Congress of Carboniferous Stratigraphy at Heerlen in 1958 (1960) is definitive. This proposal reads "the strata containing the earliest occurrence of *Cravenoceras leion* Bisat be taken as the base of the Namurian as proposed by Bisat in 1930 and 1950". This definition is not so meaningful where goniatites are rare, as in the Yoredale facies in Northern England and Scotland. Neverthless considerable progress has been made recently in relating these rare and sporadic goniatite occurrences (Johnson and others 1962) to the established Yoredale limestone sequence, and it is now possible with a fair degree of confidence to say that the base of the Namurian in the Yoredale limestone sequence lies somewhere within about 100 ft of strata extending upwards from a few feet below the Great (or Main) Limestone to a few feet above it. The evidence (*op. cit.* 1962) is as follows: goniatites from the uppermost sub-zone of *Posidonomya* (P_{2c}), and thus of Lower Carboniferous age, have been collected from the Mount Pleasant Borehole near Barnard Castle at a horizon said to overlie the Undersett (or Four Fathom) Limestone, while some 50 miles farther north, at Greenleighton Farm, Northumberland, *Cravenoceras leion* has been found in tip material from beds that overlie the Great Limestone, its likely horizon being in shales about 12 ft above the top of that limestone. This latter horizon would qualify as the base of the Namurian were not this occurrence of *C. leion* unique in the Yoredale limestone sequence, so that it is possible that this zonal fossil may later be found at a somewhat lower horizon.

Support for a divisional line at the top of the Great Limestone is provided by the rich and full standard limestone fauna of that formation. It is typical of the Upper Viséan and is not dwarfed, stunted or transitional in type. Details of assemblages are given in Chapter X and Appendix I; here we may illustrate the point by listing the coral genera found in the Great Limestone, viz. *Chaetetes, Aulophyllum, Caninia, Dibunophyllum, Diphyphyllum, Koninkophyllum, Lithostrotion* and *Lonsdaleia.* Consideration of this assemblage leads to the conclusion that the Great Limestone is best placed in the Avonian, and thus in the Lower Carboniferous.

Moreover in the area under description the Four Fathom and the Great limestones commonly unite, and the only available divisional line for mapping purposes is then the top of this joint limestone.

Thus the balance of evidence favours taking the top of the Great Limestone as the divisional line between Upper and Lower Carboniferous. It follows that the overlying Hensingham Group falls wholly within the Upper Carboniferous, and it is so indicated on One-inch Geological Sheet 23.

Upper Carboniferous. These rocks are divided traditionally into Millstone Grit Series and overlying Coal Measures. As previously indicated the Geological Survey of Great Britain equates the Millstone Grit Series with the Namurian. In the Hensingham Group of this area, however, there is no fossil evidence to indicate higher Namurian strata than the genus zone of *Eumorphoceras*, and it is considered that the higher zones of the Namurian are here absent because of non-sequence (Trotter 1952, p. 104).

A threefold classification for Geological Survey maps of the Coal Measures of England and Wales, on the basis of marine bands carrying diagnostic goniatites, was put forward by Stubblefield and Trotter (1957). The band taken for the base of the Coal Measures is that of *Gastrioceras subcrenatum* (Frech), first suggested by Jongmans (1928). The divisional line between Lower and Middle Coal Measures is taken at the marine band which has *Anthracoceras vanderbeckei* (Ludwig) as its characteristic goniatite, and that between the Middle and Upper Coal Measures is taken at the top of the marine band in which *A. cambriense* Bisat is the characteristic goniatite. Although these marine bands are remarkably persistent they do not invariably carry their diagnostic goniatites.

Gastrioceras subcrenatum was first recognized in Cumberland by Sir James Stubblefield from the cores of a bore in Whitehaven (Trotter 1953, p. 33), and later from other boreholes in that vicinity (Taylor 1961, p. 3). The band appears to fail northwards and has not been found within the area under description. Fortunately, where present, it closely underlies the Harrington Four Feet seam, and this practical divisional line has been used in preference to the marine band throughout most of the West Cumberland Coalfield (Eastwood 1930; and Eastwood and others 1931), including, where possible, the present district.

The West Cumberland equivalent of the *Anthracoceras vanderbeckei* Marine Band is the Solway Marine Band (Stubblefield and Trotter 1957, pl. i), although as yet it has not yielded the diagnostic goniatite. Apparently its distribution is restricted locally to the area south of Workington (Taylor 1961, p. 10 and pls. i and ii), but it may be present on Sheet 23, in Chalk Beck, in reddened beds devoid of coals (see p. 205). Because of its rarity in the area under discussion the Lower and the Middle Coal Measures are grouped together.

A widespread and important marine band characterized by the goniatites *Anthracoceras hindi* Bisat and *A. aegiranum* H. Schmidt was first found in Cumberland in Pow Gill within Sheet 23 (see p. 202). In the St. Helens No. 11 and No. 13 boreholes its stratigraphical position was proved to lie above the Brassy seam and about 300 ft below the St. Helens Marine Band. It is known as the Bolton Marine Band and it carries both diagnostic goniatites. The occurrence of this marine band in reddened strata in Pow Gill, $2\frac{1}{2}$ miles south of Wigton, initially suggested that it lay within the Whitehaven Sandstone Series, and the 6-in geological maps of this area were published under this supposition. Now that the position of the Bolton Marine Band within the sequence is known, it follows that the strata south of Wigton in which it occurs should be classed as Middle Coal Measures (reddened), and they so appear on One-inch Geological Sheet 23. Taylor (1961, p. 19) has suggested that, as the term 'Whitehaven Sandstone Series' has ceased to have any useful meaning, its use should be discontinued.

It is doubtful whether the *A. cambriense* Marine Band has been found in Cumberland, although Taylor (*op. cit.*, p. 16) suggests that the St. Helens Marine Band, found by Eastwood at depths of 208 ft and of 215 ft in the St. Helens No. 11 and No. 13 boreholes respectively, may represent this band. It is, however, possible that the position of the *A. cambriense* Marine Band lies higher in the sequence, but has been cut out by an unconformity at the base of the Upper Coal Measures.

Upper Coal Measures nowhere appear at the surface on Sheet 23 in normal sequence above the Middle Coal Measures. They are found as a faulted outlier to the south-east of Welton, where they yield fossil plants of undoubted Upper Coal Measures age. Also they have been proved beneath the New Red Sandstone in boreholes to the north-east of Aspatria (see p. 207).

RED BEDS

There can be little doubt that the red shales which occur in the Basement Conglomerate Series are primary red beds. For the most part the pebbles of the conglomerates with which the red shales are interbedded exhibit their original coloration but some are reddened. It is evident that these red shales of the Basement Series have been derived from a land surface that was weathering under oxidizing conditions. Parts of this old reddened land surface are still visible on Skiddaw Slates to the south of Whittas Park, and on Borrowdale Volcanic Rocks near Ruthwaite.

No red beds occur in the overlying Seventh Limestone, but in places secondary reddening (Trotter 1939) affects the upper beds of the Carboniferous Limestone Series, the Millstone Grit Series and the Coal Measures. The red beds are found in juxtaposition to the base of the New Red Sandstone Series, and the reddening results from the oxidation of the ferrous iron contained in the Carboniferous rocks mostly as siderites. The reddened rocks include sandstones, mudstones, fireclays and thin limestones. They display red coloration of varying degree ranging from bright red to pale pink, from deep to pale purple, and brown. Red fireclays contain nodules of bluish purple hematite.

In immediate juxtaposition to the base of the New Red Sandstone Series the contained iron in all of the Carboniferous rocks is in the form of hematite, and this reddish purple mineral causes the mudstones and fireclays, which normally contain appreciable amounts of iron, to take on a deep coloration; the feldspathic sandstones, with relatively less iron, are not so deeply coloured red-purple; highly quartzitic sandstones and pure limestones (such as the First or Great) containing little or no iron either display no reddening, or but faint reddening, limited to the close proximity of joints. Subordinate grey and green lenses or 'eyes' occur within the reddened rocks.

In all of the rocks that are iron-bearing the intensity of the red coloration decreases away from the outcrop of the base of the New Red Sandstone, and the maximum distance to which the coloration extends from that outcrop is four miles, in the area southward from Lowling almost to Caldbeck. Nevertheless, faults of later date than the reddening, bring unreddened measures against reddened beds.

In Lancashire, where a number of boreholes have been examined (Trotter 1954), it has been shown that a zone of complete reddening by oxidation immediately underlies the base of the New Red Sandstone Series, and at lower levels the beds are reddened in a zone or zones of partial oxidation. It is probable that the situation is the same in the present district where, however, the evidence lies mainly at the surface. Certainly in the area in which the reddened rocks occur, the reddening becomes fainter away from the base of the New Red Sandstone Series, and on its periphery there is incomplete oxidation of the sideritic ironstones. Also the reddening decreases with depth in the High Head No. 2 Borehole [4115 4433]. This and the High Head No. 1 [4117 4409] lie just beyond the eastern margin of the district, on the River Ive, a tributary of Roe Beck. Without having seen the cores it would be unwise to attempt to separate the zones of complete reddening and partial reddening in these bores. In the No. 1 bore reddened measures of the Hensingham Group are recorded to the bottom of the hole at 511 ft 3 in with a 2-in band of iron-ore (hematite) recorded at 502 ft 8 in. In the High Head No. 2 bore the reddened measures extend to the base of the Hensingham Group at 981 ft 7 in with the last record of iron-ore (hematite) a 3-in band, at 972 ft 10 in. Thereafter in the Carboniferous Limestone Series there are alternations of reddened measures and grey measures to 1193 ft 1 in with 'traces of ore' recorded, and below that depth, to the base of the hole at 1402 ft 7 in, the measures are recorded as being dominantly grey, the lowest coloured bed being 'reddish grey sandstone' 5 ft thick at 1373 ft 7 in. The depth to which the reddening has penetrated is thus of the same order as occurs in Lancashire.

The range in horizon of the beds affected by secondary reddening is illustrated by the following examples of sections in the field which have yielded fossils of diagnostic value:-

(1) In Chalk Beck, left bank, and in bed of streams, north of the Lowling Fault and from three to four furlongs S. 20° W. of Chalk Lodge. Patchily reddened sandstone lies below the Four Fathom or 2nd Limestone.

(2) In Roe Beck south of Middlesceugh, and also in Castle Beck, a tributary of Roe Beck. The beds are heavily reddened marine shales in the Hensingham Group.

(3) In the higher reaches of Chalk Beck east of Broadmoor. The horizon of the reddened beds is at the normal junction of the Hensingham Group with the Coal Measures.

(4) In a stream joining the River Caldew from the west and 450 yd S. of Lonning Head. The horizon is in red mudstones low in the Coal Measures sequence.

(5) In Chalk Beck east-north-east of Broadmoor. The horizon is in red mudstones of the Middle Coal Measures.

(6) At the foot of Pow Gill, a tributary of the River Waver. The reddened beds include the Bolton Marine Band.

It is important to realize that all the localities indicated above are in near proximity to the outcrop of the New Red Sandstone Series. Where not so situated the same strata are grey. The reddened beds include the measures that carry all of the workable coals of the West Cumberland Coalfield. Indeed the heavily reddened measures of the Broad Moor–Chalk Beck–Sebergham area lie in the *Anthraconaia modiolaris* and Lower *Anthracosia similis–Anthraconaia pulchra* zones that are normally prolific of coal seams throughout Great Britain. Nevertheless they are here devoid of workable coals, a fact rendered all the more remarkable because within the outcrop of the reddened measures there is an upfaulted area of grey Middle Coal Measures south of Tracentree that carries good coal seams (p. 203). We are not, therefore, dealing with progressive deterioration of the coal seams in an easterly direction from the main part of the West Cumberland Coalfield, but with secondary reddening caused by local conditions that have resulted in the oxidation of the ferrous iron contained in the strata and in the destruction of the coal seams.   F.M.T.

REFERENCES

BISAT, W. S. 1924. The Carboniferous goniatites of the north of England and their zones. *Proc. Yorks. geol. Soc.*, **20**, 40–124.

EASTWOOD, T. 1930. The geology of the Maryport District. *Mem. Geol. Surv. Gt Br.*

————— DIXON, E. E. L., HOLLINGWORTH, S. E. and SMITH, B. 1931. The geology of the Whitehaven and Workington District. *Mem. Geol. Surv. Gt Br.*

EDMONDS, C. 1922. The Carboniferous Limestone Series of West Cumberland. *Geol. Mag.*, **59**, 74–83, 117–31.

FORSTER, W. 1809. *A treatise on a section of the strata from Newcastle-upon-Tyne to the Mountain of Cross Fell in Cumberland.* Newcastle upon Tyne.

GARWOOD, E. J. 1913. The Lower Carboniferous succession in the north-west of England. *Quart. Jl geol. Soc. Lond.*, **68**, 449–586.

JOHNSON, G. A. L., HODGE, B. L. and FAIRBAIRN, R. A. 1962. The base of the Namurian and of the Millstone Grit in north-eastern England. *Proc. Yorks. geol. Soc.*, **33**, 341–62.

JONGMANS, W. G. 1928. Congrès pour l'étude de la stratigraphie du Carbonifère dans les différents centres houillers de l'Europe, Pt. IV. Discussion générale. *C. r. 1re Congr. Advanc. Étud. Stratigr. Géol. Carbonif.* xxii-xlvii.

KENDALL, J. D. 1885. The Carboniferous Rocks of Cumberland, north Lancashire, or Furness. *Trans. N. Engl. Inst. Min. mech. Engrs.* **34**, 125–36.

KIDSTON, R. 1923-5. Fossil plants of the Carboniferous rocks of Great Britain. *Mem. Geol. Surv. Palaeont.*

LECKWIJCK, VAN W. P. 1960. Report of the subcommission on Carboniferous Stratigraphy. *C. r. 4me Congr. Advanc. Étud. Stratigr. Géol. Carbonif.*, Tome 1, Resolution 7. xxv.

PHILLIPS, J. 1836. *Illustrations of the geology of Yorkshire Pt. II. The Mountain Limestone district.* London.

SMITH, B. 1919. Iron Ores–Haematites of West Cumberland, Lancashire and the Lake District. *Mem. Geol. Surv., Spec. Rep. Miner., Resour.*, **8.**

STUBBLEFIELD, C. J. and TROTTER, F. M. 1957. Divisions of the Coal Measures on Geological Survey maps of England and Wales. *Bull. Geol. Surv. Gt Br.* No. 13, 1–5.

TAYLOR, B. J. 1961. The stratigraphy of exploratory boreholes in the West Cumberland coalfield. *Bull. Geol. Surv. Gt Br.* No. 17, 1–74.

TRUEMAN, A. E. (editor). 1954. *The coalfields of Great Britain.* London.

TROTTER, F. M. 1939. Reddened Carboniferous beds in the Carlisle Basin and Edenside. *Geol. Mag.*, **76**, 408–16.

————— 1952. Sedimentation facies in the Namurian of north-western England and adjoining areas. *Lpool and Manchr geol. J.*, **1**, 77–112.

————— 1953. In *Summ. Prog. Geol. Surv. Gt Br.* for 1951, 33–4.

————— 1954. Reddened beds in the Coal Measures of south Lancashire. *Bull. Geol. Surv. Gt Br.* No. 5, 61–80.

VAUGHAN, A. 1905. The palaeontological sequence in the Carboniferous Limestone of the Bristol area. *Quart. Jl geol. Soc. Lond.*, **61**, 181–307.

Chapter X

LOWER CARBONIFEROUS ROCKS

IN THE COCKERMOUTH DISTRICT major earth-movements and extensive denudation took place in the vast era of time that elapsed between the deposition of the Ordovician and of the Carboniferous rocks. If Silurian and Devonian rocks were deposited they were denuded before the onset of Carboniferous sedimentation. Areas in the Northumbrian trough of sedimentation to the north and in Edenside to the south-east had been long submerged beneath the Lower Carboniferous sea, whilst the Cockermouth district and contiguous areas on One-inch Sheets 22 (Maryport), 28 (Whitehaven) and 37 (Gosforth) remained land. In these areas sedimentation was ushered in by the deposition of basement beds, which were quickly followed by the Seventh Limestone.

BASEMENT CONGLOMERATE

The basement beds which lie below the Seventh Limestone must not be confused with the conglomerates (sometimes referred to as the Polygenetic Conglomerate) that underlie much older Lower Carboniferous rocks in parts of Edenside, and that are well exposed at Mell Fell some 3 miles south of One-inch Sheet 23. The latter contain many far-travelled pebbles; indeed they include some igneous rocks that are unknown in the Lake District. They attain great thickness, measured on Mell Fell in hundreds of feet. These polygenetic conglomerates are probably of Upper Devonian age.

By contrast the Basement Conglomerate of the Cockermouth district is almost certainly of Carboniferous age. It contains only locally derived pebbles. It rarely attains a thickness of 100 ft, and is present in this order of thickness only where it lies upon the Borrowdale Volcanic Series or where these rocks crop out nearby. On the softer Skiddaw Slates the Basal Conglomerate is either absent or thin. The basal series contains shaly beds as well as conglomerates, and shaly beds also occur in the lower part of the Seventh Limestone, in which thin bands of conglomerate are not uncommon. There is thus a passage from the Basement Conglomerate into the Seventh Limestone.

On the southern outcrop of the Borrowdale Volcanic Series around Calder Bridge (One-inch Sheet 37), boreholes have proved a thin basement conglomerate up to 10 ft thick consisting of pebbles of Borrowdale Volcanic rocks and vein-quartz. Northwards as far as Cockermouth the base of the Lower Carboniferous rests on Skiddaw Slates, and no basal conglomerate is present either at outcrop or in the numerous boreholes of the West Cumberland iron-orefield. At Cockermouth the Basement Conglomerate reappears and its outcrop continues for about 4 miles to the north-east to the vicinity of Sunderland. From Sunderland to Bothel the conglomerate is not visible. It may, however, be present beneath Drift, for an obscure and faulted outlier occurs farther east near the junction of the Bothel and Whitrigg-Bassen-thwaite roads.

In the Bothel–High Ireby area the junction between the Carboniferous and older rocks is a faulted one, but the Basement Conglomerate appears at the surface at Ruthwaite where it includes red shales. To the east, in the Uldale area, the conglomerate is composed of Borrowdale Volcanic pebbles to such an extent that it was mapped as a tuff within that formation on the Old Series One-inch Map. Small outcrops of the conglomerate have been found at intervals eastwards to Fellside where faulting again is the cause of its failure to crop out. It is absent, possibly by overstep, to the east of the Caldbeck Fells.

The Basement Conglomerate is present close to the Carrock Fell igneous complex and it is noteworthy that no pebbles of that complex have been found in it. This is in striking contrast to the abundance of pebbles of Shap Granite in the Basement Conglomerate close to the outcrop of that granite. The rocks of the Carrock Fell complex are hard and readily form pebbles, so their absence from the basement series indicates that the complex was not available to denuding agencies at the time of the formation of the conglomerate.

T.E., F.M.T.

DETAILS

Cockermouth to Bothel. The most southerly exposure [1177 3122] is in an old bluff of the Derwent, 200 yd S.E. of Hames Hall near Cockermouth. Here over 5 ft of well-consolidated breccia with fragments of slate, quartzitic sandstone and igneous rocks are visible. To the north-east there are many exposures along the Derwent near Wood Hall. The conglomerate hereabouts is 30 or 40 ft thick; actual contacts with the Skiddaw Slates below and the basalt above are not seen, but the obscured ground in each case amounts to less than 5 ft. The pebbles include vein-quartz, quartzitic sandstone and slate from the Skiddaw Slates, sporadic tuff and rhyolite from the Borrowdale Volcanic Series, and some decomposed rocks of doubtful origin; many of them are subangular. Beds of yellow sandstones are present in this region but the bulk of the rock is a coarse conglomerate or breccia.

There are good sections in the basal conglomerate, sandwiched between sandstones of the Skiddaw Slates and basalt, in Tommy Gill, Redmain.

The conglomerate is not seen *in situ* again until Park Wood is reached. Near the north-western corner of that wood, in a small stream flowing down to Isel Mill, a few feet of calcareous breccia appear

beneath the basalt but this particular outcrop is terminated to the east and west by faults. An exposure [1694 3482] in Blumer Beck, 800 yd W.N.W. of Linskeldfield, shows 2 ft of fine red conglomerate, on 18 in of slightly sandy red shale, that probably represent an old surface deposit that rests with a sharp junction on 5 ft of contorted dark Skiddaw Slates. A section [1700 3486] about 100 yd farther upstream, shows 8 ft of conglomerate.

Between Sunderland, Bothelcrags and Bothel there is no sign of the conglomerate but a peculiar outlier of it has been preserved in the low ground farther east. Here, in a small stream [2041 3618] 200 yd S. of the junction of the Whitrigg–Bothel–Bassenthwaite roads there are about 6 ft of coarse red sandstone and conglomerate exposed. T.E.

Ruthwaite to Uldale. In this area beds of the Basement Conglomerate are faulted against the Borrowdale Volcanic Series and occupy the featureless slopes south of the Ellen from Ruthwaite to Chapel House. A small outlier [2336 3664] is brought in to the south of the main outcrop by an east-west baryte-bearing fault, seen in a stream 450 yd W. 15° S. of the crossroads in Ruthwaite. The beds (consisting of a coarse conglomerate, fine-grained grey sandstone, and gritty grey mudstone with carbonaceous markings) occur in the stream for 30 to 40 yd south-west of the fault, and dip northwards at 20° to 30°. They rest on Borrowdale lavas.

Along the main outcrop exposures are few. At Ruthwaite the boundary fault is mineralized, and open-cast workings have exposed red and purple shales of the basement beds along the baryte vein whilst the mine-tip includes fragments of coarse conglomerate and purple sandstone.

Grey, green and red micaceous mudstones of this series are exposed in a stream 800 yd S. 5° E. of the cross-roads in Uldale; and conglomerates with fragments of andesite and tuff from the Borrowdale Volcanic Series, vein-quartz and quartzitic sandstone, red and grey sandstone, and grey mudstone, are exposed in the bed and in the southern banks of the River Ellen 870 yd S.E. of the cross-roads.   F.M.T.

Uldale to Berrier. This belt of country is largely drift-covered. Coarse red conglomerate is not seen definitely *in situ*, but large blocks of strictly local origin are plentiful in the sides and beds of the

numerous small gullies draining the high ground to the south between Sworley and Branthwaite. The principal fragments are volcanic rocks of various types, fine-grained sandstones probably derived from the Skiddaw Slates, and vein-quartz.

Grey slates with limestone bands and red and green shales, presumably lying above the main conglomerate horizon, are exposed at several points, e.g. [2844 3685] 300 yd S.S.W. of Greenhead. Here the direction of dip—north at 20° to 35°—is similar to that of the nearest limestone outcrop.

Along the road north-east of Fellside the Carlisle R.D.C. pipe-track from Roughton Gill proved red, golden and cream-coloured shale and marl with some reddish grey conglomerate.

In the borehole journals of the Berrier area 40 to 60 ft of red and blue shales have been recorded below the Seventh Limestone. They may represent the shaly facies that comes between the Seventh Limestone and the basal conglomeratic beds west of Hesket Newmarket, or be washed-up debris of local origin.   S.E.H.

COCKERMOUTH LAVAS

In the western part of the area the Basement Conglomerate is succeeded by a series of basalts to which the name of Cockermouth Lavas has been given (Eastwood 1928). Apart from minor interruptions due to faulting, the outcrop of these lavas stretches from the Derwent valley west of Cockermouth nearly to Bothel—a distance of about 8 miles. For the greater part of this distance they rest on the Basement Conglomerate and are succeeded by the Seventh Limestone, with which they agree in general strike and dip, so that it is obvious that they cannot be Borrowdale rocks as indicated on previous geological maps but must be of Lower Carboniferous age. These lavas are not present in the iron-orefield of West Cumberland and appear to die out with some rapidity between Bothelcrags and Bothel; in the latter region their strike is almost at right angles to that of the Borrowdale rocks on which they here may rest. In the region between Bothel and Greystoke, where these lavas might be expected to crop out, none have been found. A narrow dyke of similar rock traverses Skiddaw Slates [1232 3206] near Wood Hall, but its relationship to the Conglomerate a few feet above is obscure. This intrusion is too small to have acted as a feeder to the lavas; the point of eruption is unknown, but probably lay to the west of the present outcrop.

The lavas occur in 4 or 5 flows, the tops and bottoms of which are markedly vesicular, and in one case at least there is a considerable development of 'bole' between two flows. In the Wood Hall region where they are excellently exposed the lavas reach a total thickness of about 300 ft.

The lavas are olivine-basalts, and when fresh and non-scoriaceous are dark blue or grey, finely granular rocks. From occasional vesicles in an otherwise compact rock, all stages to markedly scoriaceous are shown, but the 'clinker' type is not always confined to the superficial parts of the flows. Many of the vesicles contain quartz, agate, or calcite, and in some cases these, and occasionally whole masses of rock, are stained green. The green colour has led to prospecting for copper in at least one instance to the south-west of Redmain. Although many of the vesicles are distorted they show little or no linear arrangement due to flow.

In addition to vesicles the rocks have occasional veins and irregular patches of dark purple flinty material a few inches across which die out downwards. These are only known near Redmain. The margins are sharp in some cases, but in others the rock appears to pass into 'bole'.

The following notes on these lavas, supplied by the late Dr. H. H. Thomas, are quoted verbatim from the original account (Eastwood 1928, pp. 15–22).

"The lavas of this group are remarkably consistent, showing only slight variations in composition and structure. In their compact or less decomposed portion they are dark grey and microcrystalline, with occasional porphyritic felspars up to 1 cm in greatest length [E 13975]. As a group they fall between micro- and macro-porphyritic basalts and by the scarcity of porphyritic felspars may be classed as a somewhat coarse variety of Dalmeny type.

"Their microscopic structure is generally that of micro-porphyritic basalt in which abundant small pseudomorphs after olivine are the dominant feature. The rest of the rock consists of granular to sub-ophitic augite and a plexus of labradorite laths that involve grains of augite and finely divided magnetite. The felspar laths frequently show a poorly developed fluxional arrangement.

"Occasional porphyritic felspars of the composition of bytownite can be observed but they are rare [E 13975].

"Some of the rocks, possibly the interior of the thicker flows, have a more doleritic aspect. In these [E 13976] the augite is more definitely ophitic. In other cases, where fine-grained, the rocks might be described as tholeiites [E 13898]. They contain original glass and an abundance of chlorophaeite, a mineral common in the Carboniferous intrusions of the Lothians.

"Olivine in these lavas is abundant, generally pseudomorphed by the usual limonitic and chloritic secondary products, but occasional remnants of olivine are preserved in fresh condition [E 13898].

"The augite is quite frequently fresh but when decomposed passes into carbonates.

"Felspars do not appear to have been albitized to any considerable extent but have been involved in a general replacement by carbonates.

"As a suite they are quite unlike not only any Borrowdale volcanic rocks with which I am acquainted but also any Lower Palaeozoic rocks that I have met with. They can be matched amongst the Lower Carboniferous lavas of Fifeshire and there is no doubt that their chief likeness is to the Carboniferous lavas of Scotland and to some of the Carboniferous intrusions of the north of England."   T.E.

CHIEF LIMESTONE GROUP

There are few boreholes in the Carboniferous Limestone Series of the Cockermouth district. The vertical sequence of these limestone measures was not given on the original One-inch Map and nothing has been written concerning their lithology, though Earle (1921 and 1922) briefly dealt with the more important faunal horizons. Mr. C. Edmonds rendered valuable assistance during the resurvey. He visited the area on several occasions and his detailed knowledge of the limestone sequence of West Cumberland was always at our disposal.

The district adjoins that of West Cumberland where the 'Lower Carboniferous' is divided into the Chief Limestone Group and the overlying Hensingham Group, but as previously indicated, the Hensingham Group is now considered to be of Namurian age. The Chief Limestone Group of the district falls naturally into two subdivisions—a lower, consisting dominantly of limestone, and an upper, which on the northern and eastern crops consists of alternations of limestones, sandstones and shales (see Fig. 14). In the extreme south-west, however, around Cockermouth, the West Cumberland sequence obtains and a dominantly marine limestone facies persists from the Seventh to the First Limestone.

OUTCROP AND STRUCTURE

The outcrop of the Chief Limestone Group forms a broad arcuate belt round the northern end of the Lake District—the general direction of dip being outwards from the Lower Palaeozoic rocks. Inliers occur beyond the main outcrop at Hazelspring, Brocklebank, Lowling and in Chalk Beck to the north of Greenquarries.

The main outcrop enters the area from the south-west to form a region of high-lying moorland that is broken only by the Ellen, the Caldew, and the latter's tributary Gillcambon Beck. Between this region (which in general represents the escarpment of the Carboniferous Limestone Series) and the outcrop of the Lower Palaeozoic rocks, a broad depression or valley has developed along the outcrops of the Basement Conglomerate Series and the lower beds of the Chief Limestone Group. In the west the escarpment rises to about 800 ft O.D. at Moota Hill and trends to the north-east as far as Bothel where it fades towards the valley of the River Ellen; this is termed the western crop. To the east and north of that river it is continuous at 1000 to 1200 ft O.D. from Sandale to the River Caldew, and this section is hereinafter referred to as the northern crop. Beyond the Caldew valley the main limestone outcrop rises from 800 ft O.D. at Hewerhill to 1100–1200 ft O.D. at Berrier—the south-south-easterly trend of this outcrop, here termed the eastern crop, being parallel to the syncline of Edenside.

On the whole the Carboniferous Limestone escarpment is fairly free from drift, but there are drift-covered tracts bordering the rivers Ellen and Caldew, and also in the valley at the foot of the escarpment, from Intack to Hesket Newmarket, occupied in part by the Cald Beck.

The dominant structural element is block-faulting, but subsidiary folds are also developed, as for example the westerly plunging syncline on Faulds Brow and the anticline at Brocklebank. There are two dominant fault systems trending to the north-west and to the east-north-east respectively. The latter are mostly major fractures that commonly bound the outcrop of the Chief Limestone Group, as for example the Gilcrux Fault. The former are more numerous, but usually end against the latter. A group of these north-westerly faults on the eastern crop is responsible for the inlier of Borrowdale rocks and the repetition of much of the limestone sequence to the east of Gillcambon Beck.

LOWER CHIEF LIMESTONE GROUP

The generalized sequence is as follows:

		ft
Rough Beds (or Limestone)	.. ..	30– 40
White Beds (or Limestone)	.. ..	60– 90
Fifth Limestone..	.. ..	60–160
Sixth Limestone	.. ..	60–120
Seventh Limestone	.. ..	160–300

Subordinate bands of shales with sandstones are developed between and within these limestones. These bands are normally less than 10 ft thick, but exceptionally and locally they may swell out to 30 ft.

Seventh Limestone. Calcareous shales and shaly limestones usually succeed the Basement Conglomerate Series except in the west. These calcareous shaly measures, rich in lamellibranchs, attain a thickness of 50 ft at Blindcrake but thin towards the east. Where the Basement Conglomerate Series is not developed impersistent bands of conglomerate and quartzitic sandstone appear at several horizons in the lower part of the Seventh Limestone.

The main mass of the Seventh Limestone is characterized by shallow water rock-types that include grey-white limestones, polyzoan limestones, calcite mudstones, cherts, sandy limestones and calcareous sandstones that are frequently false-bedded or 'diagonally' bedded. The sandy types are usually impersistent and pass laterally into limestones, but a sandy phase near the top of the limestone is fairly persistent and is succeeded by the Bryozoa Band—a limestone crowded with crinoids and polyzoa. Crinoidal limestones rich in polyzoa are also present at lower horizons in the western area.

The sandstones and shales above the Seventh Limestone, although only a few feet thick, include a coal horizon. The seam is reported to be 14 in thick at Uldale, and is apparently of workable thickness east of Park where several shallow shafts have been sunk to it.

Sixth Limestone. On the western and northern crops this limestone is 80 to 120 ft thick, and consists of grey-blue limestone with white limestone in the upper part and occasional subordinate bands of shale which in places include a thin coal. Between Uldale and Caldbeck nodules and lenses of chert are developed near the base. To the east around Berrier the limestone is 60 to 100 ft thick, and is split into two by shale bands up to 15 ft in thickness. In each part there is a repetition of an upward sequence passing from grey-blue limestones to grey-white limestones followed by cream-coloured clays and calcareous shales.

Fifth Limestone. This consists of a lower limestone, grey-blue to black in colour, usually well bedded with minor shale partings, and an upper massive grey-white limestone that is pseudo-brecciated in the upper posts. In the western and central districts the thickness of the Fifth Limestone is difficult to estimate but may be 60 to 100 ft. In the east and south-east the incoming of bands of shale with subordinate sandstones in their lower part increases the thickness to 160 ft. One such band thickens locally to 30 ft.

White Beds (or Limestone). Around Cockermouth the White Beds constitute the lowest part of the Fourth Limestone, but farther to the north-east, where there is a Yoredale facies and the Fourth Limestone is represented by several separate limestones, these measures are known as the White Limestone. This is probably the purest limestone in the district. The lower posts usually consist of well-bedded dark grey limestone that, in upward sequence, gives place to massive white and pseudo-brecciated limestone interbedded with minor bands of calcite mudstone. (A similar upward passage is characteristic of the Fifth, and to a less extent the Sixth limestones.) This rhythmic tendency resembles that in corresponding beds in the Melmerby Scar Limestone of the Brampton district (Trotter and Hollingworth 1932, p. 48). Another point in common is that on both sides of the Eden valley the greatest development of light grey to white limestone is to the south-south-east.

Rough Beds (or Limestone). This is a dark grey limestone up to 40 ft thick that has yielded *Girvanella?* in the western and eastern areas. It rests on the White Limestone as far east as Snowhill, but to the east and south-east of that locality thin shales separate the two limestones.

The top of the Rough Limestone represents a horizon which is underlain, essentially, by massive limestone 400 to 700 ft thick. In consequence, this horizon is commonly marked by a well-defined set of solution holes (swallow holes) making it readily identifiable in the field.

UPPER CHIEF LIMESTONE GROUP

This group includes the strata from the top of the Rough Limestone to the top of the First or Great Limestone. The sequence at several localities is given in Fig. 14, from which it will be seen that the beds vary considerably, the principal changes being as follows: the massive limestones[1] of the Cockermouth area split up in a north and north-easterly direction due to the incoming of sandstones and shales; the equivalent of the Potholes Beds, missing at Cockermouth but present farther south (Eastwood 1930, p. 22), reappears; and there is lateral alteration in the lithology of some of the limestones. These changes are best described in a clockwise direction along the outcrop.

Spotted Beds and associated measures. Except in the Cockermouth area where the Spotted Beds immediately overlie the Rough Beds, dark blue shales up to 50 ft thick rest on the latter and are succeeded along the northern and eastern crops by a massive grey sandstone varying in thickness from 30 to 100 ft.

At Cockermouth the Spotted Beds, some 10 ft in thickness, are pale grey in colour. The lower beds contain cherts and there is a development of dark irregular spots (pseudo-breccias) in the upper beds. Towards Gilcrux this limestone swells to 60 ft, but the lithological characters mentioned above are

---

[1]These fall within the Fourth Limestone of West Cumberland which is there subdivided (Edmonds 1922) into a series of beds known in upward sequence as the White, Rough, Spotted, Potholes, 'Saccammina', *junceum* and Chert beds.

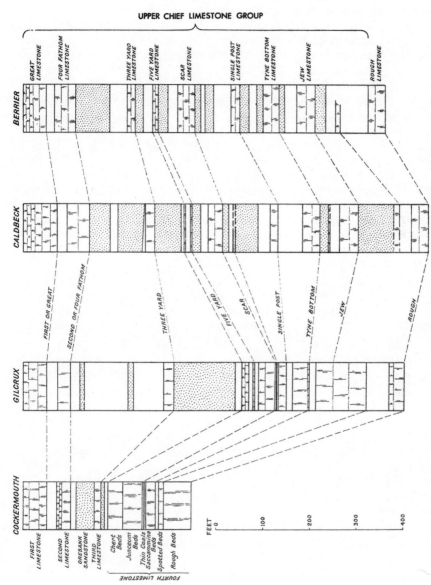

FIG. 14. Vertical sections of Carboniferous Limestone Series above Rough Limestone

absent. Farther east the limestone has not been recognized and although exposures are poor, it appears to be absent. It is again present in the Caldew near Newlands and has been mapped intermittently at several places farther south.

Jew Limestone. The equivalent of this limestone is not identifiable at Cockermouth; elsewhere it maintains a thickness of 30 to 40 ft and displays distinctive faunal and lithological characters. A basal pale porcellanous limestone with spots is overlain by well-bedded grey and grey-blue limestone that is crowded with *Saccamminopsis fusulinaformis*[1]; *Caninia juddi* is abundant near the top of the limestone immediately above posts with an abundance of *Lithostrotion*.

'Saccammina' Beds and the Tyne Bottom and Single Post limestones and associated measures. The 'Saccammina' Beds of Cockermouth are most probably equivalent to the Tyne Bottom and Single Post limestones (see Fig. 14). The lower part of the 'Saccammina' Beds consists of dark and grey limestone with abundant *Saccamminopsis* and these features also characterize the Tyne Bottom Limestone. The upper part of the 'Saccammina' Beds consists of spotted grey-white limestone as does the Single Post Limestone. Additionally the *Erythrospongia* Band, although only recognized in the district by the presence of *Erythrospongia?*, occurs at the top of the 'Saccammina' Beds in West Cumberland and in the Single Post Limestone of the Pennines (Dixon *in* Eastwood and others 1931, p. 77).

The Tyne Bottom Limestone, 30 to 40 ft thick, is grey-blue in colour and abundant in *Saccamminopsis*. It is separated from the Jew Limestone below by measures up to 40 ft thick which include, in the Hesket Newmarket area, a 3-ft band of limestone with black cherts. The cherts that occur in the basal beds of the 'Tyne Bottom Limestone' farther south near Howhill may be due to the union of this 3-ft limestone with the true Tyne Bottom.

The Single Post Limestone, 12 to 15 ft thick, is pale cream, with darker spots; it is separated from the Tyne Bottom Limestone by strata that thicken to 60 ft along the northern and eastern crops.

Thin coals, associated with shales, and limestone bands with large Productids, occur immediately above the 'Saccammina' Beds at Cockermouth and above the Single Post Limestone at Gilcrux, but at Caldbeck are separated from the latter limestone by a considerable thickness of sandstones and shales and overlain by a 3-ft limestone. The last named, and possibly the Productid limestone, are probably the equivalent of the Cockleshell Limestone of the Pennine area. East of Berrier a coal has been worked at approximately this same horizon.

The *junceum* and Chert beds and their equivalents the Scar and the Five Yard limestones. Limestones with reefs of *Lithostrotion junceum*, and containing chert in their upper part, are known as the *junceum* and Chert Beds at Cockermouth. Farther north, at Gilcrux, the equivalent beds consist of massive grey limestones in the lower part, and shales and thin limestones in the upper part; *Lithostrotion junceum*, although present, is not found in abundance in reefs except in the highest beds, and chert is absent. The interbedded shales are highly fossiliferous and yield a normal shale phasal fauna (see p. 161). To the

---

[1]The names of the authors of the species of Lower Carboniferous fossils are given in Appendix I.

east these lower and upper beds retain their distinctive character, and have been mapped as the Scar and the Five Yard limestones respectively, being separated by 15 to 25 ft of shales overlain by 20 to 25 ft of massive quartzitic sandstone.

Third or Three Yard Limestone and underlying measures. Shales followed by sandstone, together not more than 15 ft thick, underlie the Third Limestone at Cockermouth (see Fig. 14). The sandstone thickens rapidly but erratically to a maximum of 150 ft at Gilcrux; thence in an east to south-easterly direction it thins progressively, the minimum being 20 ft near Howhill.

Between Cockermouth and Gilcrux the Third or Three Yard Limestone is a dark grey earthy crinoidal limestone with few identifiable fossils. Eastwards to Faulds Brow it is poorly exposed, but there and farther east it is a pale grey, highly crinoidal limestone containing nests or colonies of *Saccamminopsis fusulinaformis* and sporadic small nodules of grey-white chert.

Orebank Sandstone. A variable series of terrigenous sediments is grouped under this name. In the extreme south-west the beds are dominantly sandstone, but consist of shales with minor sandstone bands at Gilcrux where they attain their maximum thickness of 200 ft. Along the northern crop, between the rivers Ellen and Caldew, coarse massive feldspathic grits account for the greater part of the group, and grits characterize the upper beds along the eastern crop.

Second or Four Fathom Limestone. Usually of dark grey limestone, 20 to 30 ft thick, these beds are characterized by nodules and lenses of black chert along the northern and eastern crops. They are separated from the First Limestone by 0 to 20 ft of sandstones and shales.

First or Great Limestone. The lowest beds, up to 12 ft thick and infrequently exposed, consist of dark grey limestones with thin partings, indistinguishable from the limestone of the underlying Four Fathom Limestone. They are overlain by massive, light grey coralline and crinoidal limestones 20 to 25 ft thick, followed by 20 to 30 ft of well-bedded dark grey limestones in 6-in to 3-ft posts separated by partings of calcareous shale. This lithology persists throughout the area and the coralline limestones and overlying beds (Tumbler Beds) yield a distinctive faunal assemblage (see p. 161).

CONDITIONS OF DEPOSITION

The Lower Carboniferous rocks of Northern England show that during deposition there was an interplay of marine and deltaic conditions of sedimentation. In north-east Cumberland and Northumberland these rocks were formerly divided into the Tuedian and Bernician, but the Carboniferous Limestone sequence of the Cockermouth district lies wholly within the Bernician of this classification. In these rocks and their equivalents throughout Northern England there is a repetition of the sequence: shale, sandstone and limestone, frequently with a coal beneath the latter. This repetition may be explained by alternating periods of relatively slow and quick subsidence. During the former, deltas at various periods advanced from the north and were built up to sea level, thereby permitting the outward growth of the plants that ultimately formed coal. A quicker rate of subsidence allowed the clear-water sea to the south to invade the deltaic area and initiate the formation of marine limestone.

In the Lower Chief Limestone group the periodicity of subsidence is reflected chiefly in the type of limestone and to a less extent by the presence of terrigenous sediments. Thus in the Seventh Limestone shallow water deposits such as porcellanous, polyzoan and sandy limestones, and calcite mudstones are interbedded with normal limestones, yielding a standard fauna, that were formed in deeper water. Again the repetition in upward sequence of calcareous shale, dark grey limestone and light grey or grey-white limestone found in the Sixth, Fifth and White limestones represents rhythmic deposition within an essentially limestone environment.

During Upper Chief Limestone times there was a south-westerly advance of deltaic areas, for while clear-water conditions persisted to the top of the Third Limestone in the extreme south-west, rhythmic sedimentation, involving terrigenous deposits, commenced immediately above the Rough Limestone over the rest of the area. The rhythmic units, however, do not attain the perfection displayed in North Cumberland and in the Pennines. In particular coal seams are poorly developed and it would appear that the district lay on the margins of the deltaic region, mostly beyond the limits of the coal swamps. This peripheral area may have been subject to periods of relative elevation as the result of excessive loading on the main part of the delta, which may account for the absence, by non-deposition or contemporaneous erosion, of the Potholes Beds around Cockermouth (although they are typically developed to the southwest) and it may also account for the marked variation in thickness of several of the limestones.

FAUNAL NOTES AND ZONAL CLASSIFICATION

With the exception of the corals, the fossils of the Chief Limestone Group have been identified by Sir James Stubblefield, and revised by Dr. W. H. C. Ramsbottom in 1962. The corals were identified by the late Dr. S. Smith and their nomenclature has been brought up to date by Mr. M. Mitchell in 1963. Assemblages have been collected from numerous localities and these collections form the basis of the fossil lists given in Appendix I. Faunas from selected representative localities of important horizons are given in the Details (pp. 161–78).

The Chief Limestone Group falls within the Viséan and includes the *Nematophyllum minus*[1] Zone at the base, and the overlying Lower and Upper *Dibunophyllum* zones.

Nematophyllum minus Zone (S_2). This zone is restricted to the Seventh Limestone. '*Linoproductus*' *corrugatohemisphericus* is found only in this limestone. As in the Gosforth area of West Cumberland, *Davidsonina carbonaria* is restricted to the basal beds of this limestone. The Bryozoa Band containing the characteristic brachiopod *Punctospirifer scabricosta* associated with *P. redesdalensis*, occurs at the top of the zone; but the zonal fossils *Lithostrotion* [*Nematophyllum*] *minus* and '*Linoproductus*' *corrugatohemisphericus* range upwards into the White Beds. *Gigantoproductus maximus* and *Dibunophyllum*,

---

[1]*Nematophyllum minus* was described by McCoy from the Kendal district and Garwood (1913, p. 472) retained the name in order that the exact form characterizing his subzone of *Nematophyllum minus* might be recognized with certainty, although he realized that it was a *Lithostrotion*. The late Dr. Stanley Smith has identified the forms collected from One-inch Sheet 23 as *Lithostrotion minus*. In this account the zone is named *Nematophyllum minus*, and the fossil identification is given as *Lithostrotion* [*Nematophyllum*] *minus* (McCoy).

fossils normally restricted to the Lower *Dibunophyllum* Zone, make their first appearance in the uppermost part of the Seventh Limestone.

Lower *Dibunophyllum* Zone (D₁). Strata from the top of the Seventh to the base of the Rough Limestone are included in this zone. *Davidsonina septosa* and *Delepinea comoides* are restricted to this zone as elsewhere in the North-West Province, and *Megachonetes siblyi* appears to be confined to it.

Gigantoproductus maximus is abundant near the base of the Sixth Limestone where *Lithostrotion junceum* makes its first appearance. In the Fifth Limestone *L. portlocki, Lonsdaleia duplicata* and *L. floriformis* are abundant; all of these, however, range into the overlying zone.

Upper *Dibunophyllum* Zone (D₂). The *Girvanella* Band of Garwood marks the base of the Upper *Dibunophyllum* Zone and is found in the Rough Beds (or Limestone) of the district. But agreement has not been reached on the upper limit of this zone. Garwood (1913, pp. 479–84 and 547) placed the overlying strata up to the Botany Beds in it. Lower horizons have been suggested by subsequent workers. In this account no attempt is made to delimit a still higher zone in the Viséan and so the base of the Millstone Grit Series marks the top of the zone.

The most important faunal horizons above the *Girvanella* Band are in the Jew, Five Yard and Great limestones.

In the Jew Limestone *Saccamminopsis fusulinaformis* makes its first appearance in abundance and ranges upwards to the Great Limestone. On the other hand *Orionastraea* cf. *phillipsi* would appear to be restricted to the Jew Limestone and its equivalent the Potholes Beds of the Fourth Limestone.

The Five Yard Limestone is characterized throughout the district by a prolific normal shale phasal fauna that includes polyzoa, small Productids, lamellibranchs and trilobites (see p. 171).

The First or Great Limestone is the highest horizon wherein corals are common. *Lonsdaleia floriformis laticlavia* is restricted to this horizon. The Great Limestone is characterized by a distinct faunal assemblage that includes *Saccamminopsis, Aulophyllum fungites, Caninia juddi, Chaetetes septosus, Dibunophyllum bipartitum bipartitum, Lithostrotion junceum* and *Gigantoproductus latissimus.*   F.M.T.

DETAILS

Redmain and Ward Hall Common. This area includes the ground between the Gilcrux Fault introducing Coal Measures on the north and the outcrop of the Cockermouth Lavas bordering the Derwent on the south, and between a line from Parsonby to the east of Blindcrake and the western margin of the district. In it the full sequence of the Carboniferous Limestone Series is exposed. It is crossed by several faults which disturb, but do not greatly obscure, the arcuate outcrops caused by rocks with a westerly dip traversing the high ground between the Ellen and the Derwent. Drift masks some of the lower ground and it is frequently difficult to delimit the outcrops of the various limestones.

The lowest beds are the basal shales with thin beds of limestone of the Seventh Limestone. They may be seen in a gully near Belle Vue, 1000 yd S.W. of Annshill, but they are better exposed in the gill [1494 3456] descending from Blindcrake to the Derwent, where they succeed the Cockermouth Lavas although the contact is not seen. They probably total 50 ft in thickness though of this amount only about half is visible. The shales are succeeded by a breccia 2½ ft thick. This has some foreign pebbles, including quartz, but many of the fragments are of bluish green limy mudstone, presumably formed by having been dried, then partly washed up, and finally cemented in a calcareous matrix. The succeeding 8 ft of shales are very fossiliferous and yield a typical shale fauna as follows: *Archaeocidaris sp.*, cf. *Gigantoproductus sp.*, *Productus* cf. *redesdalensis*, *Aviculopecten* cf. *eskdalensis*, *Limipecten* cf. *dissimilis*, *Edmondia senilis*, *Sanguinolites* cf. *plicatus*, *S.* cf. *variabilis*, *Sulcatopinna mutica*, cf. *Wilkingia elliptica*, and cf. *Aphelaeceras discum*. The shales are followed by 2 ft of dull grey, very sandy limestone and a limestone made up of crinoids of which 4 ft are visible in the highest exposure of the gill. The latter rock is probably at the same horizon as a crinoidal limestone which crops out at the foot of a scar [1443 3410] by the side of a field-path 900 yd S.W. of the inn in Blindcrake. The succeeding 17 ft of non-crinoidal limestone there carry *Caninia juddi*.

In the next 300 ft or so of strata, most of which are limestones referable to the Seventh Limestone, there are many small quarries in the area between Annshill and Blindcrake, but nowhere in this region is there a continuous section. There are two or three bands of sandstone and of crinoidal limestone, but they are not individually sufficiently distinctive to be regarded as indices in the sequence of the Seventh Limestone.

In the park at Wood Hall, there are two bands of siliceous sandstone interbedded with limestones that in addition to being markedly crinoidal contain many polyzoa. Other limestones are compact rocks with corals and brachiopods, and some development of chert.

In the Seventh Limestone to the north-east of Annshill there are alternations of crinoidal and more compact limestones that are believed to overlie the sandstone-bearing measures which are introduced by minor faults to the north and south.

Farther to the north-east similar measures crop out between Redmain and Blindcrake. Here there are two sandstones, each about 20 ft thick: the lower, which is closely associated above and below with crinoidal and polyzoan limestones, lies about 250 ft above the top of the Cockermouth Lavas,

while the other, marking the top of the Seventh Limestone, is about 100 ft higher still. Limestones below the sandstones have yielded fossils which include many Productids, *Actinoconchus planosulcatus* and *Lithostrotion martini*, while those between the sandstones provide, amongst others, *Gigantoproductus* cf. *maximus* and *L. martini*.

The sequence is believed to continue without serious interruption towards Moota (see p. 165) but little is seen of the Sixth and Fifth limestones on account of drift, while farther west beds[1] of *Dibunophyllum* age come on in the trough fault area about Bridekirk. These beds, however, are well exposed about Ward Hall Common and Parsonby. A large quarry [146 389] at the latter place shows 58 ft of strata, mainly dark limestone, dipping north-west at from 12° to 15°. Thick-bedded material is confined to the lower portion; in the upper third thin-bedded and nodular limestones are interrupted by 9 ft of measures which are regarded as the parting between the Sixth and Fifth limestones. The uppermost 5 ft consist of fine evenly bedded sandstone; these rest on 18 in of conglomerate, made up of small pebbles of limestone in a sandy matrix, that succeed white clay and dark shale. A sandstone at probably the same horizon may be seen near Plumbland Cottage about 1 mile S. of the Parsonby quarry.

High Close Quarry [147 382] about ½ mile S. of Parsonby provides a section of the succeeding beds of the Fifth Limestone, though some are rather inaccessible. About 60 ft of strata are exposed, of which all but a 3-ft band of light to dark grey shale 4 ft from the top consist of limestones. These, with the exception of the topmost 4 ft, which are white, porcellanous and nodular, and the beds immediately below an irregular 6-in band of limestone, which are fairly light grey, vary from moderately dark grey to almost black. The 6-in band, which occurs 16 to 17 ft down, maintains its thickness but abruptly changes its position with regard to the bedding planes of the adjacent limestones and behaves more like a sill of igneous rock than a limestone.

Fossils are fairly abundant especially just below the light grey limestone and

---

[1] Some of these beds were penetrated by the Annshill Borehole (see Kendall 1885).

include *Lithostrotion junceum, L. [Nemato-phyllum]* cf. *minus, L. pauciradiale, Echinoconchus punctatus, Gigantoproductus* cf. *edelburgensis* and *G.* cf. *latissimus.*

There is a considerable gap between the beds just described and those in the quarry [1435 3835] at the foot of Parsonby Brow 400 yd W. of High Close, and there may be some repetition by faulting. From Parsonby Brow westwards, however, there is an almost continuous section exposed in quarries, though natural sections are poor.

The lowest quarry on Parsonby Brow shows 19 ft of limestones beneath 6 ft of shales. When fresh these rocks are dark but weather light grey. The shales must be closely succeeded by the beds in the next quarry [1434 3828] to the south-south-west. Here the lower 7 ft are a dark blue, compact limestone[1]. Then comes a 12-in blue-black splintery limestone, followed by blue-grey limestone with many partings and wisps of shale, topped by 8 ft of white limestone with nodular beds. These beds can be picked up at intervals to the south. They are referred to the White Limestone horizon. To the west they are closely succeeded by the rocks of the long and narrow third quarry [143 381] of Parsonby Brow. Here the lowest 15 ft consist of dark limestone[1] in thick posts, followed by about 10 ft of limestone with frequent partings of shale. Shale then comes on in force and the total thickness may amount to 50 ft, but of this only 20 ft are visible in the quarry. Wherever seen these shales are dark though some are sandy and micaceous and weather brown.

A dark limestone with *Girvanella?* is also to be seen in the quarry [140 387] 1000 yd W.N.W. of High Close.

The limestones above the shale belt are poorly exposed rough-looking grey rocks, and the next position of note is the easternmost of the Wardhall Quarries [139 382] 500 yd N.E. of Eweclose, of which a section, in descending order, is given below:

	ft
Limestone, dark, weathers rough ..	3
Limestone, pale grey, brown-skinned, sandy	1
Limestone, compact, light grey, some dusky patches	3

	ft
Limestone, nodules of, in shale ..	1
Sandstone, fine, grey-blue, with brachiopods	$\frac{2}{3}$
Shale and clay, soft, sandy, with nodules of pyritous limestone ..	$1\frac{1}{2}$
Sandstone, hard, fine, white .. average	$\frac{2}{3}$
Fireclay, white, sandy	3
Sandstone, pale blue, shaly	3
Shale, sandy, pale blue with occasional dark bands	2
Limestones, grey to white, occasionally nodular	35
Shale, dark	$\frac{2}{3}$
Limestone, grey, pseudobreccia seen for	2

Saccamminopsis fusulinaformis is abundant throughout the 35 ft limestone; other fossils of note include *Caninia juddi, Corwenia rugosa, Lonsdaleia duplicata, L. floriformis,* and Smith (1928) records *Nemistium edmondsi.* The brachiopods include *Echinoconchus punctatus, P. (Gigantoproductus)* cf. *edelburgensis, P. (G.) latissimus, Spirifer* cf. *duplicicosta* and *S.* cf. *trigonalis.*

Near the entrance to this quarry there is a down west reversed fault of about 5 ft, but the section just described is continued upwards in the middle quarry [1393 3803] of the Wardhall group and may be summarized as follows:

	ft
Sandstone, thin-bedded	3
Shale, grey-black, slightly sandy ..	3
Shale, soft, black	2
Coal, inferior, with sandstone floor	$\frac{1}{2}$
Not exposed	4
Limestone, mostly blue-grey, frequently nodular and in part 'spotted'	$31\frac{1}{2}$
Limestone, pale grey	1

The lowest 1 ft of limestone is certainly the 1-ft bed near the top of the quarry to the east; it succeeds a pale, rather porcellanous limestone which floors part of the quarry and in places appears to contain fragments of the lower rock, while at others it becomes almost a ganister.

Saccamminopsis is again abundant almost throughout; other fossils include various species of *Lithostrotion, Aulophyllum fungites, Avonia davidsoni* and *Echinoconchus elegans.*

[1]We are indebted to Mr. C. Edmonds for pointing out that this is his *Girvanella* Limestone though the fossil occurs somewhat rarely.

Between the above mentioned quarry and the large one that extends for over half a mile to the south from Ward Hall Guards there are probably 20 ft of strata, but of these only a few feet, of pale grey limestone, referred to as the Single Post Limestone, are exposed. The large quarry [1357 3819] shows the following sequence, the highest beds being visible on the north and west.

	ft	in
Sandstone, white to pink, fine to coarse	8	0
Shales, dark, with thin earthy limestones rich in *Lithostrotion junceum*	12	0
Limestone, thin-bedded in upper part, many fossils	15	0
Shales, dark, with thin pyritous limestones at top, small ironstone nodules below; many fossils ..	9	0
Limestone, thin-bedded	3	9
Shale, dark, blue-grey	2	0
Limestone, compact, pale grey with dark spots; nodular and brown-skinned in places	1	0
Shales, dark, with earthy limestone in middle	4	0
Limestones, mainly grey, with two shale bands in upper half	25	0
Coal, top poor and smutty, better below		6
Fireclay, dark, weathering yellow ..		2
Shale, dark	1	0
Limestone, earthy, nodular in part, many large Productids .. 6 in to		8
Coal, good, bright .. .. 7 in to		8
Fireclay, dark grey		2
Limestone, dark, earthy, seen for ..		1

The coal seams are undoubtedly those seen in the large quarry at Broughton Craggs (Eastwood 1930, p. 22), about 2 miles W. of Cockermouth, and like them show that the growth of coal *in situ* was interrupted by an incursion of the sea.

The limestone between the coals includes *Gigantoproductus latissimus;* the main limestone is not particularly fossiliferous, but the beds above it have yielded a large and varied fauna, which includes *Fasciculophyllum* cf. *densum, Lithostrotion junceum, Echinoconchus elegans, Gigantoproductus* cf. *latissimus, Plicochonetes* cf. *buchianus, Pustula pustulosa,* and *Rhipidomella michelini.* There can be no doubt that the limestones represent the *junceum* and Chert Beds at the top of the Fourth Limestone of West Cumberland.

The overlying sandstone contains casts of fossil wood. It is believed to be of considerable thickness but is not well exposed. Between it and the limestone quarried 200 yd W. of Eweclose, a few feet of shales intervene. This limestone, which is the Third of West Cumberland, is about 20 ft thick and is succeeded by a broad belt of dark shales, with two or three thin sandstones, amounting to about 200 ft in thickness. Some of the shales pass into mudstones; others contain septarian nodules: some are very fossiliferous; others appear barren; and a few are pyritous. Some of the sandstone bands are ganister-like; others are thin-bedded and micaceous. These argillaceous measures represent the Orebank Sandstone which only 2 miles to the south-west at Tallentire Hill consists, as in West Cumberland, largely of sandstone.

The succeeding Second and First limestones are exposed on Ward Hall Common but call for little comment.

West of Leathers Gill the sequence from the Orebank Sandstone upwards is repeated by a fault which ranges south by east for 2 miles from Gilcrux and then curves towards Bridekirk. Near Tallentirehill Farm there is a large old quarry in the First Limestone, while on the Hill there are several quarries in that limestone and in the measures below.

The *junceum* and Chert Beds occur in a quarry about 1500 yd S. of Tallentirehill Farm, and a coal is again present beneath them, but the thick sandstone above them at Ward Hall appears to have thinned here almost to vanishing point, though it reappears as ganister to the north-east of Tallentirehill. The Orebank Sandstone consists mainly of yellow sandstone, which has been quarried at two horizons south of the hill, but a fair thickness of shale intervenes between the sandstone and the Second Limestone to the north.

East of Tallentire Hill a sequence from the top of the Fourth Limestone to the First Limestone may be made out. The former crops out near Millstonemoor and is closely followed by a hard, fine, white, siliceous sandstone that makes a 20-ft bank in the wood north of the farm. To the north-east a similar sandstone is brought in by faulting and affords some clue to the sequence on Moota Hill but the ground between this point and Ward Hall Common is puzzling; exposures are poor though it is obvious that there are several faults.

Limestone forms the summit of Moota Hill and the sandstone just referred to crops out on the dip slope to the north-west. The limestone is mainly light grey in colour, but becomes darker below and rests on a fine sugary sandstone, white to pale purple in colour, which gives rise to a bank 30 ft high. To the east this sandstone is cut off by a fault bringing up a limestone that succeeds the beds of Moota Quarry to the south-east, which in turn follow still lower limestones. These latter are best exposed 1000 yd N. 14° E. of Moota House, and 800 yd E.N.E. of Moota Hill Beacon, in a small quarry [1512 3663] that lies to the west of a fault that brings in higher beds to the east. The quarry shows 6 ft of dark limestone with frequent partings of shale and two bands of black chert. *Megachonetes* cf. *papilionaceus* is abundant here, along with *Gigantoproductus* cf. *maximus* and *Spirifer* cf. *duplicicosta*. These beds are probably low in the Fifth Limestone.

Between these beds and those of Moota Quarry [148 362], limestones, both pale and dark grey, intervene, but are poorly exposed. The quarry, 400 yd N. of Moota House, shows 42 ft of limestone, dark with the exception of 10 ft near the top which vary from pale grey to white though with many dusky patches. There is some development of white calcite mudstone, generally 2 ft in thickness, either at or not far above the base of these light beds and this rock has been traced almost continuously for 1000 yd to the south-west of, and nearly the same distance to the north-west of Moota Quarry. It thus provides a fairly useful index of position and enables us to estimate the local throw of two faults —one 200 yd W. of Moota House, which also shifts the rocks of Moota Hill, as 20 ft down west, and the other, 600 yd W. by S. of that house, as 15 ft down east.

Fossils are not uncommon in the beds worked at Moota Quarry, but are not sufficiently diagnostic to determine the exact horizon. Some clue, however, is provided by outcrops to the west, in particular

one in a quarry [1436 3583], 750 yd E. of Millstonemoor. Here the lowermost 10 ft are dark blue limestone while the upper 8 ft consist of alternations of white compact and nodular limestones. *Nemistium edmondsi*, characteristic of the upper part of the Fourth Limestone of West Cumberland, occurs here, and as these beds lie 50 ft or so above the white calcite mudstone band it is presumed that the greater part of the rocks from Moota Hill to Moota House, including those of Moota Quarry, belong to the Fourth Limestone.

Isel Park, Plumbland and Bothel. In this area there is considerable faulting, drift obscures much of the ground, and the detailed sequence is frequently in doubt.

A fault ½ mile E. of Blindcrake brings basalt against limestone of the Seventh Limestone, the two rock-types being found within a few yards of each other. Nothing is seen of the basal shales but a flat shelf between the lowest limestone and the top of the basalt of Park Wood probably marks their outcrop. In this neighbourhood sandstones in the Seventh Limestone appear to be absent, though some of the limestones are sandy. Sandstones reappear between Sunderland and Bothel but even here do not exceed 10 ft in thickness. The best exposure is in Dobby Quarry [1805 3672], 800 yd E.N.E. of Threapland Moss, which shows buff sandstone, fine to coarse with lenticular bedding. Some parts are markedly calcareous. The upper surface, on which rest masses of *L.* [*N.*] *minus* and *Chaetetes septosus*, is very uneven and suggests that emergence may have taken place before the deposition of the succeeding limestone. This sandstone may be traced about a mile to the north of the quarry. A sandstone in the beds above the quarry is only 18 in thick and is crinoidal. In the limestones associated with these sandstones two bands of remarkably crinoidal limestone, commonly rich in polyzoa and lamellibranchs, are generally present, and are well displayed in the Park Wood area. The other limestones vary from light to dark grey; some are chert bearing. They have yielded a mixed fauna.

There is no easily distinguishable boundary between the Seventh and the Sixth Limestones although the alternations of light and dark grey limestones above the

700 ft contour at Isel Park, and between Threapland Moss and Bothel are referred to the Sixth Limestone. In the latter locality the strata appear to be affected by gentle rolls giving a great breadth of outcrop, and two shale bands are present towards Bothel. One in a small quarry [1761 3797], 480 yd E. of the milestone (Wigton 9) on Wharrels Hill, has yielded *Lingula* cf. *squamiformis*, *Plicochonetes sp.*, *Productus* cf. *concinnus*, *Streblochondria anisota*.

In a roadside quarry [1778 3840], 900 yd S.W. of Bothel School, dark shales with a 2-ft limestone are said to include a thin coal. The underlying limestone has yielded *Lithostrotion pauciradiale* approaching *L. martini*, *Palaeosmilia murchisoni* and *Pugilis* cf. *pugilis*. The horizon is probably midway in the Sixth Limestone, and this shale appears to continue northwards through Bothel village. The succeeding limestone, mainly dark, seen 300 yd E.N.E. of the milestone on Wharrels Hill, contains *Aulophyllum fungites* but no fossils of diagnostic value.

North of Bothel there is a large old quarry, known as Gillands, [1833 3946], situated between the main Cockermouth–Carlisle road and Bothel Beck. This quarry, along with the beck, presents a section of some interest. The location to the east of Bothel Limeworks would appear to indicate a position low down in the sequence and this is borne out to some extent by the rocks themselves. *Orionastraea*, however, has been found in the limestone floor of the beck and this fossil is usually regarded as being characteristic, if not diagnostic, of beds much higher in the sequence.

Gillands Quarry shows 21 ft of very dark, rather thin-bedded limestone with a 3- to 6-in gently undulating band of dark chert about the middle. Above the chert bed there is a tendency to nodular structure but the rest of the limestone is very compact. There are reefs of *Lithostrotion pauciradiale* and *L. maccoyanum* just below the chert and *Spirifer* cf. *bisulcatus* also occurs in the same post.

The beck to the west of Gillands Quarry runs partly along the strike; it exhibits the following section [1827 3937]:

	ft
Limestone, rough, grey, paler in upper part .. .. .. *about*	20

	ft
Sandstone, white, ganister-like in places..	3½
Fireclay, light grey, shaly to stony ..	3½
Shale and mudstone, dark .. *about*	2
Limestone, thin-bedded, dark, with *Orionastraea*	4½
Limestone, light grey, with pseudo-breccia; some red and purple staining	2½
Limestone, dark, partly nodular, surface hummocky	4

The lower limestones floor the beck for about 300 yd below the road bridge, while the sandstones and shales occupy the western bank before descending to stream level. The fossils include *Erythrospongia?*, *Chaetetes depressus*, *Clisiophyllum* cf. *multiseptatum*, *Hexaphyllia mirabilis*, *Orionastraea phillipsi*, *Avonia davidsoni* and *Echinoconchus elegans*. This assemblage cannot be regarded as coming from a horizon lower than the Fourth Limestone.

At Bothel a sandstone and shales lie between the Sixth and Fifth Limestones. The sandstone has been quarried on the west side of the road at a point [1745 3832] 450 yd N.E. of the milestone on Wharrels Hill. It is there a massive, false-bedded fairly coarse buff and reddish sandstone over 12 ft in thickness. The sandstone appears to be succeeded by the shales underlying Bothel Limeworks quarry [176 391], 800 yd W.N.W. of Bothel school. A sump in this quarry penetrated 6 ft of these shales which are here rich in brachiopods. The succeeding 35 ft of limestone (of the Fifth Limestone) are mainly dark and have yielded *Lithostrotion pauciradiale*, *L. junceum*, *L. [N.]* cf. *minus*, and *Lonsdaleia duplicata*.

The beds just described are believed to lie direct beneath those in the large quarry which are referable to the upper part of the Fifth Limestone [171 382] on Wharrels Hill. Of the 37 ft of limestone visible here all except 5 ft at the base and an 8-ft bed near the top, which are almost white, are dark grey or blue, though some of the beds weather rusty brown. Fossils are abundant, the most prolific horizon being the 8-ft white limestone which in places is a shell-bed of Productids. These include *Gigantoproductus* cf. *maximus*, a large thick shelled '*Linoproductus*' of ovoid shape and spreading tail, and other forms not specifically identifiable. At the base of this 8-ft bed there are masses of *Lonsdaleia floriformis floriformis*. *Davidsonina septosa* also occurs in this quarry and was first noted by Mr. C. Edmonds.

The scars and quarries to the north-west of Threapland Moss show a white limestone with numerous Productids similar to those of Wharrels Hill quarry; detailed confirmation of exact correlation is lacking, however, and the presence of *Lithostrotion martini*, and '*Linoproductus*' cf. *corrugato-hemisphericus* may possibly indicate a somewhat lower position in the sequence.

The Fifth Limestone covers a considerable tract of the high ground north of Isel Park, which in places consists of bare rock with wide open joints or 'grikes'. Some of the measures roll considerably and there is undoubtedly a fault on the south. Light and dark limestones alternate with each other, and there is some development of pseudobreccia, but the most characteristic band is a pale grey to white porcellanous limestone or calcite mudstone. This may be traced in the easterly facing escarpment from near Thackray Cottage (midway between Sunderland and Blindcrake) to near the point where the road from Plumbland Cottage joins the main road. A limestone a few feet lower in the sequence, and exposed in a small quarry [1587 3694] on the north side of the main road 500 yd S.W. of Threaplandgill Bridge, has yielded *Davidsonina* cf. *septosa*, *Delepinea* aff. *comoides* and a thick shelled '*Linoproductus*' with a spreading tail, identical with forms from Wharrels Hill quarry.

About 100 ft above the calcite mudstone there is a shale band exposed in a roadside quarry [1560 3712] 1000 yd S.S.E. of Plumbland Cottage. The sequence here is identical to that in the quarry at the foot of Parsonby Brow (p. 163). Higher beds hereabouts are masked by drift, but at a point 700 yd S.S.E. of this quarry a scar [1584 3652] 300 yd in length emerges and shows white limestone on black splintery limestone similar to those of the second quarry of Parsonby Brow (p. 163), and referred to the White Limestone at the base of the Fourth Limestone.

Farther north, between Plumbland and Bothel much of the ground is obscured by boulder clay but it is evident that there is considerable faulting. One fault may be seen in Adam's Gill, 250 yd E. of High Close, where it brings dark limestone on the west against sandstone on the east; since the hade is easterly the fault is presumed to throw down in that direction. The sandstone passes up into dark shales with a thin earthy limestone, which are quickly lost to view under drift, but are presumably followed by a pale limestone, seen downstream on the west side of Plumbland. This is succeeded by dark shales with sandstones, all somewhat disturbed.

In a stream descending north-easterly from Plumbland Cottage there is a section which consists of dark blue limestone dipping north followed in upward succession by 8 ft of dark shales with many lamellibranchs, limestone-breccia 6 in, sandstone about 12 ft and limestone—compact, light grey in the lower part, blue in the middle, and nodular above. These may represent the rocks seen in the quarries at Threapland but present some differences.

The next section of importance is in Threapland Gill between Threaplandgill Bridge and the village of Threapland. Light grey limestone predominates in the upper part of this gill into which the stream frequently disappears down swallow-holes. *Nemistium edmondsi* occurs at a point [1582 3824] 850 yd N.E. of Plumbland Cottage and is closely followed by: limestone, granular, with nodular top; fine white, red mottled sandstone with traces of shells, about 1 ft; limestone, grey granular passing up into dark blue red-mottled, about 8 ft; hard fine siliceous sandstone passing up into sandy fireclay ?10 ft; blue black shales with traces of brachiopods, about 10 ft; grey and blue limestone with *Saccamminopsis*. A fault then comes in and introduces a few feet of rough sandstone beneath limestone. The latter is light grey and porcellanous at the base, then rough and sandy before it becomes dark and nodular and eventually grey; *Saccamminopsis* is common and the rock is pseudo-brecciated. There can be no doubt that this limestone is that quarried lower down stream at Thrushgill Quarries, Threapland, and the lower part recalls the measures of the middle quarry at Wardhall (p. 163).

The stream then passes over shales with lamellibranchs and brachiopods whereas the banks show some pale limestone, but these measures are better exposed in the Thrushgill Quarries. Here, in the south-eastern quarry [1555 3915], about 30 ft of limestone are to be seen, dark and compact in the lower part and with a fine development of pseudobreccia at the top, followed by 8 to 10 ft of blue-black shales. Similar measures were worked in the north-western quarry [155 392], but the upper part is more complete and in addition it is possible to make out the position of the Gilcrux Fault, to within a few feet; the section is:

	ft
Limestone, pale, base nodular seen for	3
Sandstone, soft, white..	4½
Shale, sandy .. .. .. about	2
Shale, smooth, blue-black	7
Main limestone of both quarries ..	

The most important fossils from the main limestone (collected from the south-eastern quarry) are *Caninia juddi*, *Nemistium edmondsi*, and *Lonsdaleia duplicata*. These recall the eastern quarry of Wardhall (p. 163) but the rocks themselves are more like those of the middle quarry there (p. 163).

Threapland to Bothel is a region of few exposures, but it is fairly certain that there is a fault with a large downthrow east between these two places. There are signs of an adit [1619 3942], 100 yd N. of the road and 550 yd E. of Threapland Hall, which we believe was driven on a mineralized part of this fault. In the small dump, con-sisting mainly of fine white sandstone with a little dolomite, there are traces of chalco-pyrite, malachite and galena, along with barytes, calcite and quartz.

About 600 yd to the south-east of the adit there is a quarry showing 20 ft of dark grey limestone which may be the Third Limestone. In the upper part the rock is rather earthy and is crowded with large *Saccamminopsis*.

Torpenhow. East of Bothel much of the ground is covered by boulder clay but it is fairly certain that the Carboniferous Limestone Series to the east is separated from the Borrowdale rocks by a north-westerly trending fault. The lowest measures exposed crop out near Stangerhill, but there is evidence of limestone still farther south in the dump [2012 3763] from an old adit, 350 yd S.W. of Bird House, which is com-posed of Carboniferous sandstone, and sandy limestone as well as Borrowdale rocks. The vein stuff in the dump appears to be largely tuff with strings of quartz and pinkish baryte with traces of malachite. No mining details are available; the adit has been driven westwards towards the bounding fault that lies about 60 yd ahead of the adit mouth.

Immediately west of Stangerhill, 7 ft of a white partly nodular limestone rest on dark limestone and are closely succeeded by a calcareous sandstone seen to a thickness of 9 inches in the floor of Stangerhill Quarry [204 382] across the road. Fossils include *Dibunophyllum sp.*, *Lithostrotion* cf. *martini*, *Gigantoproductus latissimus* and *G. maximus*. The succeeding 4 ft of limestone comprise a dark pseudobreccia which is followed by 12 ft of dark limestone with nodular bands. These beds are tentatively assigned to the Sixth Limestone. These and suc-ceeding beds with a thin coal seam appear to be cut off to the east by a fault along the road through Whitrigg.

The next exposures of note are in and about the two quarries[1] to the north-west. The rocks quarried are mainly dark thin-bedded limestones but in the southern quarry there are 7 ft of very compact almost white limestone near the top which must overlie the highest bed of the other quarry, and there is another and higher bed of white limestone exposed in scars to the east and south-east. Fossils are fairly abundant and include *Lonsdaleia floriformis flori-formis*, *Palaeosmilia sp. nov.?*, *Megacho-netes siblyi*.

Exposures to the north of the east-south-easterly fault mentioned above are not good in the vicinity of Torpenhow, but there is sufficient evidence to indicate that the strata are referable to the measures from the Five Yard to the Three Yard Limestone. There are exposures of thin

---

[1]The northern of these, Borrowscale Quarry [1967 3880], is marked on the One-inch map; the other [1967 3855], 200 yd to the south, is not named but is indicated by a kink in the 800 ft contour.

limestones and calcareous shales (which hereabouts represent the Five Yard Limestone) in a northerly flowing stream [1960 3934] about 800 yd from the inn in Torpenhow. They yield a typical shale phasal fauna. These beds are separated by a small north-westerly fault, from sandstones lying on the same line of strike which are seen in a quarry [2015 3930] on the east side of the Whitrigg road from Torpenhow. The sandstones of which 10 ft are seen in the quarry are white, with red and brown specks and rather soft in the upper layers, but ganister-like below. They represent the upper portion of a rather thick series of sandstones with shales which lies above the Five Yard Limestone and which has been traced eastwards from that quarry for about a mile into a northerly flowing stream from Snittlegarth (Cockshott Beck of 6-in map).

In a wood (Cockshott Wood of 6-in map) south of where Cockshott Beck crosses the eastward trending road from Torpenhow, the following section [220 393] is exposed:

		ft	in
15	Shale, dark grey	1	0
14	Coal, poor		2
13	Fireclay, light grey, sandy ..	1	6
12	Sandstone, grey white to brown *about*	25	0
11	Shales, dark, with ganisters and septarian ironstones .. *about*	10	0
10	Coal, good		6
9	Ganisters and fireclay	8	0
8	Shales, dark, with shells .. *about*	5	0
7	Limestone, dark to grey	11	0
6	Mudstone with *Fenestella* ..	10	0
5	Limestone, dark	2	6
4	Shale, brown, limy	1	6
3	Limestone, grey, crystalline ..	1	3
2	Shales, dark, with ironstone; many lamellibranchs	5	0
1	Limestone, light grey, crystalline seen for	6	0

Beds 1 to 7 inclusive represent the Five Yard Limestone and yield the characteristic shale phasal fauna of that limestone. The 25-ft sandstone constitutes the lower part of the sandstone with shales mentioned above which lies between the Five Yard and the Three Yard limestones. The measures between it and the 11 ft limestone are repeated in the beck owing to the shape of the ground.

There are no further sections in the stream for some distance to the south, but limestones associated with sandstones and shales emerge from the boulder clay about Whitecroft. In a stream 1000 yd E. of that farm a grey limestone rests on dark shales with crinoids, polyzoa and small brachiopods, which must succeed the limestone of the quarry where the road bends towards Ireby. This quarry [2310 3836] is in 12 ft of fairly light grey limestone rich in *Saccamminopsis*.

Between the belt of sandstones with shale and the Gilcrux Fault, which must range near Torpenhow, there is little evidence beyond the facts that south of the village a swallow-hole [2043 3955] shows a few feet of pale limestone, that a well [2025 3973] near the inn in Torpenhow is said to have passed through 36 ft of limestone into 4 ft of shale, and that the main street is on limestone. These rocks probably represent the strata from the Third or Three Yard Limestone to the Second or Four Fathom Limestone.

North of the Gilcrux Fault at Newbiggin Grange the First or Great Limestone crops out in the stream and has been quarried nearby. Faulting brings up a chert-bearing limestone to the east, which may be part of the Four Fathom Limestone.

T.E.

Uldale–Ireby and Sandale. This area is illustrated in Fig. 15 and includes the strata from the Basement Conglomerate to the Great Limestone. The general direction of dip is northwards and varies between 4° and 30°. A trough bounded by three faults lies to the east of Aughertree. Subsidiary fractures cross it, notably the Green How Fault which with northerly downthrow cuts out, at the east end, beds between the White and Five Yard limestones. The Snowhill and Thornthwaite faults, with southwesterly and northerly throws respectively are tear faults that form convenient boundaries to the area; east-north-easterly faults around Sandale end against them.

The Seventh Limestone averages 150 ft in thickness and may be traced from small quarries north-west of Ruthwaite across the River Ellen via Uldale to the Snowhill Fault. The best exposures are around Uldale. In a crag and small quarries [2524 3689] 300 to 400 yd E.S.E. of the crossroads

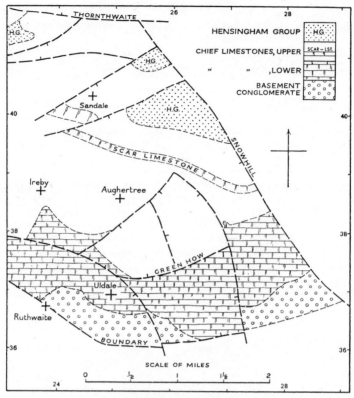

FIG. 15. *Sketch map illustrating geology of Aughertree area*

in that village, 20 ft of dark grey-blue limestone overlie 10 ft of false-bedded calcareous sandstone—the 'diagonally bedded' limestones of the West Cumberland area. The limestone includes highly crinoidal beds with abundant polyzoa and the horizon represents Garwood's Bryozoa Band. The fauna includes *Syringopora sp., Fenestella sp., Hemitrypa* cf. *hibernica, Stenodiscus compactus, Actinoconchus planosulcatus, Pleuropugnoides*[*Camarotoechia*]cf.*pleurodon, Echinoconchus elegans, E. punctatus, Fluctuaria* cf. *undata, Productus garwoodi,* '*Linoproductus*' aff. *globosus, Pugilis* cf. *pugilis, Spirifer* cf. *bisulcatus,* and the following forms identified by Mr. C. Edmonds: *Lithostrotion martini,* '*Linoproductus*' *corrugatohemisphericus* and *Punctospirifer scabricosta.*

The strata immediately above the Seventh Limestone are not well exposed but include sandstones and shales with a coal seam reported to be 14 in thick at Uldale where it has been worked to a slight extent.

The combined thickness of the overlying Sixth and Fifth limestones (which are not mapped separately in this area) is 270 ft. Good exposures are restricted to quarries. That [2560 3700] 750 yd E. 4° N. of the cross-roads in Uldale displays 27 ft of dark grey limestone with bands and nodules of black chert near the base of the Sixth Limestone. Similar beds are displayed in the roadside quarries [2540 3720] 350 yd N.E. of Uldale church where the fauna includes *Lithostrotion junceum, L. paucira-diale, Megachonetes siblyi, Gigantoproductus* cf. *bisati, G. maximus* and *Pugilis* cf. *pugilis.* Some 24 ft of the Fifth Limestone are exposed in a quarry [2645 3720] 650 yd N.N.W. of Baggra Yeat and yield a fauna similar to that from Snowhill quarry given on p. 172.

The White and Rough limestones are mapped together; the former is poorly exposed and the latter is best seen in the River Ellen north of Uldale Mill. The massive grey-white sandstone, in this area

25 to 30 ft thick, that underlies the Jew Limestone is seen on the left side of the Ellen valley at Ireby behind the corn-mill, and again in the banks of the stream to the north of Aughertree.

The Jew and Tyne Bottom limestones are mapped together, being separated by only a few feet of sandstone and shale. There are good exposures on Green How, between Daleside and Snowhill and along the stream to the north of Aughertree. The best section of the Jew Limestone, however, occurs in a roadside quarry [2576 3734] 800 yd E. 25° N. of the church in Uldale, and the sequence there displayed and set out below, may be taken as typical of this limestone as far east as Newlands.

		ft
4.	Limestone, dark grey	3
3.	*Lithostrotion* band	$\frac{1}{2}$
2.	Limestone, dark grey, well-bedded, splintery	18
1.	Limestone, grey-white, in places almost porcellanous, with red spots	6

Faunally, bed 1 here and elsewhere, is characterized by numerous *Lonsdaleia floriformis, Gigantoproductus* aff. *crassus* and *G.* aff. *latissimus*. Throughout bed 2 *Saccamminopsis fusulinaformis* is abundant and corals are frequent, notably *Aulophyllum fungites, Dibunophyllum bipartitum bipartitum* and *Nemistium edmondsi*. Bed 3 is composed almost exclusively of reefs of *Lithostrotion pauciradiale*, and *Saccamminopsis* is again abundant in bed 4 along with *Caninia juddi*.

The strata from the Tyne Bottom to and including the Scar Limestone are not well exposed. The Five Yard Limestone and the underlying grey-white siliceous sandstone are seen in a quarry [2617 3761] on Aughertree Fell $\frac{3}{4}$ mile E.N.E. of Uldale church. The former consists of a lower 3-ft bed of limestone separated from an upper 1-ft bed by 10 ft of highly fossiliferous calcareous shale yielding a shale phasal fauna that includes *Fasciculophyllum* cf. *omaliusi, Heterophyllia* cf. *grandis, Hexaphyllia maccoyi, Lithostrotion junceum, Fenestella membranacea, F. nodulosa, F. polyporata, Penniretepora* aff. *grandis, Productus* cf. *redesdalensis, Pugilis* cf. *scoticus, Rhipidomella michelini, Spirifer* cf. *duplicicosta, Aviculopecten* cf. *knockonniensis, A.* cf. *murchisoni,*

Nuculopsis gibbosa, Palaeoneilo cf. *laevirostris,* and the trilobite *Weberides mucronatus.*

Strata from the Three Yard or Third Limestone to the Great are present in the Aughertree trough and trend from the Snowhill Fault to Sandale and Catlands Hill. In the trough the Great and Four Fathom limestones come together and this is also the case north of Newlands where they form lines of crags; but from Sandale westwards 12 to 15 ft of strata, mostly sandstone, intervene between these limestones. The Four Fathom is best seen in a quarry [2471 4077], 650 yd N.N.W. of Sandale, where black cherts are abundant in 14 ft of dark grey limestone. The Great Limestone is well exposed in numerous quarries, (notably Angerton Bank and Headend quarries of 6-in maps) in which the lithology may be matched almost bed for bed. Some 10 ft of dark grey-blue limestone split up by shale partings are succeeded by 20 ft of pale grey to creamy limestone, which in turn are followed by 20 ft of dark grey, thinly-bedded limestones separated by shale partings. The fauna is similar to that from the Great Limestone at Brocklebank given on p. 174.

Parkend and Faulds Brow (between the Snowhill and Caldbeck Faults). The sequence ranges from the Basement Conglomerate to the Great Limestone. As far east as the north-west fault past Thistlebottom the dip is to the north-north-west and the strata are traversed by four north-westerly trending faults of which that of Clay Gap, with a maximum throw down north-east of 300 ft, is the most important. Between this fault and the Whelpo Fault the beds dip to the north-north-west in the south, but in the north, on Faulds Brow, a syncline with a westerly pitch is developed. The Whelpo Fault fans out to the north and several of the branch faults end against the Thornthwaite Fault. The throw down east of the main fracture is 150 ft to the south-west of Upton but increases to 750 ft on Faulds Brow. This dislocation is a tear-fault and shifts the axis of the above mentioned syncline 1½ miles to the south; in consequence the dip between it and the Caldbeck Fault is north-westerly in the south and south-westerly in the north. These major faults are connected, to the north of Whelpo, by two accommodation fractures of westerly downthrow; their maximum displacements are 250 ft for the western, and 450 ft for the eastern fault. The Thornthwaite Fault which bounds the area on the north swings to the south-south-east to form the Caldbeck Fault which attains a maximum throw of 1000 ft down east ½ mile N.W. of Caldbeck.

Isolated exposures mark the crop of the Seventh Limestone, the best being in Parkend Beck, where fine-grained limestones and calcite-mudstones are succeeded in turn by the diagonally-bedded calcareous sandstones and the calcareous shales and interbedded limestones of the Bryozoa Band. At a locality [2976 3853] 500 yd S.W. of Parkend the fauna of this Band includes: *Fenestella nodulosa*, '*Linoproductus*' aff. *globosus*, *Pleuropugnoides* cf. *pleurodon*, *Productus* cf. *garwoodi*, *Punctospirifer redesdalensis* and *P. scabricosta*.

The Sixth Limestone is well exposed from a point [3200 3972], 600 yd W.S.W. of Caldbeck church, to Fairy Bridge in the beck (Cald Beck of 6-in map) where some 60 ft of dark grey-blue limestone are seen. A band near the top of the limestone contains *Gigantoproductus* cf. *maximus;* other forms collected from this locality include *Heterophyllia grandis*, *Lithostrotion portlocki* and *Megachonetes* cf. *siblyi*. *L.* [*Nematophyllum*] *minus* is recorded from a point [3192 3973] 700 yd W. 15° S. of Caldbeck church. Lower beds of the Sixth Limestone are seen in the stream east of Upton where black cherts are found as lenses and nodules.

The Fifth Limestone is well displayed in this area at Snowhill, around Thistlebottom south of Whelpo Heads, and in a quarry 100 yd E. of Townhead. The section at Snowhill Quarry [2796 3879], 250 yd N. of Snowhill, may be taken as typical. Corals are abundant in the lower 20 ft of dark grey limestone, and include *Chaetetes septosus*, *Lithostrotion junceum*, *L.* [*Nematophyllum*] *minus*, *L. portlocki*, *Lonsdaleia duplicata*, *L. floriformis* and *Palaeosmilia murchisoni*. Brachiopods prevail in the upper 10 to 12 ft of massive light grey limestone and include *Davidsonina* aff. *septosa*, *Delepinea* aff. *comoides*, *Gigantoproductus* cf. *maximus*, and *Striatifera striata*.

Pseudobreccias of the White Limestone are seen in the stream 430 yd W.N.W.

of Thistlebottom, but the best section of this limestone is in the quarry [3029 3987] 400 yd S.S.E. of Paddigill. Here some 10 ft of dark grey limestones are followed by 8 ft of dark limestones and shales, which in turn are overlain by 12 ft of pale grey to creamy limestone. The bottom beds yield few fossils. *Megachonetes siblyi* is abundant in the shales of the middle beds, whilst the top beds include *Lithostrotion maccoyanum*, *L.* [*Nematophyllum*] *minus*, and *Lonsdaleia floriformis floriformis*.

The beds from the Rough to the Great limestones are well displayed on Faulds Brow where shales and sandstones as well as the individual limestones have been mapped. The sandstone below the Jew Limestone reaches its maximum thickness of 100 ft. The Jew Limestone, well displayed in a quarry [2978 3992] 500 yd N. of Faulds, has the following forms additional to those cited on p. 171: *Lithostrotion junceum*, *L. portlocki*, *Palaeosmilia murchisoni*, *Gigantoproductus edelburgensis*, and *Pugilis* cf. *pugilis*. The pale creamy, faintly pseudo-brecciated Single Post Limestone is best seen in the small crags 400 yd N.E. of Paddigill. The Scar Limestone is exposed in a line of quarries [304 409], 500 to 900 yd N.N.E. of that farm. Here the upward succession is: (a) dark grey limestone, 2 ft; (b) calcareous shale, 9 in, with abundant *Aulophyllum fungites;* (c) massive grey limestone in 7-ft posts, 14 ft, with scattered *Saccamminopsis fusulinaformis* and *Lithostrotion junceum;* (d) dark grey, thinly-bedded limestone and thin shale partings, 12 ft, with *Zaphrentites delanouei* and *Z.* cf. *disjunctus*. Old quarries to the west of those in the Scar Limestone show the overlying white quartzitic sandstone and the Five Yard Limestone, which is faunally and lithologically identical to that described on p. 171. The pale grey, highly crinoidal, Three Yard Limestone with small nodules of white chert is seen 750 yd N.W. of Paddigill, where it is overlain by the Orebank Sandstone, here a coarse feldspathic grit some 80 ft thick.

Caldbeck, Hesket Newmarket and Newlands. This area includes the valleys of the Cald Beck below Caldbeck and the River Caldew from Haltcliff Hall to Sebergham, the limits being defined by the base of the Hensingham Group to the north and to

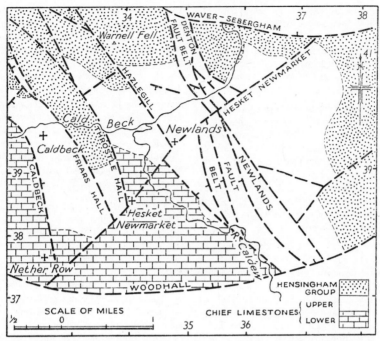

FIG. 16. *Sketch map illustrating geology of Caldbeck and Newlands area*

the east, and by the Woodhall Fault to the south. The area is divided by a north-easterly tear-fault through Hesket Newmarket and Newlands—the Hesket Newmarket Fault. The general direction of dip to the north-west of this fracture is northerly, but to the south-east of it the dip is easterly. There are also faults of north-westerly trend, some of considerable throw.

The Friars Hall and Throstle Hall faults that let down a wedge of Hensingham Group east of Caldbeck have throws of 600 to 800 ft. The eastern member of the Denton Fault-belt (see Fig. 16) has a throw of 500 ft down east. The four faults of the Newlands fault-belt all throw to the south-west with a combined displacement of 1000 ft and the fracture which joins the Hesket Newmarket Fault, ¼ mile S.W. of Hesket Newmarket, has a north-easterly downthrow of 500 ft.

The Sixth and Fifth limestones are the lowest beds exposed but their outcrops to the south-east of Hesket Newmarket are mostly covered by drift. In this area the Rough Limestone lies directly upon the White Limestone; they are well exposed in several

small quarries near Nether Row east of the Caldbeck Fault.

In this area measures from the Jew Limestone to the Great Limestone are particularly well exposed in the valleys of the Cald Beck and the River Caldew. The following section between the Jew and the Tyne Bottom limestones, is exposed at and about the confluence [343 399] of the Caldew and the Cald Beck.

	ft
Tyne Bottom Limestone: dark-blue splintery limestone in posts up to 2 ft	32
Sandstone, grey, massive	15
Limestone, grey-blue, with black cherts	4
Shale, blue	1
Fireclay	4
Ironstone	1
Sandstone	5
Jew Limestone .. .. at least	20

The fauna of the Tyne Bottom Limestone includes *Saccamminopsis fusulinaformis, Lithostrotion junceum, L. maccoyanum, Dielasma* cf. *hastatum, D. sacculum, Avonia* cf. *youngiana, Echinoconchus elegans,*

Gigantoproductus aff. *giganteus, G.* cf. *latissimus, Quasiavonia aculeata.* East of the Throstle Hall Fault a 10- to 12-in coal has been worked immediately beneath a 3-ft limestone (probably the Cockleshell Limestone) that lies a short distance below the Scar Limestone.

In the highly crinoidal Three Yard Limestone, which forms a crag to the south of Parkhead, *Saccamminopsis fusulinaformis* is abundant in patches, and small nodules of grey chert occur. There are also cherts in the overlying Four Fathom Limestone. Numerous quarries at and near Parkhead mark the outcrop of the Great Limestone which here presents its usual faunal and lithological characters.

In the southern part of the area at a point [3539 3822] 200 yd S.S.W. of Banks the Jew Limestone yields *Orionastraea* cf. *phillipsi,* thus suggesting the correlation of this limestone with the Potholes Beds of West Cumberland. Hereabouts the strata between the Scar Limestone and the Three Yard Limestone are well exposed, the outcrops being thrice repeated by the fractures of the Newland fault-belt.

Thornthwaite Beck and Brocklebank (north of Thornthwaite Fault). In this area there are two separate outcrops. The westerly one is in Townthwaite Beck, where the Great Limestone is somewhat poorly exposed. Its identification is confirmed by the fauna which includes *Lonsdaleia floriformis laticlavia* collected from an exposure in the Beck [2898 4210], 700 yd W. 35° S. of Hilltop.

In Townthwaite Beck, north of an east–west fault, a grit, dipping west at 35°, is overlain by a poorly exposed limestone. If the grit be that which occurs farther south, then the limestones represent the Four Fathom and the Great. The fauna indicates the presence of the latter and the overlying Little Limestone Coal crops out in the stream nearby.

A fracture of considerable magnitude with an easterly downthrow must intervene between the Great Limestone in Townthwaite Beck and quarries in this limestone at Brocklebank one and a quarter miles farther east where the dip is westwards at 10°. In these quarries 9 ft of dark blue, well-bedded limestones are followed by

16 ft of massive grey limestone—the main posts—which are overlain by 30 ft of dark blue limestone with thin shale bands. A representative Great Limestone fauna from the southern quarry [3054 4292], 1250 yd E. 25° N. of Hilltop, includes *Saccamminopsis?, Aulophyllum fungites, Caninia juddi, Dibunophyllum bipartitum bipartitum, Diphyphyllum lateseptatum, Lithostrotion sp., Londsaleia floriformis laticlavia, Dielasma sacculum, Eomarginifera* cf. *derbiensis, Gigantoproductus latissimus, Phricodothyris* cf. *lineata, Quasiavonia aculeata, Schizophoria* cf. *resupinata, Edmondia sulcata.*

Lowling and Kirkstead (north of Lowling Fault). The double throw of the Lowling fault, which forms the southern boundary, has already been referred to (see p. 18 and Fig. 17). The trend of the north-north-easterly fault past Lowling and the outcrop of the Great Limestone to the east of it are based on an exposure of limestone in an old quarry 250 yd S. of Lowling and on four borings nearby. An abbreviated record of No. 3 Borehole [3149 4676], 60 yd W. 10° S. of the south-west corner of Lowling, is as follows:

	Thickness	Depth
	ft	ft
Surface deposits	7	7
Sandstones and shales of Hensingham Group ..	40	47
Great Limestone	57	104
Shales and sandstones ..	11	115
Four Fathom Limestone ..	23½	138½
Sandstone (Orebank Sandstone)	60	198½

The Great Limestone is also recorded from Lowling No. 5 Borehole [3143 4646], 350 yd S. 17° W. of the south-west corner of Lowling, where it is has yielded *Lonsdaleia floriformis laticlavia.*

The grey-white sandstones in Chalk Beck east of Kirkstead are probably referable to the Orebank Sandstone. Farther north, in Chalk Beck immediately east of a north-westerly fault, a few feet of creamy and red dolomitic limestone immediately under the basal breccia of the New Red Sandstone, have a fauna suggestive of the Great Limestone.   F.M.T.

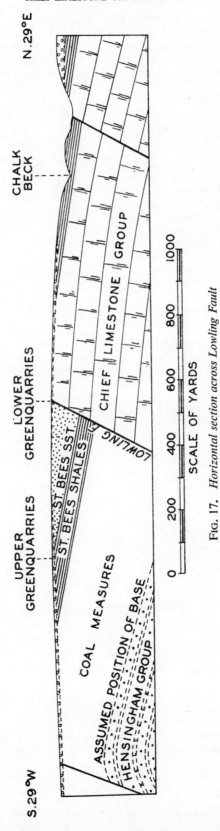

Fig. 17.   *Horizontal section across Lowling Fault*

Deerrudding to Berrier. South of the Woodhall Fault the strike of the Carboniferous Limestone is towards the south-south-east. The contact with the Borrowdale Volcanic Series to the west is obscured by drift; minor strike-faulting cutting out the lowest beds is possible, but a normal unconformable contact has been assumed. On the east this area is bounded by the Gillcambon Fault and its offshoot the Church Stile Fault (p. 177). A long escarpment ridge, the crest of which is usually formed by the Fifth Limestone, trends to the south-south-west to form the divide between the Caldew and Gillcambon Beck valleys. It is highest in the south-east where it merges into a broad limestone plateau at 1050 to 1150 ft O.D. and falls gradually northwards and disappears beneath boulder clay in the angle between the River Caldew and Gillcambon Beck. The structure is simple, a general east-north-easterly dip at rather less than 10° broken by a few comparatively small and unimportant faults.

The Seventh Limestone with its associated beds of thin sandstone is about 200 ft thick, and occupies the lower part of the escarpment, and exposures are rare except where it rises to the level of the plateau mentioned above. There are small outcrops of sandy detrital limestones, associated with thin-bedded flaggy limestones rich in polyzoa, probably the Bryozoa Band at about 950 ft O.D. on the scarp west of Hutton Roof.

Small quarries [387 307] on both sides of the Berrier road ¾ mile S.E. of Murrah Hall show the following (composite) upward sequence: obscure buff weathering limestone 6 ft; pale creamy white fine-grained limestones (calcite-mudstones) 24 ft, with diagonally bedded calcareous sandstone and a little white chert near the base, and a bed of coarse sandstone, 2 ft 8 in thick, pebbly at the base lying 13 ft from the top; dark grey limestone with shale partings and a 2-ft bed of sandstone 6 ft from the base. These beds probably lie about 30 to 70 ft above the base of the Seventh Limestone. The full sequence of the latter is proved in two of a group of four boreholes put down in search of iron-ore on the scarp ½ to 1 mile N.N.W. of Berrier. A band of conglomerate recorded from No. 1 [3921 3061] borehole probably corresponds with the pebbly sandstone of the

above section. In No. 4 [3900 3099] borehole the higher sandstone of the quarries is present. A third sandstone horizon near the top of this limestone is proved in the boreholes, and has been mapped south of Berrier. A sandy phase at this horizon is widespread but as is evident in the borehole records sandstones in this part of the sequence are irregular in their occurrence.

The Sixth Limestone, 60 to 80 ft thick, is mostly dark bluish grey limestone with shale partings. Pale grey limestone with pseudobreccias is sometimes developed at the top of the beds of dark limestone. As shale beds are common throughout this limestone and the adjoining parts of those above and below it, limits are ill-defined. Exposures are comparatively few; among these may be mentioned quarries 350 yd E. of Normancrag [3681 3432], below the 1000 ft contour north of the road west of Hutton Roof [3708 3400], 300 yd N.W. of Bank House [3709 3363], and a richly fossiliferous quarry [3808 3194], ¼ mile N.E. of Murrah Hall. The latter has yielded *Caninia juddi, Caninia* sp. [= *Campophyllum* aff. *murchisoni*], *Dibunophyllum* spp., *Heterophyllia sp., Lithostrotion pauciradiale, L. maccoyanum, L. martini, Lonsdaleia duplicata, Palaeosmilia murchisoni, Fenestella nodulosa, Hemitrypa* cf. *hibernica, Megachonetes* cf. *siblyi*, and several Productids, lamellibranchs and gastropods. An abundant fauna of similar type from the scarp slope of Highbanks Wood N.W. of Berrier includes *Dibunophyllum bipartitum bipartitum, Heterophyllia grandis* and *Megachonetes papilionaceus*.

The Fifth Limestone appears to range from 120 ft thick in the north to 170 ft in the south. It is divided into two parts by 20 ft or more of sandstones or sandy shales. The lower part is mostly dark limestones and some shales with pale limestones towards the top; in the upper part there is a similar upward change from dark to light coloured pseudobrecciated limestones but the latter are predominant.

At Haltcliff Bridge the medial parting of sandstones and sandy shales 14 ft thick is seen resting on 3 ft of pale pseudobrecciated limestone and followed after a short gap by 20 ft of dark limestone, of which the lowest 5 ft are dolomitic. There are many exposures of the limestones around

Hutton Roof and on the crest of the scarp north-west of Berrier. At the former locality fireclay and a 2-in coal seam were developed in the medial sandstones. The fauna from a limestone scarp [3909 3083], $\frac{1}{4}$ mile E.S.E. of the north-west corner of Highbanks Wood north-west of Berrier, includes *Carcinophyllum* cf. *vaughani*, *Dibunophyllum bipartitum bipartitum*, *Lithostrotion paucira-diale*, *Davidsonina* aff. *septosa*, *Quasiavonia aculeata*. A nearby exposure [3897 3092] 300 yd E. 17° S. of the north-west corner of Highbanks Wood yielded *Lithostrotion maccoyanum*, *L. martini*, *Gigantoproductus* cf. *maximus* and '*Linoproductus*' cf. *corrugato-hemisphericus*.

The White Limestone, 60 to 80 ft thick, is well exposed in natural and quarried scarps [3735 3513] immediately N.W. of Thwaite Hall. The sequence here is:

	ft
Limestone, grey-white in 1 to 2 ft beds	13$\frac{1}{2}$
Chinastone, cream-coloured ..	1$\frac{1}{2}$
Not exposed	1$\frac{1}{2}$
Limestone, pseudobrecciated, a small-grained type	1$\frac{1}{2}$
Limestone, massive greyish white ..	12
Chinastone, massive, with rectangular blocky jointing	1$\frac{3}{4}$
Pseudobreccia with *Lonsdaleia sp.* ..	11$\frac{1}{4}$
Limestone, massive greyish white, with two 1$\frac{1}{2}$-ft bands of chinastone	8$\frac{1}{2}$
Not exposed	10
Limestone, compact grey-white (cal-cite-mudstone)	14
Gap with pink and greenish grey mudstone	10
Pseudobreccia (top of Fifth Lime-stone)..	15

The fauna of the upper part of these beds includes *Caninia subibicina*, *Carcinophyllum vaughani*, *Dibunophyllum bipartitum bipartitum*, *Lithostrotion pauciradiale*, *Lonsdaleia floriformis*, *Davidsonina septosa* and *Delepinea* aff. *comoides*.

North and north-west of Scale, and east of Highbanks Wood, there are many good scarps of bare limestone with associated bare dip slopes showing excellent examples of griked surfaces. The general dip here is 8° to 10°.

The Rough Limestone usually occurs at the bottom of a long dip-slope of White Limestone and is poorly exposed. An old quarry [3809 3344] immediately east of Scale shows 23 ft of dark grey to black limestone. The fauna includes *Dibunophyllum bipartitum bipartitum*, *Echinoconchus punctatus*, *Gigantoproductus giganteus* and *Pustula pustulosa*. Over a triangular block of country south-east of Scale higher beds than those to the north and south are brought in by the north-north-easterly trending fault past Scale and the west-south-westerly trending Gully Fault. They comprise strata from the Fifth Limestone to the Tyne Bottom dipping east-north-east at low angles. South of the Gully Fault up to 500 ft of limestones, sandstones and shales of the Upper *Dibunophyllum* Zone from the Rough Limestone to the Five Yard Limestone form a regular succession of scarps trending first to the south-south-east and then to the south-east. The Rough Limestone yields *Girvanella*-like organisms half a mile north of Berrier. Of the higher limestones the Jew, Tyne Bottom, Single Post and Scar are all fairly well exposed in the area $\frac{3}{4}$ mile N. of Berrier. Here a 1-ft seam of coal lying between the Tyne Bottom and Single Post limestones has been worked from numerous bell-pits. Its horizon appears to correspond with that of the Reagill Coal which outcrops a few miles south of Penrith.

East of Gillcambon Beck. The dominant structural feature of this area is the north-north-westerly fault (Gillcambon Fault) which has an upthrow east of 1000 ft or more in the southern part of the area where it brings the Borrowdale Volcanic Series (1 mile E. of Scale Plantation) against Carboniferous Limestone Series to the west. About 1 mile E. by N. of Scale this fault divides; one part continues the north-north-westerly line of the Gillcambon Fault while the other (here termed the Newsham Fault) trends north, and beyond Newsham swings into a N.E. by N. course. This branch has much the larger throw. The offshoots from the northern part of the Gillcambon Fault in a north-westerly direction meet the Woodhall Fault, and appear to be accommodation fractures in the angle between the Woodhall and Gillcambon faults. In the vicinity of Howhill there are two north-north-westerly faults and one north-easterly fault which represent minor adjustments in the angle between the

Newsham Fault and the northern part of the Gillcambon Fault.

The westernmost offshoot of the Gillcambon Fault (the Church Stile Fault) has a negligible downthrow (to the north-east) south of Church Stile but this increases to the north-west. Downstream from Sowerby Hall strata from the Tyne Bottom Limestone to above the ?Scar Limestone are exposed. North-west of Sowerby Hall the following upward sequence is visible: blue-grey limestone (Tyne Bottom) 12 ft, sandstone 8 ft, *not exposed* 15 ft, soft brown sandstone 8 ft, fireclay with 2-in coal 2½ ft, grey limestone upper part pseudobrecciated (Single Post) 8 to 9 ft. Farther downstream the following upward sequence is observable: sandstone 30 ft, shale 24 ft, sandstone 25 to 30 ft, shale 2½ ft, sandstone 9 ft, limestone 30 ft. The dip is E. 40° N. at 20° to 30°. The limestone is cut off by a fault parallel to the Church Stile Fault, and 300 yd east of the latter. This dislocation is well exposed 500 yd W.S.W. of Low Moordyke. It brings in the Four Fathom Limestone which here is rather cherty, and dolomitic in its lower part. The limestone is underlain by mudstone 3 ft thick and containing a 3-in coal, and this mudstone rests on siliceous and calcareous sandstone 6 ft thick. Secondary dolomitization of limestones adjacent to faults is of frequent occurrence in this area.

Around Newsham to the east of the Gillcambon Fault, strata ranging from the White Limestone to the grit below the Four Fathom Limestone form a regular series of scarps broken by a strike fault which cuts out the Single Post to Five Yard Limestone group of beds. *Girvanella?* is present in the Rough Limestone.

From Howhill, northwards to High Dean and Chapter and Inglewood Edge, beds from the Tyne Bottom to the Great Limestone are present; the dip varies from E.N.E. to a little east of north, indicating a north-easterly pitching synclinal fold between the two faults. In an old quarry [3934 3605], on the west side of the road 200 yd E.N.E. of Howhill, the Tyne Bottom Limestone is directly overlain by sandstone as in Gillcambon Beck. The fauna, which is similar to that from the latter area, includes *Plicochonetes* cf. *buchianus*, *Gigantoproductus latissimus* and *Tornquistia polita*.

The Newsham Fault with an upthrow east of 600 to 800 ft brings up strata, mainly massive limestones, from the Sixth Limestone to the Jew Limestone. These crop out as a series of small scarps on the plateau-like area south-east of Howhill where the dip is 12° to 14° to the north-east. They disappear beneath boulder clay to the south but reappear as a regular series of bare limestone scarps on the higher ground to the south-east of Thanetwell Cottage.

The Tippy Hills Fault, trending south-eastwards from the Newsham Fault ¾ mile S. by E. of Newsham, forms the boundary between the limestone and the inlier of Borrowdale lavas to the south, and cuts out the Seventh Limestone. A narrow strip of Fifth Limestone and White Limestone is let down by a north-north-westerly fault crossing the broad angle between the Newsham and Tippy Hills faults.

Near the eastern margin of One-inch Sheet 23 the Rough Limestone is indicated principally by a line of large swallow holes in the outcrop of the overlying shale, but the Jew Limestone is well exposed in Lamonby Quarries [4007 3588], 1000 yd E. of Howhill. A feature in the latter is the large reefs of *Lonsdaleia floriformis* in the quarry floor.   S.E.H.

References

EARLE, K. W. 1921. The Lower Carboniferous rocks of West Cumberland. *Abstr. Proc. geol. Soc. Lond.*, No. 1076, 9–10.

———— 1922. The Lower Carboniferous rocks of Cumberland. *Geol. Mag.*, **59**, 523–6.

EASTWOOD, T. 1928. The Cockermouth Lavas, Cumberland—a carboniferous volcanic episode. *Summ. Prog. Geol. Surv. Gt Br.*, for 1927. Pt. II, 15–22.

———— 1930. The Geology of the Maryport District. *Mem. Geol. Surv. Gt Br.*

———— DIXON, E. E. L., HOLLINGWORTH, S. E. and SMITH, B. 1931. The Geology of the Whitehaven and Workington District. *Mem. Geol. Surv. Gt Br.*

EDMONDS, C. 1922. The Carboniferous Limestone Series of West Cumberland. *Geol. Mag.*, **59**, 74–83, 117–31.

GARWOOD, E. J. 1913. The Lower Carboniferous succession in the north-west of England. *Quart. Jl geol. Soc. Lond.*, **68**, 449–586.

KENDALL, J. D. 1885. The Carboniferous rocks of Cumberland and North Lancashire, or Furness. *Trans. N. Engl. Inst. Min. Eng.*, **34**, 125–37.

SMITH, S. 1928. The Carboniferous coral *Nemistium edmondsi*, gen. et sp. n. *Ann. Mag. nat. Hist.*, (10), **1**, 112–20.

TROTTER, F. M. and HOLLINGWORTH, S. E. 1932. The geology of the Brampton District. *Mem. Geol. Surv. Gt Br.*

Chapter XI

UPPER CARBONIFEROUS ROCKS

THE UPPER CARBONIFEROUS falls into two divisions, the Millstone Grit Series and the overlying Coal Measures. Within measures yielding a sequence of goniatite species-zones the Geological Survey of England and Wales regard the Namurian as being synonymous with the Millstone Grit Series and in goniatite-bearing rocks the latter is defined as lying between specific goniatite bands. Reasons have been given, however (p. 145), for taking the base of the Hensingham Group, the local representative of the Millstone Grit Series in this area, at the top of the First or Great Limestone. It remains here to discuss the divisional line between the Millstone Grit Series and the Coal Measures in the absence of the *Gastrioceras subcrenatum* Marine Band, the horizon accepted as the divisional line between the Namurian and Westphalian on the continent and representing the base of the Coal Measures in this country. Elsewhere in the West Cumberland Coalfield this basal Coal Measures band has been found a few feet below the Harrington Four Feet and this seam forms a mappable base to the Coal Measures where it is present. Unfortunately the basal Coal Measures goniatite-band is not present in the Cockermouth district and over much of the area the Harrington Four Feet is also absent. Where this is the case the upper limit of the local Millstone Grit Series is taken at a line drawn to separate the highest measures yielding marine fossils of Hensingham Group type and the lowest measures yielding mussels diagnostic of the Lower Coal Measures.

Although the Hensingham Group yields a diverse marine fauna, which taken as an assemblage is characteristic (p. 182), individual fossils of diagnostic value are nevertheless few, being as follows: *Productus carbonarius*[1], *Tylonautilus nodiferus* and *Anthracoceras glabrum*, the last-named found at one locality only. These are in conformity with the current practice of placing the Hensingham Group in the Arnsbergian (E_2) Stage. No fossils diagnostic of the Pendleian (E_1) Stage have been found and it is considered possible that over much of the area there may be a non-sequence at the base of the Group (see p. 182), although the evidence is admittedly meagre.

The evidence for a non-sequence at the top of the Hensingham Group is found in Chalk Beck, about two miles north of Caldbeck, where, in a continuous sequence, measures yielding a typical Hensingham Group fossil assemblage are separated by about only 10 ft of strata from a mussel-band yielding forms which according to Mr. M. A. Calver are probably indicative of the lower part of the *Anthraconaia modiolaris* Zone. A major non-sequence is clearly indicated: for here the Chokierian (H_1), Alportian (H_2), Kinderscoutian

---

[1]The authors of the names of species of fossils in the Upper Carboniferous rocks are given in Appendix II.

(R_1), Marsdenian (R_2) and Yeadonian (G_1) stages are missing as well as the Coal Measures non-marine lamellibranch Zone of *A. lenisulcata* and probably all of the *C. communis* Zone.

HENSINGHAM GROUP

The fossils from this group were mainly collected by Mr. S. W. Hester and were identified by Sir James Stubblefield. Identifications were revised, where necessary, in 1962 by Dr. W. H. C. Ramsbottom.

The strata from the top of the Great Limestone to the base of the Coal Measures are referred to the Hensingham Group, a name given for similar measures in the Maryport and Whitehaven districts. The thickness of the Group, although subject to local variations, nevertheless shows a pronounced regional increase towards the north. At the type locality of Hensingham, a suburb of Whitehaven, the group is only 150 ft thick, with a medium to coarse grit (the Hensingham Grit) at the base lying directly upon the First Limestone. In the Whitehaven area the non-sequence at the top of the Millstone Grit Series lies wholly within that Series; the Hensingham Group, with the typical E_2 form of *Tylonautilus nodiferus* described by Pringle and Jackson (1928) near the top, is overlain by a marine band carrying *Gastrioceras cumbriense*, which in this area is succeeded by the *G. subcrenatum* Marine Band. Northwards from the Whitehaven area the Hensingham Group thickens; it is 400 ft near Workington, and still farther north in the Bank End and Blue Dial boreholes near Maryport (Smith 1921) 1600 ft of these measures were encountered without the base being proved. Eastwards from Maryport the measures thin to some 400 ft around Crosby, the thinning being attributed (Eastwood 1930) to the initiation of an anticline or low ridge after the deposition of the Great or First Limestone. This ridge, of east-north-easterly trend, extends to the Aspatria area in the present district, where the Group is about 400 ft thick. Farther to the east, however, to the south of Mealsgate and to the north of Caldbeck, the Hensingham Group expands to about 1200 ft and just beyond the eastern margin of the district a boring near High Head commenced within the Group and proved 806 ft of strata above the Great Limestone. Thus apart from the local thinning around Crosby and Aspatria there is clear evidence of thickening of the Hensingham Group northwards toward the Northumbrian trough of sedimentation, which Trotter and Hollingworth (1927, p. 105; 1932, p. 17) suggested had a south-westerly extension from mid-Northumberland beneath the New Red rocks of the Carlisle Basin to the northern end of the Isle of Man.

The Hensingham Group consists of sandstones, medium to coarse grits, shales with marine fossils, sporadic thin bands of marine limestones and a few thin coal seams. Apart from the basal beds, which nowhere exceed 120 ft, and which contain laterally persistent marine beds, the strata are variable, and in this respect are unlike beds of the same age that lie in a similar situation with respect to the Northumbrian trough of sedimentation. Thus to the north-east in the Brampton district Trotter and Hollingworth (1932) recognized some 20 persistent marine horizons above the Great Limestone, and Smith (1927) found many of these same strata in boreholes at the northern end of the Isle of Man.

At outcrop the basal grit (Hensingham Grit) is present throughout the area of Sheet 28 (Whitehaven), Sheet 22 (Maryport), and in the western part of

Sheet 23 as far east as the Snowhill Fault, but it is not recognizable farther east. On Sheet 23 at a slightly higher horizon a thin coal seam and an overlying limestone have been proved in boreholes in the western part of the sheet, and these possibly may represent the Little Limestone Coal and the overlying Little Limestone respectively. Correlation with these horizons is more definite in the eastern part of the district, where, however, the Hensingham Grit is not present. In these eastern areas, around Sebergham, there are three separate but closely associated coal seams, two, and in places three, of which unite to form a workable seam. The highest coal horizon lies directly beneath a limestone 12 to 18 ft thick, lying some 120 ft above the Great Limestone. In these respects the measures are identical with the Little Limestone coal and the overlying Little Limestone of the Brampton district.

It is possible that there is a non-sequence below the Hensingham Grit. As previously mentioned Eastwood noticed intra-Carboniferous movements commencing above the Great Limestone, and no fossils diagnostic of E_1 have been found in the Hensingham Group. This Grit is not developed in the area where the Little Limestone Coals and Little Limestone can be recognized with some degree of confidence, and there the suggested non-sequence would have disappeared. Whether or not the Hensingham Grit represents the basal member of sediments deposited after a non-sequence, it is clear that the over-lying beds of the Hensingham Group are lithologically variable, in marked contrast to the limestones of the underlying Chief Limestone Group found in the same area.

The abrupt change in sedimentation above the Great Limestone is reflected in the fauna of the Hensingham Group. Corals almost disappear; crinoids are present in the limestones; fenestellids are not uncommon, with *Fenestella plebeia* the prevailing species. Productids of the smaller varieties are well represented and include *Antiquatonia muricata*, *Productus carbonarius* and *P. concinnus*; other common brachiopods are *Pleuropugnoides pleurodon*, *Schizophoria resupinata* and *Spirifer* cf. *bisulcatus*. The lamellibranchs include *Aviculopecten* cf. *subconoideus*, *Edmondia* cf. *laminata*, *Palaeolima* cf. *simplex* and *Sanguinolites* aff. *clavatus*. Gastropods are also common including *Bucanopsis* cf. *flemingi* and *Euphemites* cf. *urii*. Of the cephalopods *Tylonautilus nodiferus* has been found at several localities but *Anthracoceras glabrum* from one only.   T.E., F.M.T.

DETAILS

Gilcrux, Aspatria and Aldersceugh. The Hensingham Group was penetrated in several borings near Aspatria. In one [1197 4114] situated 1000 yd W. of Hall Bank a 19-in coal was encountered at a depth of 114 ft from the surface. This seam may be the Albrighton—it is certainly no higher in the sequence. The boring was continued to a total depth of 740 ft though only a 6-in coal was met with at 719 ft. There are nearly 40 ft of black shales commencing within a few feet of the top of the coal and a core from 704 ft has yielded *Productus*, *Orbiculoidea*, and *Campylites*. *Productus* was also got from a 4-ft band, recorded as ironstone but possibly bastard limestone, at a depth of 426 ft. Sandstone predominates between this band and the black shales, but higher measures are mainly shaly.

Lancar Beck Borehole [1300 4275], 1400 yd E. of Aiglegill, passed from the New Red Sandstone at a depth of 629 ft into reddish sandstones. A thin calcareous grit with marine fossils, at 776 ft, and a 2-ft limestone at 894 ft suggest that these beds belong to the Hensingham Group; the hole was abandoned at a depth of 903 ft.

A borehole, situated [1334 4038] 300 yd

N.E. of Ellen Villa, passed through reddened Coal Measures sandstones into grey Coal Measures, proving a coal, probably the Ten-quarters, at 350 ft from the surface. Below this coal one or more faults must have been encountered for some of the lower strata are certainly not Coal Measures. The hole ended at a depth of 1102 ft in 12 ft of sandstone beneath 68 ft of limestone —the latter referred without hesitation to the First Limestone. On this rest 10 ft of shales and about 50 ft of red and grey sandstone, followed by some sandy shales and another sandstone on which lies an 8-in coal at a depth of 925 ft. Since this coal is followed 7 ft above by 11 ft of limestone these two may be regarded as the Little Limestone and Coal. The next 150 ft of overlying measures are mainly shales but in them are a 6-in limestone at 847 ft, another of 45 in at 842 ft, and a thin coal at 808 ft. A thick sandstone with a shaly parting towards the middle lies above the shale belt; above the top of this at 620 ft there is doubt as to the age of the measures until the Ten-quarters is reached at 350 ft.

The Dub Pot borehole [1382 4017] 800 yd E. of Ellen Villa is also interesting for it too reached the First Limestone which was penetrated for 35 ft. The Hensingham Grit, if present, is poorly developed and a 7-in coal at 771 ft is possibly the Little Limestone Coal. It is followed by 6 ft of shale but unless the material recorded as red and grey rock represents the Little Limestone that horizon is not recognized. The higher measures are shales with ironstones, and sandstones up to a coal believed to be the Albrighton or the Harrington Four Feet at a depth of 441 ft from the surface.

A borehole [1622 4077] 300 yd S.S.E. of Fitz (1 mile S.E. of Aspatria) commenced in Coal Measures and after passing through various seams, including the Little Main at 20 ft, feeble representatives of the Upper and Lower Three-quarters at 182 and 208 ft, and possibly the Albrighton at 248 ft, entered measures with limestones. These latter comprise a 6-ft limestone at 289 ft, one of 3 ft at 315 ft and a 10-ft lime-

stone at 389 ft. The last rests on gritty sandstone, in which the hole continued to a total depth of 408 ft, and though coal is absent this 10-ft bed may be the Little Limestone.

Near the western margin of the district there are exposures in the Hensingham Group near Gilcrux. South of that village they are confined to the basal or Hensingham Grit; to the south-east, however, in and around Leathersgill in the stream by Goosey Brackens and High Flat, a second grit is to be seen; this is separated from the basal one by a considerable thickness of shales with some thin decalcified limestones. Fossils are fairly abundant but call for no special comment.

Some of the measures encountered in the borehole near Fitz (above) may be seen in the adjoining Gilgooden Beck, which in its higher part is also known as Bothel Beck, but individual beds in the Hensingham Group cannot be identified. Shales rich in fossils, including *Tylonautilus nodiferus*, come in immediately below the basal sandstone of the Coal Measures, at 1100 yd S.E. of Fitz. Upstream there are two fairly thick sandstones amidst shales and this sequence is repeated by No. 3 Pit Fault (see p. 193). Some of the shales are calcareous but the only true limestone noted is one 2 ft in thickness near the Gilcrux Fault west of Overgates. Fossils are abundant, not only in the shales and limestone but also in the sandstones. A typical locality is [1680 4031] in Gilgooden Beck, 350 yd E. by S. of Gilgooden where the following were collected: crinoid columnals, *Fenestella sp.*, Trepostomatous polyzoa, *Actinoconchus* cf. *planosulcatus*, *Antiquatonia* aff. *costata*[1], *Derbyia sp.*, *Echinoconchus* cf. *punctatus*, *Eomarginifera* cf. *setosa*, *Eomarginifera sp.*, *Punctospirifer sp.*, *Rugosochonetes* cf. *laguessianus*, *Schizophoria resupinata*, *Spirifer* cf. *bisulcatus*, *Spirifer sp. nov.* [*S. trigonalis* group], *Euomphalus sp.*, *Aviculopecten sp.*, *Reticycloceras* cf. *koninckianum*, *Tylonautilus nodiferus* and orthocone nautiloids.

Sections are furnished by the River Ellen above Aldersceugh, and its tributary Cock-

---

[1]This appears to be a new species; it has a longer trail and coarser radial costae than has the form of *P. costatus* figured from the Orchard Limestone by H. Muir-Wood (1928, pl. x, figs. 1–2). It has two long prominent spines on the trail as well as two rows of spines on the flanks.   C.J.S.

shot Beck near Park House in the ground which lies to the north of the Gilcrux Fault. This ground is crossed by other faults but the sequence down to and including the First Limestone is reasonably clear. In the River Ellen there are gentle folds, and near Park House there is some sharp folding of north-westerly trend, but the general direction of dip is to the west-south-west at about 10°.

There are outcrops of four or five distinct sandstones. That of the lowest sandstone (separated from the First Limestone by 10 or 20 ft of black shales and comparable with the Hensingham Grit of West Cumberland) is split into two by a thin shale belt that probably contains a thin coal. This sandstone is to be seen in the River Ellen near Newbiggin Grange. Towards Park House two other sandstones crop out in the beck and the higher may be traced downstream to the River Ellen. North of that river it was quarried to supply material for White Hall. Two thin limestones occur in the shales between these sandstones. The highest of the sandstones of this tract crops out in the River Ellen near Cock Bridge and also near High Woodnook.

Fossils are common at various horizons but the most prolific locality is [2148 4006] 350 yd E. of Park House which has yielded Zaphrentid indet., *Antiquatonia muricata*, *Athyris?*, '*Camarotoechia*' *sp.*, *Chonetes sp. s.l.*, *Echinoconchus sp.*, *Eomarginifera* cf. *lobata*, *E. sp. Pleuropugnoides* cf. *pleurodon*, *Spirifer* cf. *bisulcatus*, and *S. sp. nov.* [*S. trigonalis* group].

Pow Gill. The next section of note is about 3 miles E. of Mealsgate in Pow Gill and its tributary. Faults separate the Hensingham Group from the Carboniferous Limestone Series on the south, and from the Coal Measures on the north, though in the latter case possibly no more than 200 ft of strata are faulted out. The measures are affected by a low anticline pitching to the west. Shales predominate but there is a 3½-ft bed of sandy limestone about 100 yd N. of Powbank, and a 9-in coal followed by sandstone alongside the road to the south of that farm. The sandstone and about 30 ft of the measures below possibly should be referred to the Coal Measures, for the shales [2537 4210] 70 yd S. of Powbank have yielded fossils which according to the

late Sir A. E. Trueman resemble mussels from the *A. lenisulcata* and *C. communis* zones. Mr. M. A. Calver in his 1962 re-examination of these mussels states that the "fossils are thought to be definitely Coal Measures, and most likely the shell-band between the Albrighton and Lower Three-quarter coals". His identifications are as follows: *Carbonicola* aff. *bipennis*, *C.* cf. *martini*, *C. torus?*, *Geisina arcuata* and fish remains including *Rhizodopsis sp.* On the other hand a sandstone, believed to be the one overlying the mussel-band, crops out in the tributary to the east, and is succeeded by dark shales with brachiopods and *Koninckophyllum*. Because of this it has been thought advisable to include all the measures thereabouts in the Hensingham Group.

The rocks in Pow Gill below Powbank [2538 4232] are very fossiliferous. The fossils collected include *Archaeocidaris sp.*, crinoid columnals, *Fenestella* cf. *plebeia*, cf. *Antiquatonia muricata*, *Avonia? sp. nov.*, *Buxtonia sp.*, *Composita ambigua*, *Derbyia sp.*, *Dielasma* cf. *hastatum*, *Meekella?*, *Plicatifera? thomasi*, *Productus carbonarius*, *Schellwienella?*, *Schizophoria resupinata*, *Spirifer* cf. *striatus*, *Bucanopsis sp.*, *Donaldina sp.*, *Euphemites ardenensis*, *E. urii*, *Hypergonia* cf. *quadricarinata*, *Sphaerodoma?*, *Aviculopecten* cf. *knockonniensis*, *A.* cf. *murchisoni*, *A.* cf. *textus*, *A. sp.* [coarsely plicate], *Edmondia* cf. *unioniformis*, *Limipecten* cf. *dissimilis*, *Palaeolima* cf. *simplex*, *Palaeoneilo* cf. *laevirostris*, *Parallelodon* cf. *fallax*, *P.* aff. *walciodorensis*, *P.* cf. *walciodorensis*, *Polidevcia attenuata*, *P.* cf. *attenuata*, '*Pseudamussium*' *sp.*, *Sanguinolites striatogranulosus*, *S.* cf. *striatus*, *S. sp.*, *Schizodus* cf. *depressus*, *Solemya* cf. *excisa*, *Sulcatopinna flabelliformis*, *Wilkingia elliptica*, *Stroboceras sp.* s.l., *Tylonautilus* cf. *nodiferus*, orthocone nautiloid, *Anthracoceras glabrum* and *Rhizodopsis sp.* [scale].

The occurrence of *A. glabrum* suggests that the horizon here is within the *Cravenoceratoides nitidus* Zone (E$_2$b).   T.E.

Hilltop, Warnell Fell and Warnell Hall. The area is crossed by numerous north-westerly and two easterly trending faults several of which have throws of considerable magnitude. Bounding faults on the south and west are the easterly trending Thornthwaite Fault that joins the north-westerly trending Caldbeck Fault. The bounding fracture on the north and east is the Waver–Warnell Fell–Sebergham Fault. As a consequence of the faulting the outcrop of the Hensingham Group is split into 'boxes' that are defined by faults, or on one side of the 'box' by the outcrop of the Great Limestone. The 'box' in the extreme north-west is largely drift-covered, but contains a section in Townthwaite Beck. In the right bank of that stream [2842 4252] 870 yd W. 40° S. of Hazelspring, the Little Limestone Coal, here only 6 in thick, crops out and is overlain downstream by some 30 ft of blue shales with minor bands of sandstone, followed by a 6-ft bed of sandy limestone and calcareous sandstone, considered to be the equivalent of the Little Limestone. In the next 'box' to the east sandstones of the Hensingham Group occur on the hill with summit marked by triangulation point 993, and to the south, east of Waverhead, the Little Limestone Coal crops out around the core of a subsidiary dome. To the east of its outcrop the seam has been worked sporadically from numerous shallow pits as far as the north-westerly bounding fault that crosses the head of Chalk Beck, and to the south and south-east the coal has been worked beneath the hill, with summit marked by triangulation point 891, to its outcrop on Lowthwaite Green where it is reported to be 18 to 20 in thick and overlain by 2 to 4 in of cannel.

Farther to the north-east another 'box' lies to the north-east of, and beyond, Brocklebank, and to the east of Gill the Little Limestone Coal has been worked from shallow shafts. An adit [3151 4340] 800 yd E. 5° N. of that place, made in 1921, proved the seam as 15 in thick overlain by 1½ in of cannel.

The next 'box' to the east and south-east contains the important Chalk Beck section in the Hensingham Group. At the head of Chalk Beck faults repeat the outcrop of the Little Limestone Coal here reported to be 18 in thick with a cannel roof, and worked in the past from numerous shallow shafts. Succeeding strata of the Hensingham Group are exposed in Chalk Beck as far as the junction with the overlying Coal Measures, and consist of reddened sandstones and shales (some of which yield marine fossils) that dip to the east-north-east at

8° to 35°. Their thickness cannot be accurately measured because two faults cross the section, cutting out an unknown amount of strata, but the thickness above the Little Limestone to the base of the Coal Measures is estimated at 800 to 1000 ft. The section in Chalk Beck [3227 4271] 200 to 240 yd W. of, and upstream from, the junction of Nine Gills displays the junction of the Hensingham Group with the Coal Measures. After clearance of vegetation the critical part of the section was seen to be continuous and unfaulted. It showed no indication of the unconformity or non-sequence which must be present. Here are the Hensingham Group details measured in the right bank of the stream. The Coal Measures details are given on p. 204.

		ft	in
(14) Shales, red and green, with marine fossils			9
(13) Limestone, sandy, crinoidal near top		2	0
(12) Shales, red and purple, sandy, with marine fossils		3	0
(11) Shales, purple and green, with marine fossils			6
(10) Shales, purple and red, sandy ..		1	0
(9) Ironstone band, with many marine fossils			4
(8) Shales, red purple and grey, with marine fossils		6	0
(7) Shale, sandy and shaly sandstone alternations, red and purple		5	0
(6) Obscure, some red shale ..		4	0
(5) Sandstone, red, flaggy		8	0
(4) Sandstone, red, blocky .. *about*		20	0
(3) Shale and mudstone, red and purple, somewhat obscure, fossils near top and near base *about*		20	0
(2) Limestone, purple, sandy, crinoidal			9
(1) Sandstone, red and purple, flaggy, calcareous, fossiliferous *at least*		3	0

These reddened measures lie within the zone of oxidation but on its outer fringe. The following identifications are referred to the beds in which they were collected by the numbers given in the above section. Bed (1): *Orbiculoidea* cf. *nitida*, *Buxtonia sp.*, *Schellwienella rotundata;* Bed (3), near base: *Chonetes sp.* s.l., *Palaeoneilo sp.*,

Posidonia corrugata, ostracod; Bed (3), near top: *Palaeoneilo sp.*, *Prothyris sp.*; Bed (8): *Lingula squamiformis*, *Aviculopecten sp.*, *Promytilus sp.*, *Sanguinolites* cf. *clavatus*, *Sedgwickia sp.*; Bed (9): crinoid columnals, *Fenestella sp.*, Trepostomatous polyzoa indet., *Antiquatonia muricata*, *Buxtonia? sp.*, *Eomarginifera sp.*, *Lingula mytilloides*, Rhynchonellid indet., *Schellwienella sp.*, *Schizophoria resupinata*, *Aviculopecten* cf. *subconoideus*, *Dunbarella sp.*, *Edmondia* cf. *laminata*, *E.* cf. *primaeva*, *E.* cf. *senilis*, *Leiopteria* cf. *thomsoni*, *Nuculopsis gibbosa*, *Palaeolima* cf. *simplex*, *Parallelodon sp.*, *Schizodus* cf. *orbicularis*, *Sanguinolites* aff. *clavatus*, *Streblochondria sp.*, *Bulimorpha* cf. *flemingi*, *B.* cf. *manni*, *Donaldina* cf. *elongata*, *Euphemites* cf. *urii*, *Hypergonia quadricarinata*, '*Loxonema*' *oweni*, *Meekospira?*, *Naticopsis sp.*, *Epistroboceras sp.*, orthocone nautiloids, and ostracods; Bed (11): *Fenestella sp.*, Productid spines, *Edmondia* cf. *primaeva*, *Leiopteria sp.*, *Limipecten dissimilis*, *Palaeolima* cf. *simplex*, *Promytilus sp.*, *Sanguinolites* cf. *v-scriptus*, *Schizodus* cf. *orbicularis*, *Epistroboceras sp.*, and *Weberides sp.*; Bed (12): *Antiquatonia* cf. *muricata*, *Derbyia sp.*, *Schizophoria resupinata* and *Schellwienella sp.*; Bed (14): *Schellwienella sp.* and *Spirifer* cf. *bisulcatus*. This assemblage taken as a whole is fairly representative of a Hensingham Group fauna, though *Schellwienella rotundata* is the only form diagnostic of E_2. Shales 9 ft above contain a non-marine lamellibranch fauna of Coal Measures age (see p. 205).

Farther downstream in Chalk Beck, beyond the faulted outlier of reddened Coal Measures, beds of the Hensingham Group are exposed as far as the Waver–Warnell Fell–Sebergham Fault. They dip to the north-east at about 15°. They lie within the zone of oxidation and include purple massive sandstones, purple and grey shales and thin pink limestones.

Farther south between the Friar Hall and Throstle Hall faults (see Fig. 16) there is a lozenge-shaped area occupied by the Hensingham Group and good exposures are seen in the Cald Beck [334 399], east of Friar Hall, where some 12 ft of grey limestone are succeeded by about 50 ft of sandstone and shale, capped by a 2 in coal. The limestone may represent the Little Limestone. Higher measures, seen in the streams that join the Cald Beck hereabouts from the north, are reddened and include sandstones, mudstones and thin limestones.

Between the Throstle Hall Fault and the Denton Fault-belt the Little Limestone Coal crops out on the southern flanks of Warnell Fell, and numerous shafts indicate that the seam has been extensively worked. Its thickness is said to vary between 1½ and 2½ ft.

A plan dated 1847 shows workings in the Little Limestone Coal north-east of the Denton Fault-belt from the Water Wheel [3557 4129] and Steam Engine [3559 4115] pits of Denton Holme Colliery situated respectively 1100 yd W. 34° S. and 1150 yd S.W. of the church in Sebergham. The coal was said to be 20 in thick at a depth of 162 ft in the Water Wheel shaft and the following is an abridged account of the other shaft:

	Thickness ft in		Depth ft in	
Soil, clay and gravel (Alluvium)	23	6	23	6
Post and metal	88	0	111	6
Limestone (Little Limestone)	13	4	124	10
Post and metal	17	6	142	4
Coal (LITTLE LIMESTONE) ..	1	8	144	0
Post and grey metal ..	24	0	168	0

A borehole [3554 4146] 1050 yd W. 24° S. of the church in Sebergham is of interest for it shows that, as in the Brampton district, the Little Limestone Coal is represented by three coal horizons. The section is as follows:

	Thickness ft in		Depth ft in	
Superficial deposits ..	13	6	13	6
Metal and post	33	0	46	6
Limestone, bastard ..	3	0	49	6
Metal with post	45	0	94	6
Limestone (Little Limestone)	16	0	110	6
Coal, slaty		4	110	10
Strata..	3	0	113	10
Coal		5	114	3
Strata..	9	0	123	3
Coal	1	4	124	7

Dobcross Hall and High Head. To the east of the Roe Beck East Fault, sandstones, grits, shales and mudstones of the

Hensingham Group dip eastwards in Bassen Beck and the tributary that joins Roe Beck near High Head Castle. In the latter stream the rocks are reddened and in places hematitized. The section which is on the eastern boundary of Sheet 23 continues on to Sheet 24 and there the measures have been bored in search of hematite. High Head No. 1 Borehole [4117 4409], 1300 yd E. 42° N. of High Head Castle, proved 511 ft of the Hensingham Group. No. 2 Borehole [4115 4433], 1470 yd N. 39° E. of the Castle, proved Drift to 75 ft, Hensingham Group to 981 ft, and the Chief Limestone Group of Yoredale type, with a 39-in coal at 1334 ft, to 1402 ft. The sandstones of the Hensingham Group are red and grey, some are calcareous and others are recorded as having 'joints of gypsum'. A 39-in limestone occurs at a depth of 851 ft, and a 14½ ft bed, almost certainly the Little Limestone, at 897 ft. Occasional bands of iron-ore up to 4 in thick are also recorded. Marine fossils were collected at depths of 265 ft, 645 ft, 869 ft and 870 ft.

Middlesceugh. There is a small triangular inlier of Hensingham Group, bounded by faults, which is exposed only in Roe Beck. The beds here are reddened and consist of sandstone and shales. An exposure of shales on the left bank of Roe Beck [3931 4193], 470 yd E. 7° N. of Cockleythwaite, yielded the following assemblage which is fairly representative of the group:- *Fenestella sp., Antiquatonia* cf. *muricata, Derbyia* cf. *hindi, Orbiculoidea sp.,* costate Productid indet., *Rugosochonetes sp.,*

Schellwienella sp., Schizophoria sp., Edmondia sulcata, Palaeoneilo aff. *laevirostris, P.* cf. *laevirostris, Promytilus sp., Sanguinolites* aff. *variabilis, Bucanopsis* cf. *exilis, Donaldina sp., Euphemites* cf. *urii* and *Naticopsis?*

Sowerby Row. The area is bounded to the north by the Waver–Warnell Fell–Sebergham Fault and to the south by the Woodhall Fault. The general direction of dip is to the east-north-east at 4° to 8°, but in the west the outcrop of the Little Limestone Coal appears to indicate the presence of a shallow syncline. Here the rocks are drift covered and the crop of the coal is based upon numerous shafts and outcrop workings. Surface workings also indicate the crop of a seam, probably the Little Limestone Coal, in Cockley Beck. Higher measures are exposed in Roe Beck and the streams including Whelpo Beck that join it from the south-west. Many of the sandstones and shales are fossiliferous and the fauna from the red and grey-green shales which outcrop [3971 4076] along the Beck 300 yd W. 15° N. of Longlands may be taken as representative of the beds of this area. The assemblage includes *Calamites sp.,* cf. *Fenestella nodulosa, Derbyia sp., Megachonetes* cf. *volva, Orbiculoidea* cf. *nitida, Euphemites* cf. *urii, Bucanopsis* cf. *exilis, Aviculopecten* cf. *semicostatus,* cf. *Limatulina scotica, Palaeoneilo laevirostris, Polidevcia* cf. *attenuata, P. sp., Sanguinolites* aff. *variabilis, Schizodus axiniformis, Wilkingia elliptica* and an orthocone nautiloid. F.M.T.

Coal Measures

The previous local classification of grey Productive Measures unconformably overlain by red Whitehaven Sandstone Series (regarded as of Upper Coal Measures age) had the merit of rendering easy the identification of both subdivisions. Now that it is realized that on the eastern part of Sheet 23, Lower and Middle Coal Measures have been converted by oxidation into reddened beds lithologically indistinguishable from typical Whitehaven Sandstone Series the identification of the three (Upper, Middle and Lower) subdivisions of the Coal Measures rests wholly on fossil evidence. Whilst on faunal evidence the three subdivisions can be readily identified in the rocks of the area, it is otherwise with their divisional lines. This can be readily seen from the table below which lists the non-marine lamellibranch zones, normally found in British Coalfields, with notes on their occurrence in the Cockermouth district.

Upper Coal Measures	*Anthraconauta tenuis* Zone	proved in two boreholes
	Anthraconauta phillipsii Zone	not found

Middle Coal Measures (top at Top Marine Band, not found; base at Solway Marine Band, proved at only one locality)	Upper *Anthracosia similis-Anthraconaia pulchra* Zone	not found
	Lower *A. similis-A. pulchra* Zone	proved in grey beds in west and red beds in east
	Upper *Anthraconaia modiolaris* Zone	

Lower Coal Measures	Lower *A. modiolaris* Zone	proved in grey beds in west and red beds in east
	Carbonicola communis Zone	proved in grey beds
	Anthraconaia lenisulcata Zone	not found

It will be noted that the divisional horizon (the marine band known elsewhere in the Cumberland Coalfield as the Solway Marine Band) between Lower and Middle Coal Measures has been found in reddened beds only, and only at one locality; neither the zones of Upper *similis-pulchra* and *A. phillipsii* nor the marine band which normally separates them have been found.

Palaeobotanical evidence, although in conformity with faunal evidence, affords no additional help in classifying the Coal Measures of the district. Of the Pre-Yorkian, Yorkian, Staffordian and Radstockian floral stages (now grouped together under the Westphalian), assemblages indicative of the Yorkian, which equates with the upper part of Westphalian A, Westphalian B, and the lower part of Westphalian C, have been found in grey measures and in reddened measures. One small area of reddened measures has yielded an assemblage indicative of either high Staffordian (upper part of Westphalian C) or low Radstockian (Westphalian D). As the base of the Upper Coal Measures on the basis of fossil plants is taken at the base of the Staffordian the plants also afford clear evidence of the presence of Upper Coal Measures.

F.M.T.

LOWER AND MIDDLE COAL MEASURES

The Lower and Middle Coal Measures are largely argillaceous, although they include several thick sandstones somewhat lenticular in character, which in the productive and western part of the field are usually named from the coal seams immediately below. Some of the shales, mudstones and fireclays contain nodules or bands of clay-ironstone, but none has been mined within the district.

In the western area centred on Oughterside, Aspatria, and Allhallows the coal-bearing measures are upwards of 1000 ft thick, and the sequence at various localities is indicated in Fig. 18. In the main part of the West Cumberland Coalfield to the south-west coal seams of workable thickness and quality occur fairly evenly distributed, though the best coals occur about the middle of the

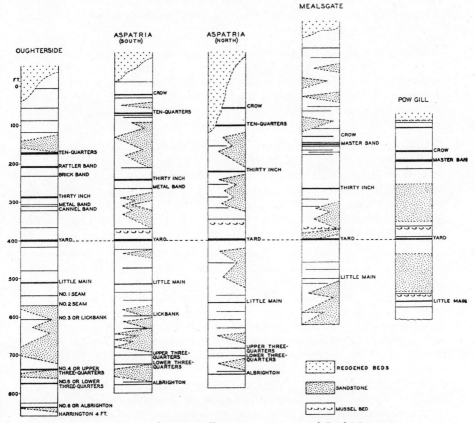

FIG. 18. *Vertical sections illustrating sequence of Coal Measures*

sequence. Traced to the north-east into the western part of the present district
many of these seams deteriorate, and this applies particularly to the valuable
seam known as the Main Band of the Whitehaven–Workington area, which
splits to the north of the river Derwent into the Cannel Band and the Metal
Band. The deterioration in the Main Band, however, is compensated in part by
the improvement in the Yard Band which in the western and productive part
of the district is 4 to 5 ft thick and of excellent quality, though here, the lowest
seam, the Harrington Four Feet does not reach workable thickness and locally
it is wanting entirely. Within the 400 ft or so of measures between the Harrington
Four Feet and the Yard Band there are several coal seams of which the more
important are as follows: the Lower Three-quarters and the Upper Three-
quarters (approximately 30 ft apart) about a quarter of the way up, the Six-
quarters about midway and the Little Main about three-quarters of the distance
in upward sequence. All of these are bituminous coals. They have all been
worked in the past, but no colliery is working at the present time.   T.E.

The absence of coal seams in the eastern part of the district, to the north and
north-east of Caldbeck, is remarkable. Presumably it is due to two causes.
Firstly the non-sequence (see p. 180) accounts for the absence of the coals
of *A. lenisulcata* and *C. communis* age, and secondly the oxidation of the

strata on, and immediately under, the old pre-New Red Sandstone land surface
has apparently destroyed the coal seams in the reddened beds of the *A. modiolaris*
Zone and in the Lower *similis-pulchra* Zone.   F.M.T.

Fossils: Prior to the resurvey of West Cumberland, which commenced in
1920, knowledge of the palaeontology of the West Cumberland Coalfield was
meagre and was confined almost wholly to fossil plants. As a result of the
resurvey, however, fossil lists were published (Eastwood 1930, pp. 39–43;
Eastwood and others 1931, pp. 125–31). More recently the results of exploratory
boreholes in the coalfield have been given by Taylor (1961).

The fossil identifications from the Coal Measures of the present district are
of collections made during the resurvey, mainly by Mr. S. W. Hester. The fossil
plants from these collections have been identified by Dr. R. Crookall. The
non-marine lamellibranchs were identified by the late Sir Arthur Trueman and
have been revised by Mr. M. A. Calver, who has also commented on certain
mussel assemblages. The marine fossils were identified by Sir James Stubblefield,
except the goniatites, which have been named by Dr. W. S. Bisat.

Calver (*in* Taylor 1961) has delimited the non-marine lamellibranch zones
in a generalized section of the Lower and Middle Coal Measures of the West
Cumberland Coalfield, but although fossil assemblages indicate the presence
of some of the zones of the Lower and Middle Coal Measures within the
present district it is impossible from the material available to give precise
definition to the zones, even in the west where the normal sequence of coal
seams is present. However, applying there the limits given by Taylor, it would
appear that the *A. lenisulcata* Zone is represented by the measures from the
Harrington Four Feet to the Albrighton seam, followed in upward sequence
by the *C. communis* Zone to the Lickbank seam, the *A. modiolaris* Zone to
the Cannel Band, and the Lower *A. similis-A. pulchra* Zone extending upwards
to the Bolton Marine Band. Presumably the measures for several hundred feet
above the Bolton Marine Band lie in the Upper *similis-pulchra* Zone but in the
absence or non-discovery of higher marine bands or of diagnostic non-marine
fossils this zone has not been recognized in the district.

In the east, the barren reddened Coal Measures probably commence in the
lower *A. modiolaris* Zone, for a mussel-band yielding an assemblage (p. 205)
determined by Mr. Calver as probably indicative of the lower part of that
zone lies only 9 ft above measures containing a marine Hensingham Group
fauna (p. 186). Other mussel horizons in the barren reddened beds from the
same area indicate the presence of the upper *A. modiolaris* Zone and the Lower
A. similis-A. pulchra Zone, but no higher zones are known. It is noteworthy
that two marine bands occur in the reddened beds. The lower has not yielded
a diagnostic fauna, but in Chalk Beck it lies below a mussel band that yields
an assemblage which is placed by Mr. Calver in the upper *A. modiolaris* Zone,
and may therefore represent, as Calver suggests, the Solway Marine Band.
The Bolton Marine Band is the other marine horizon occurring in reddened
measures. The first record of this important band was made by Eastwood
(1931, p. 55) who stated that fossil-collecting by Mr. S. W. Hester near Bolton
New Houses confirmed the existence of a marine band low in the Whitehaven
Sandstone Series. Subsequently the band was correlated with the Skipsey's
Marine Band of Scotland (Kitchin 1932, p. 65) and with the Mansfield Marine
Band of Yorkshire. It was termed the Bolton Marine Band in the first edition

of the Regional Guide for Northern England (Eastwood 1935, p. 52) where the horizon was again given as in the lower part of the Whitehaven Sandstone Series. In the 3rd edition of this Guide (Eastwood 1953, fig. 20, p. 50) it was placed high in the Productive Coal Measures and shown as the divisional line between the Lower and Upper *similis-pulchra* zones, being there correlated with the Ashington Marine Band of Northumberland and the Ryhope Marine Band of Durham. The full list of fossils from this marine band is given on p. 203. Here it may be noted that the list includes *Anthracoceras hindi* and *A. aegiranum*, the two diagnostic fossils of the Mansfield Marine Band.

T.E., F.M.T.

DETAILS

The outcrop of the coal-bearing or productive part of the Coal Measures lies almost wholly under drift; additionally in certain areas coal seams have been worked beneath the New Red Sandstone. Thus details of the productive part of the Coal Measures come almost entirely from underground information, obtained from collieries and their managements, from agents of the old royalty owners, and from abandoned mine plans. The information is too detailed to appear on the One-inch Geological Map except in a more or less generalized form. Much more information appears on the 6-in published geological maps that cover the old working part of the coalfield lying on Sheet 23—Cumberland 35 SE, 36 SW, 36 NW, 36 NE, and 37 NE. These embrace the areas of Oughterside, Aspatria, Bolton and Mealsgate, and the description of these areas which follows is based on the 6-in geological published maps.

Oughterside. The Oughterside area forms the western portion of the Oughterside–Aspatria basin, the main axis of which trends to the east-north-east. Part of the basin falls within the confines of Sheet 22 and the entire area, including that part lying on Sheet 23, has been described in detail (Eastwood 1930, pp. 79–87 and figs. 15, 16 and 17). In consequence the Oughterside area is dealt with only briefly here although it is covered by the sketch map (Fig. 19). To the south-west, on Sheet 22, it is separated from the Bullgill Basin by the Bullgill Fault. To the north-north-west the Trias is brought in by the Maryport Fault, with a downthrow to the north of perhaps 200 to 300 ft, beyond which there have been no coal workings. To the south coal working is stopped by the Gilcrux Fault.

The most important seam is the Yard Band though it is closely approached by the Ten-quarters which is the highest seam that has been wrought; the Little Main (the lowest seam mined), the Metal Band, the Thirty Inch and the Rattler Band coals have been exploited to a minor extent. Seams below the Little Main are too thin to be of value.

The Old Domain Colliery was the most important undertaking and worked the Yard Band extensively. It was served by No. 1 Pit [127 402], situated about 500 yd W. of Ellen Villa, and No. 2 (or New) Pit [1244 4008], 500 yd E.N.E. of Butts. These pits are said to be 336 and 378 ft respectively to the Yard Band.

Aspatria. The Aspatria district comprises the north-eastern portion of the Oughterside–Aspatria basin (Fig. 19), and the most important undertaking was the Brayton Domain Colliery though Brayton Knowe Pit at Baggrow and the Old Plumbland Colliery near Threapland have obtained some coal. In this region the Yard Band is practically the only coal worked though some Thirty Inch and Ten-quarters have been tried.

The boundary to the south-west is the Old Domain Fault. This unites with another of north-easterly downthrow—the Hall Bank Fault—to the south-east near Ellen Villa, but apparently it dies out in that direction. The displacement however is continued *en échelon* by the Dub Pot Fault. To the east the limiting fault is the Baggrow Fault, a large downthrow north-east. The Hensingham Group emerges to the south-east; to the north-west New Red Sandstone rocks form an unconformable cover to the Coal Measures but are introduced in part by a fault of about 200 ft downthrow

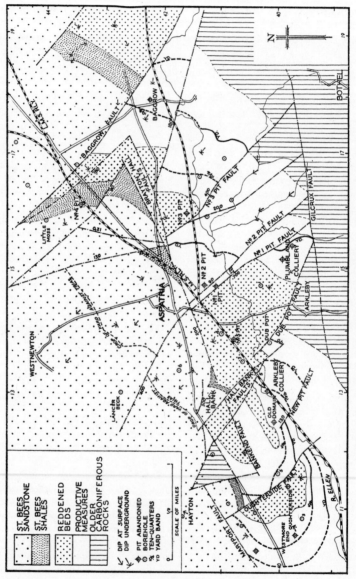

FIG. 19. *Sketch map illustrating geology of the Aspatria area*

and of east-north-east trend. The latter fault bifurcates at the eastern end of Aspatria to form the Brayton Hall Faults; in the western part of Brayton Park the northern branch attains a throw down to the north of 230 ft. The southern branch, which forms the northern limit of Brayton Domain No. 3 Pit workings, appears to have a throw down north of about 100 ft in the west and this is known to decrease to 54 ft farther east.

In addition to those mentioned the district is crossed by other faults mainly of north-west trend. South of the Maryport Fault the most important of these are named after the pits. No. 1 Pit Fault which divides the old No. 1 Pit and the northern No. 5 Pit (Fig. 19) is a downthrow south-west of 600 to 700 ft. No. 2 Pit Fault, between Nos. 1 and 2 pits has a throw of only 90 ft down to the north-east, but No. 3 Pit Fault farther east again is a large downthrow in the same direction. East of Fitz its throw is estimated at about 400 ft and as, to the north, it is joined by a 200-ft fault the throw near No. 3 Pit must be considerable.

All these faults abut against the Gilcrux Fault which brings up the main mass of Carboniferous Limestone to the south, but between No. 3 Pit Fault and the Baggrow Fault is another which unites with the latter near Cock Bridge and forms a fault of more or less east and west trend which limits the Allhallows part of the coalfield (Fig. 21).

North of the Maryport Fault the No. 1 and No. 2 Pit Faults separate the workings of No. 4 and No. 5 pits and No. 3 Pit Fault may be represented by the faults near Newtown.

In spite of the faulting the basin-like structure is obvious (see Fig. 20), and from the workings on the north side of Aspatria it is clear that the basin-making was initiated before the deposition of the New Red Sandstone. Much of the faulting is post-Triassic though probably some displacement took place earlier.

The measures below the Yard Band have been tested in many places by boreholes but in all cases the coals were proved to be thin though they may be correlated with those to the south-west. Some of the holes show that coals representing the

Harrington Four Feet at the base of the Coal Measures and the Albrighton, somewhat higher, are present in this part of the field. The two Three-quarters seams about 100 ft or so above the Harrington Four Feet occur within 30 ft of each other and the higher (Upper Three-quarters) still retains its roof of dark shales with ironstones which is usually followed by a considerable thickness of sandstone. The Six-quarters coal and the No. 2 and No. 1 seams of Crosby above it call for little comment. They are undoubtedly present in several of the borings between the Upper Three-quarters and the Little Main. The latter has a well-developed fireclay floor and is succeeded as usual by bluish shales with ironstones, but though frequently of fair quality the coals seldom exceed 18 inches in thickness.

The measures low in the sequence described above crop out in the south-eastern part of the district as discontinuous sections in streams which have cut through the boulder clay. In Bothel Beck above Gilgooden 40 ft of sandstone, varying from ganister at the top and flaggy in the middle to coarse below, which succeed the limy shales of the Hensingham Group, are taken as the basal member of the Coal Measures for, unlike the sandstones below, they contain no marine fossils. This sandstone is overlain by mixed measures of shales, fireclays and thin sandstones with at least one coal which appears to have been thick enough to work in the gully [1623 3984] 800 yd W. of Lowfield. The presence of black shales with large mussels on the small dumps and in the streams makes it almost certain that this is the Upper Three-quarters Coal.

A seam which is probably the Little Main was encountered at a depth of 20 ft in a borehole alongside Bothel Beck [1622 4077] about 500 yd N.W. of Gilgooden, and measures between that horizon and the Upper Three-quarters are to be seen at intervals in the beck. In Threapland Gill to the west, the prevalence of mudstones with ironstones about Plumbland Mill is suggestive of the belt of strata from the Six-quarters to above the Little Main. There is an outcrop of coal in the bed of the stream [1580 4053] about 200 yd below the mill which may be the Little Main itself

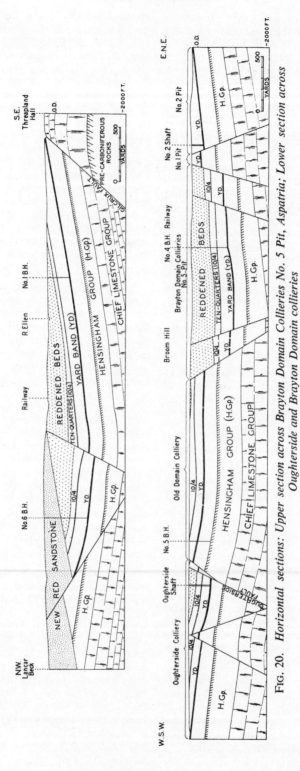

FIG. 20. Horizontal sections: Upper section across Brayton Domain Collieries No. 5 Pit, Aspatria; Lower section across Oughterside and Brayton Domain collieries

but the measures hereabouts are so disturbed that it is impossible to be certain.

The Yard Band was worked back to outcrop from Plumbland Colliery. At No. 5 Pit, Brayton Domain Colliery [1390 4072], the seam occurs at a depth of 1032 ft, with the measures dipping north-west, first at 10½° and then flattening to 8° before rising to bring the Yard Band against the New Red Sandstone cover between White-lees and Aspatria. At No. 1 pit [1472 4110] 400 yd S.E. of Aspatria station, the Yard Band is only 132 ft deep, but on finding the coal somewhat stony a borehole was sunk a further 523 ft to test the lower measures. A thin coal at 392 ft below the Yard is probably the Harrington Four Feet, and most of the other seams appear to be present but are thin. In this tract of ground there are old pits alongside the River Ellen but there are no details. The Yard at No. 2 Pit is 333 ft deep and from here the coal was wrought back to its outcrop below the boulder clay from the River Ellen to the Maryport Fault which formed the northern limit of the workings.

No. 3 Pit, at Harriston, was a large undertaking and from it about a square mile of coal was extracted. At the shaft [1601 4155] the Yard Band is 538 ft deep and rises to the south-east at 1 in 9 bringing the coal to outcrop against drift near Mechie Farm and, beyond the fault through Blenner-hasset, to the east of Baggrow. The Baggrow pits took the shallow part of the coal here; the dip is to the west at 8°; several nips were encountered in the northern part of the property.

No. 4 Pit [1611 4340], situated near Wellington, was sunk 562 ft to the Yard Band, and nearly two square miles of this seam were extracted before the pit was abandoned in 1933. In the east the dips are somewhat irregular but to the west the basin structure is obvious from the spot levels on the mining plans. It is certain that in many places the coal impinges against the New Red Sandstone cover.

In a drift-covered area the only exposure of note is to the north of the large limestone quarry at Threapland where, in the west bank of Threapland Gill, outcrop workers have located the Yard Band amidst dark blue shales with micaceous sandy shales and sandstones. Another exposure of measures just below this seam is that at the sharp bend of the River Ellen [1526 4107] ¾ mile N.E. of Arkleby Mill.

The Yard Mussel Bed occurring up to 30 ft above the Yard has been found at several places in the collieries but appears to have been overlooked in most of the borings and sinkings.

The Yard Band, the seam on which the output of this district depended, usually consists of 4 to 5 ft of coal with no partings of note, though occasionally as at Little Moss borehole [1588 4402] 1½ miles E. of Westnewton it thins to a few inches. Generally it is of excellent quality but where it approaches its outcrop beneath the Red Rocks it becomes worthless. Though it may retain its normal thickness the coal is then hard and the ash content very high.

The Thirty Inch Coal, as its name implies, is a seam about 2½ ft thick and is the sole relic of the Main Band of West Cumberland which is worthy of consideration in this region. A little of it was worked from No. 2 Pit and it has been tried in No. 5 Pit.

The Ten-quarters though frequently 4 or 5 ft thick (including a parting of a few inches of shale) is usually of too poor a quality to merit mining. It has been tried from No. 5 Pit to the north-east of Hall Bank. A thin coal near this horizon crops out in Flatts Beck to the west of Hodgson Pit at a point [1493 3974] 700 yd N. by W. of the inn at Plumbland. Many boreholes show that there is commonly a good development of sandstone between the Thirty Inch and Ten-quarters seams.

Mealsgate. This area lies between the Baggrow Fault and the Waverbank Fault (see Fig. 21). The former brings the shallow workings of Baggrow in line with the deepest part of Allhallows Colliery, and though it may be in more than one step—as appears to be the case to the west of Whitehall—the total throw is probably about 1400 ft. Near Cock Bridge it unites with the Blennerhasset Fault and running more easterly, brings Coal Measures on the north against the Hensingham Group on the south. The Waverbank Fault throws down to the north-east about 300 ft.

In addition to the bounding faults the Mealsgate area is traversed by other faults, some of which are of considerable throw.

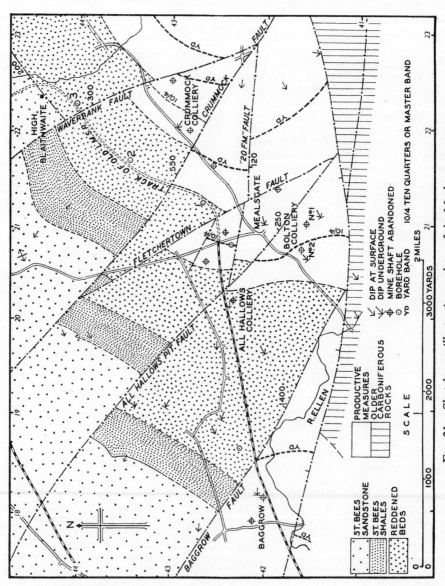

Fig. 21. *Sketch map illustrating geology of the Mealsgate area*

One, the Allhallows Fault, forms the north-eastern limit of Allhallows Colliery where north of the shafts it has been proved in two places as a downthrow to the north-east. Near Mealsgate it has a throw of about 250 ft; to the north-west beyond Crookdake the throw in the Trias may also be about 250 ft but in the Coal Measures the throw appears to be double that amount.

About two-thirds of a mile to the north-east, the Crummock Fault throws down to the north-east about 500 to 600 ft. It unites with the Waverbank and other faults about 1¼ miles E. of Mealsgate. The intervening ground is crossed by the Fletchertown Fault of north-north-west trend with a downthrow east, (though some of the old colliers believed it to be down west 72 ft near Weary Hall) and a fault which trends roughly eastwards, with a downthrow south of 180 ft in its western portion and 120 ft farther east.

Apart from faulting the structure is comparatively simple, the prevalent dips ranging from north-west to south-west, though there appears to be a tendency for the measures to rise again near Watchhill towards the extremity of the Allhallows undertaking (see Fig. 22).

We know little of the strata below the Yard Band, for boreholes and shafts stop at that seam and the only exposure of note is that of the hard fine-grained white sandstones which emerge from beneath the boulder clay at Quarryhill [223 418] and have been quarried there on a small scale. Nevertheless in the Mealsgate region more Thirty Inch and Ten-quarters, also known hereabouts as the Master Band, have been worked than in the Aspatria region.

From Allhallows Colliery about ½ square mile of the Yard Band has been taken while to the rise Bolton Colliery exhausted much of the seam. At Allhallows shaft the coal itself is cut out by a small fault but in that vicinity the Yard Band is about 630 ft and at Watchhill 1500 ft below the surface. Hereabouts the seam lies beneath New Red Sandstone rocks.

The following sections of the **Yard Band** may be taken as typical:

Allhallows Colliery
    Shale
        Coal ..   ..   13 in

Shale	6 in
Coal	54 in
Fireclay	

Bolton Colliery

Coal	14 in
Slate	2 in
Coal, with median parting	46 in
Stone	2 in
Coal	4 in

At No. 2 Pit, Bolton Colliery [2071 4158], 600 yd E. of White Hall, the Yard Band is 340 ft deep, with a dip of 6½° to the south-west.

The Thirty Inch at Allhallows, where it was worked on a considerable scale, had about 3 ft of coal devoid of partings and had a roof of dark shale and a floor of fireclay. Elsewhere it has received little or no attention. The Ten-quarters at the same colliery had a section as follows: roof, light free-stone, coal 2 in, shale 4 in, coal 30 in, shale 3 in, coal 4 in, black stone 5 in.

Beyond the Allhallows Fault there are several small pits which worked the Yard Band. The Priestcroft Pit [2060 4261], 270 yd N.W. of Mealsgate Station, reached the Yard Band at 510 ft. Next in importance is Knapethorn Pit [2078 4234]—170 yd S. by W. of Mealsgate Station and 264 ft deep to the Yard Band—with Gin Pit [2089 4242] 130 yd S.E. of the station and 156 ft deep to that seam. Farther south again is Mealsgate Pit [2094 4209], near Mealsgate Bridge; this pit reached the Yard at a depth of 198 ft and worked a patch of that seam dipping west-south-west at 1 in 4 until stopped by faulted ground alongside the Allhallows Fault which separates this pit from the Bolton Collieries.

East of the Fletchertown Fault there are many small old workings of which little is known except that the Yard Band appears to have been worked back from them to its outcrop farther east, and that the workings are divided by a west to east fault down south 120 ft. North of that fault are Roadside Pit [2161 4252] and Dip Pit [2159 4277]; they are both about 180 ft to the Yard Band and the deepest known workings hereabouts. To the west a borehole known as No. 1 or Priestcroft was put down on the west side of the railway [2122 4264], 450 yd E.N.E. of Mealsgate Station, and proved the Yard Band, 4 ft 4½ in thick, at a depth of

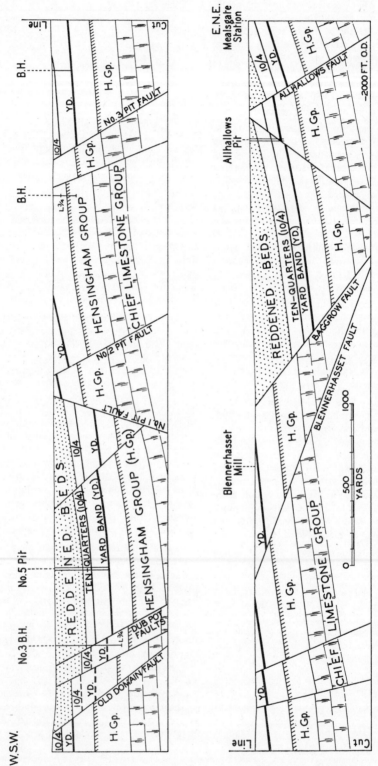

FIG. 22.   Horizontal section mainly along the Ellen valley, across the Brayton Domain, Baggrow and Allhallows Collieries

564 ft. The Thirty Inch, 154 ft higher in the sequence, is 2 ft 5 in thick, but the Ten-quarters appears to be absent, possibly through faulting unless it be represented by the black metals or shales at a depth of 313 ft.

The Crummock Colliery lies between the Crummock and Waverbank faults, and was served by several pits; those on the east worked the Yard Band (under the name of the Main Band) between its outcrop and a water level at a depth of about 300 ft, while those on the west worked the Master and Crow Coals. The deepest working to the Master Band is 230 ft at Crummock or Tile Kiln Pit [2195 4277] situated on the east side of the road 730 yd S.E. of Patten-foot. No pit at Crummock Colliery passed through all the above mentioned seams but the following section is believed to be representative.

				ft	in
CROW BAND, no partings	..	..		2	6
Metal and stone	..	..	..	16	0
Coal	..	..	..	..	1	6
Metal	..	..	..	..		3
MASTER BAND					
Coal	9 in				
Metal	4 in				
Coal	19 in			2	8
Strata..	..	..	..	180	0
'MAIN BAND' [YARD]		..	..	6	0

In Crummock Colliery a peculiar nip 135 yd wide was encountered in both the Crow and Master bands. Peile (1838, pp. 78–88), who was interested in this colliery, noted the change was immediate, perpendicular through the seams, and without preface of any small hitch. It was most singular in the Master Band for there the partings were in no way altered, the coal only being "turned into stone". The Yard Band has not been worked beneath the Master Band so it is not known whether the lower seam is affected, but to the rise in line with the nip, Peile records that the Yard Band was somewhat inferior in quality and had a rib or dyke of white freestone 1 ft thick perpendicular through the seam. Stone-dykes or rock-riders are not uncommon in Cumberland (Eastwood 1929) but the abrupt transition of coal to stone is unusual; a more gradual passage is to be noted at Wyndham Pit, Low Bolton Colliery, p. 202.

To the west and north of Crummock

Colliery the field is virgin but two bore-holes have been put down alongside the railway. In the one [2167 4341], 600 yd W.S.W. of Waverbank, the Ten-quarters is present at a depth of 610 ft; the other [2227 4400], 400 yd N. by E. of Waverbank, reached the Yard at a depth of 968 ft. If the measures maintain the strike known at Crummock Colliery there must be a fault of about 300 ft between these two boreholes and this is the downthrow known as the Waverbank Fault.

Bolton. This district stretches eastwards from the Waverbank Fault and includes Bolton Low Houses and Bolton New Houses. To the south it is bounded by the outcrop of the Hensingham Group; to the north and north-east the New Red Sandstone is brought in by faults. The eastern boundary is defined by a fault coursing to the north-west that brings in the Hensingham Group. The general structure is simple, the prevalent dip being to the north at about 10°, though it probably swings north-westerly as the Mealsgate district is approached. The most important fracture is the Bolton Low Houses Fault which ranges through Bolton Low Houses and High Pow and has a downthrow south-west of about 300 ft; near High Pow it splits but the more important branch carries on to join an east–west fault near Thornthwaite.

Boulder clay again masks much of the surface but two deeply entrenched streams provide good sections. The first is the Waver, mainly running along the strike; the second, a tributary known as Pow Gill, which enters the River Waver at Parson Bridge, is a dip stream which furnishes an almost complete section of the coal-bearing measures though the basal portion is probably cut out by a fault.

In this area mining has been confined mostly to the northern portion where the Master Band is the most important coal, though some of the lower seams have received a little attention in the south.

As indicated above on page 184, beds mapped in Pow Gill as Hensingham Group carry mussels (in dark grey mudstone and ironstone) which according to Mr. M. A. Calver are Coal Measures forms, "and most likely the shell band between the Albrighton and Lower Three-quarters coals" (i.e. a mussel horizon which lies near the base of the *C. communis* Zone). The locality [2538 4214], 70 yd S. of the bridge at Powbank, yields the following fauna: *Carbonicola* aff. *bipennis*, *C.* cf. *martini*, *C. torus?*, *Geisina arcuata* and fish remains including *Rhizodopsis sp.* A possible explanation is that there is a small down-faulted area of Coal Measures, from which this fauna has been collected, within the outcrop of the Hensingham Group.

The lowest seam exposed in the south of the district, believed to be the Upper Three-quarters, crops out near the confluence of Low Loughing Beck with Pow Gill. There are shallow and outcrop workings hereabouts, and in one [2528 4273] situated in a gully 250 yd S. of Low Loughing Bridge[1] the seam was from 2 to 2½ ft thick—mostly cannel of fair quality though in places the lowest 6 in was of bituminous coal. A fault here throws down the coal about 20 ft to the north but the dislocation dies out rapidly in an easterly direction. The fireclay beneath the coal may be seen in several places and evidently succeeds the mudstones, shales and fireclay visible in Pow Gill above its confluence with its tributary Low Loughing Beck. The coal is succeeded by about 10 ft of dark mudstones and shales some of which are canneloid and carry black ironstones while a 6-in band near the base is crowded locally with mussels. The fauna from the west bank of Pow Gill [2534 4280], 200 yd S.S.E. of Low Loughing Bridge, as identified by Mr. Calver, is: *Anthracosia regularis*, including the shell figured as *Carbonicola rhomboidalis* by Trueman and Weir (1947, pl. vii, fig. 7), cf. *Anthracosphaerium cycloquadratum*, *C.* cf. *cristagalli*, *C. oslancis*, *Naiadites* cf. *subtruncatus*, *N. sp.* intermediate between *productus* and *quadratus*, *Carbonita humilis* and *Geisina arcuata*. Mr. Calver comments that "this collection is said to be from the Three-quarter Coal horizon; this is not supported by the faunal evidence, which suggests a higher horizon, most likely the Little Main of the main Cumberland Coalfield. The presence of *A. regularis* and abundant ostracods are typical of the Little Main/ Eighteen Inch (Dovenby) positions and there is no evidence of the fauna to be expected from the Three-quarter horizon."

The 10 ft of dark mudstones and shales

mentioned above are followed by massive sandstone in Pow Gill as far north as Low Loughing Bridge. The succeeding measures are mainly mudstones with fossil plants as far as a large fault some 300 yd below the bridge. In the south-eastern bank [2530 4318], 250 to 270 yd N.N.E. of Low Loughing Bridge, the following plants were collected: *Alethopteris decurrens*, *A. lonchitica*, *Neuropteris gigantea*, *Sphenopteris* cf. *dilatata*, *Calamites suckowi* and *Sphenophyllum cuneifolium*.

The measures described above must have been penetrated in the Old Pow Gill Colliery—situated in the angle of the roads to the west and served by six pits and a water level that was driven south-west from Pow Gill 60 yd N.W. of Low Loughing Bridge—but the records preserved are meagre. The coal worked was known as the Cannel Band and was thought to be equivalent to the Main Band, but is probably the Yard Band. It had the following section: metal roof, cannel 8 in, coal 8 in, hard grey metal stone 5 ft, coal 10 in, cannel 16 in. The depths of the shafts are unknown but all are probably shallow.

Farther down Pow Gill there is an 8 in coal north of the fault, which may be seen in the stream bed [2533 4325] resting on a few inches of dark shale, and followed by 44 ft of grey brown-weathering sandstones of variable grain interbedded with sandy shales. These measures continue for about 100 yd where they terminate against a fault which is seen in the west bank to hade south-west at 20° from the vertical. This is the northern branch of the Bolton Low Houses Fault.

Continuing downstream, the gill is floored by hard, fine sandstone, 4 or 5 ft in thickness, followed in turn by 6 ft of light grey mudstones with a layer of large rough ironstone balls at the top, and 8 ft of yellow-stained, light fireclay. In 1926 outcrop workers got a coal with a section as follows: black crumbly shale 2 ft, coal 7 in, grey bastard fireclay 1½ in, coal 6 to 7 in, black shale with coaly bands 2 in, on hard fireclay. The coal roof is surmounted by a few feet of light blue-grey mudstones followed by 16 ft of dark shales with a 3-ft bed of brown and grey sandstone about the middle.

---

[1]A road bridge over Pow Gill about midway between High Pow and Powbank.

These shales are canneloid in the lower part and the bottom 12 in are rich in mussels, while at 5 ft from the top there are 3 in of poor cannel in canneloid shales with ironstone bands and traces of fish and plants. From these measures, in a section [2543 4339] on the west bank of the gill, 500 yd E. of High Pow, the following were collected: *Lepidodendron lycopodioides, Lepidostrobus sp., Calamites sp., Anthracosia regularis* and *Megalichthys sp*. Most of the other bands of dark shales weather buff; they contain poor ironstones but appear to be barren of fossils. A thick sandstone succeeds these beds.

From the appearance and position of these measures the coal beneath them is regarded as either the Upper or Lower Three-quarters and this belief receives additional support from the fact that the 3-ft bed of sandstone weathers with the same brown feathered effect as the 'Harrington Marble' occupying a similar position above these coals in West Cumberland. Mr. Calver, however, though noting that the mussels are poorly preserved, considers that they do not look like the Three-quarter Coal fauna, but are more likely to be the Little Main horizon.

One of the old plans of this district preserved at Somerset House, Whitehaven, indicates the outcrops of three coals in the beck bottom in this belt of strata. The lowest of these, marked the Little Band, though somewhat out of position, is probably the coal dug by the outcroppers; the upper one, known as the Little Kennel, appears to be the 3-in band of cannel noted above, but the middle one—the Great Kennel— does not seem to be visible though some outcroppers stated that there was a 27-in seam of coal and cannel hereabouts.

The sandstone which succeeds these measures forms the potholed floor of the gill for about 200 yd and is also exposed in the sides of the valley. It is mostly a buff weathering, blue-grey, medium- to fine-grained, massive sandstone, but is thinner-bedded below, and towards the top includes some sandy mudstone. It is possible that there may be a coal somewhere in this belt of sandstone for according to old plans a level has been driven southwards for about 200 yd from the big bend east of High Pow and on the other side of the

stream, farther south, another has been driven for nearly 300 yd. Neither venture appears to have been very successful.

The next belt of strata is mainly of pale-weathering blue mudstones with some thin sandstones, fireclays and dark shales, and is succeeded by another thick sandstone. In addition to a 3-in coal about 10 ft below the thick sandstone these measures contain a coal which has received considerable attention from outcrop workers, and in strata midway between the two seams there is a well-developed mussel-bed which indicates that this seam is the Yard. Only the lowest 9 in of the coal were visible during the resurvey, but there is said to be a further 12 in of coal above a parting of shale. This seam comes to the bottom of the ravine at the foot of the tributary from the east, 500 yd E. of High Pow, while the mussel-bed and sandstone above it may be seen in the tributary and also in the main stream below the big bend [2540 4371], 350 yd E.S.E. of Low Pow, where the fauna included: *Anthracosia* aff. *aquilina, A.* cf. *beaniana, A. ovum, A. phrygiana, A. sp. nov.* [large, elongate], *Anthracosphaerium turgidum* and *Naiadites* aff. *quadratus*. The last-mentioned sandstone occupies the valley floor to near Powgill Mill. It is usually a buff-weathering, blue-grey sandstone and has been quarried at several places along the banks of Pow Gill providing the material for building the mill. Near its top, this sandstone is interbedded with blue mudstones and shales; above it mudstones predominate and contain two workable coals. The lower one is here known as the Master Band and the upper as the Crow Coal. The Master Band outcrops around the bend in Pow Gill [2524 4403] immediately to the north of Powgill Mill and may be followed thence by cavings and old workings to the west. The Crow Coal crops 50 yd lower downstream. Above the Crow Coal in the west bank of the gill [2520 4406], 150 yd N.W. of the Mill, mudstones have yielded *?Anthraconaia librata, Anthracosia* cf. *atra, A.* cf. *concinna* and *A. simulans*. The assemblage indicates a position within the Lower *similis-pulchra* Zone.

The Master Band has been considerably exploited and workings extend beyond the Waver almost to the fault which introduces the St. Bees Sandstone. The deepest working is Engine Pit of the Low Bolton Collieries situated [2467 4460] on the north side of the Waver 430 yd below Parson Bridge. This pit was 384 ft deep to the Master Band and a water level coursing a little north of west extended from Parson Bridge through the shaft bottom to below the main road south-east of Crosshill. There are dozens of other old pits and much of the ground must be exhausted.

Recent attempts to work the Master Band comprise Dand's Pit and Pow Gill Colliery. The former [2522 4409] was situated on the east side of Pow Gill, 140 yd below the Mill; it proved the Crow Coal 2¼ ft thick at 16 ft and the Master Band 4½ ft thick at 40 ft below the surface. Dand's Pit also had an adit to the Master Band on the west side of Pow Gill.

Pow Gill Colliery consisted of a dip-drift [2484 4389] commencing on the east side of the road, 350 yd N.W. of High Pow. and an air shaft about 110 yd farther north, Beneath 20 ft of boulder clay the latter is said to have reached the Crow Coal 2½ ft in thickness at a depth of 37 ft and to bottom the Master Band at 73 ft from the surface. Meeting with old goaf in which the pillars were narrow and often crushed appears to have contributed to the failure of both these undertakings.

At the Pow Gill Colliery the Master Band was usually about 4 ft thick though in places it reached 6 ft and had an immediate roof of 4 in of black shales beneath blue metal (shale or mudstone). There is frequently a brassy or pyritous band up to 1½ in thick near the middle of the seam and the top 15 in of coal are described as free, easy to get and suitable for house coal, while the bottom 9 in are hard and more suitable for steam raising. No Crow Coal was worked here but some (averaging 2 ft 3 inches in thickness with a soft white metal roof and a hard grey metal stone floor) was got from the Low Bolton Collieries farther north. There the Master Band, 4 ft 9 in thick, had the following section: black metal roof (beneath white metal) 10 in, coal (best quality) 1 ft 5 in, slaty coal 3½ in, middle coal 4 in, brass band 1 in, coal 3 in, slaty coal 4½ in, coal 3 in, metal 1 in, coal (inferior) 1 ft 8 in, on a very soft floor of grey metal.

To the west of the Bolton Low Houses Fault the principal working was Wyndham Pit [2399 4405] situated in the spinney 500 yd S. of where the Waver passes under the main road at Bolton Low Houses. This shaft was 320 ft deep to the Master Band and a level from the pit bottom ran west for about 750 yd. Towards the end of the level a thin band of limestone appeared in the coal, thickening farther west, first to 15 in and then to 2 ft 10 in, where it appears to have replaced the whole of the seam; a leader of coal came in at the end of the level but exploration appears to have finished at this point. Some of the coal to the rise of Wyndham Pit was got from day-holes and old pits drained by an adit running north and emerging on the Waver about 120 yd below the main road bridge.

The Crow Coal hereabouts is said to be 27 ft above the Master Band and some of it was worked though there are probably considerable reserves of both it and the Master Band to the dip of the Wyndham Level. Farther west the ground, apart from the borehole north of Waverbank (p. 199), is unexplored.

Returning to Pow Gill, 400 yd N.N.W. of Powgill Mill, there is exposed sandstone that is about 15 ft thick and is of medium to coarse grain, purple to grey-buff in colour, very micaceous in part, and with some clay-galls. It is succeeded by grey and purple shales and sandstones with some light grey fireclays. No coal is visible in Pow Gill but near the head of a tributary to the west there is coal about 6 in thick resting on fireclay and capped by about 6 ft of dark blue and purplish shales that carry mussels and a few heart-shaped fish scales. The collection [2500 4426], 200 yd S. of Parson Bridge, includes: *Anthracosia atra*, *A. acutella*, *Naiadites productus* and *N.* cf. *angustus*. Mr. Calver is of the opinion that the assemblage represents the *A. atra*-*A. acutella* fauna found between the Black Metal Marine Band and the underlying coal of the main Cumberland Coalfield.

At the foot of the tributary the following section [2506 4432] is visible in Pow Gill:

	ft
Shale, thin well-bedded, purple and grey, with marine fossils (Bolton Marine Band)	3

	ft
Fireclay, red-mottled, rough, sandy..	6
Shale, purple, with irregular sandstones	6
Fireclay, grey and purple, rough sandy, with small nodules of blue hematite	3½
Shale, purple and pale grey	2½
Mudstone, purple	7½
Sandstone, purple-brown	2
Shale, purple-brown	3
Shales, blue-grey sandy, with some purple staining	15

These beds dip northwards at angles from 10° to 25°, the average dip being about 20°. Plants including *N. gigantea* and *S. cuneifolium* occur in the lower portion and the *A. atra-A. acutella* fauna occurs about 6 ft below the base of the Bolton Marine Band. The fauna of the Bolton Marine Band has been collected in the gill at adjacent localities respectively [2506 4433], 190 to 200 yd S. of Parson Bridge, and [2509 4432], 200 yd S. by E. of the bridge. The fauna from these localities includes: cf. *Crurithyris carbonaria*, *Dictyoclostus craigmarkensis*, *Lingula mytilloides*, *Orbiculoidea* sp., *Bucanopsis* sp., *Donaldina* cf. *ashtonensis*, *Dunbarella macgregori*, *Palaeolima* cf. *simplex*, *Pernopecten carboniferus*, *Posidonia sulcata*, *Schizodus* cf. *antiquus*, *Solenomya* cf. *primaeva*, '*Orthoceras*' aff. *asciculare*, '*O*' cf. *conquestum*, *Reticycloceras* cf. *koninckianum*, *Metacoceras* cf. *perelegans*, *Huanghoceras costatum*, *Anthracoceras hindi* (including juv.), *A. aegiranum*, *Politoceras politum* [= *Homoceratoides jacksoni*], 'Goniatite, Gen. et sp. nov.' [Currie and others 1937, pl. iv, figs. 9, 10], *Cypridina* ?, Conodonts, *Listracanthus wardi* and *Rhabdoderma sp.*

Little is seen of the higher measures until the River Waver is approached. That stream for half a mile above and below Bolton Low Houses has cut a course through reddened measures, but unfortunately it is a strike stream hereabouts. No great thickness of measures is exposed and though the river is crossed, near the bridge carrying the main road, by a fault of 250 ft to 300 ft down south-west, the rocks show no marked differences. Purple is the prevalent colour but near the faults and slips, of which there are several in addition to the large fault, the rocks are frequently bright red in colour. Sandstones, shales and sandy mudstones with several fireclays, are all represented. It may be noted too that some of the ironstone nodules in shales and fireclays have been partly or wholly converted to hematite in the vicinity of slips. Some 200 yd E. of Shaking Bridge—the bridge carrying the main road—and on the upthrow side of the 300-ft fault, there are some grey measures; these carry an 8-in coal of which the lower half is good, but the rest hard and stony. This coal lies about 250 ft above the Master Band.

Farther north a small inlier of reddened measures has been noted by Mr. Rose in the Wiza Beck south of Raise Lodge.   T.E.

Westward Park and Tracentree. To the south the area is bounded by the Waver–Warnell Fell–Sebergham Fault, and a north-south line through Rosley delimits it to the east. The St. Bees Shales overlap to the north and west, but the extension of the Coal Measures northwards beneath the New Red rocks is limited by the Lowling Fault, as Carboniferous Limestone and Hensingham Group lie to the north of that fracture. The area was shown as Millstone Grit on the Old Series geological map, but coals of workable thickness crop out in it and mussels from Wiza Beck suggest that there the measures fall within the lower part of the *A. modiolaris* Zone.

The area is mostly drift-covered, but solid rocks appear in the banks of Wiza Beck and its tributaries, and from these exposures it would appear that the general direction of dip is to the north.

Intermittent sections are seen in the stream that joins the Wiza at Westward Park. Here, near the Waver–Warnell Fell–Sebergham Fault, 18 ft of sandstone with mudstones dipping northwards at 2° overlie a 2-in coal; farther north outcroppers have worked a coal, reported to be 2 ft thick, in the right bank [2894 4468], 180 yd S.S.E. of Westward Park.

East of Westward Park on the southern bank of Wiza Beck there are intermittent exposures of sandstone and shale associated with two coal seams. The lower and probably the upper seam have been worked at shallow depth from the numerous old shafts situated in and to the south of the wood (Lords Wood of the 6-in map) to the south of

Tracentree. The upper seam was proved 1 ft thick at a depth of 10 ft in a trial boring—sunk in connexion with a proposed reservoir —[2992 4486], 1150 yd E. of Westward Park.

Outcrop workers have raised coal from the lower seam (thought to be the Little Main) along the southern bank of Wiza Beck, and here in 1927 an adit situated [3059 4486], 700 yd S. 34° E. of Tracentree, driven southwards struck the seam 25 yd from the Beck to prove the following section: coal 2 ft, with roof of red clay and marl, clay 1 ft 6 in, coal 1 ft 5 in, on floor of black shale. The thickness of the coal and of the contained partings varied considerably and the venture soon closed. The seam dipped northwards at 7°. Farther east an exposure of overlying shales and mudstones on the south bank of Wiza Beck [3072 4486], 1000 yd S.S.W. of Causeway Grange, yielded *Anthracosia regularis*, *Carbonicola* cf. *oslancis*, *Naiadites sp.* and *Geisina arcuata*. Mr. Calver comments that this assemblage indicates "Lower Coal Measures, and most likely the Little Main or possibly Eighteen Inch (Dovenby) position".

Still farther east the measures exposed in a small stream south-west of Rosley are separated from the measures just described by a west-north-west fault, seen in the stream [3163 4480], 370 yd W. by S. of Intake. The dip is to the west and north of west at 10° to 15° and the sequence is as follows:

	ft	in
Mudstone, grey and purple, with 6-in band of carbonaceous shale	8	0
Mudstone, grey sandy	1	0
Sandstone, grey blocky	8	0
Shale, grey purple with two sandstone bands	6	9
Shale, blue-black platy	12	0
Coal, 3 in seen, but reported to be	1	3
Fireclay with lenticular bands of sandstone	5	0
Not exposed	8	0
Coal, not seen but reported to be	4	0

Outcroppers have worked both coals. It is reported that in the lower seam they encountered old flooded workings. The upper beds show red and purple coloration and this deepens eastwards in the intermittent exposures of sandstone and mudstone (on both banks of the Wiza Valley) which dip eastwards at angles up to 30°.

Welton and Sebergham. With the exception of a small infaulted outlier in Chalk Beck, this area is bounded to the south-west by the Waver–Warnell Fell–Sebergham Fault, to the east by the River Caldew, and to the north by the outcrop of the St. Bees Shales. In this area also underground extension of the Coal Measures beneath newer rocks is limited by the Lowling Fault.

The general dip is to the north-east, but northerly and easterly dips are common. Several faults are exposed in the streams and others may traverse drift-covered areas. Good exposures are available in Chalk Beck and in a stream that joins the Caldew from the west at Sebergham.

Although fireclays are common, not a single outcrop of coal has been found; there are no signs of old workings and we have obtained no record of coal mining here. Mussels indicate that the *A. modiolaris* and Lower *A. similis-A. pulchra* zones are present, but the coal seams normally found in the strata of these zones are apparently absent.

All the Coal Measures of this area and farther east are reddened. The coloration is regional and also affects the Hensingham Group, but it is not associated with any known line of faulting. The sandstones take on a purplish ashen hue, shales and sandstones are dull red to purple, whilst fireclays, although dominantly purple, frequently present a mottled appearance.

In the faulted outlier of Coal Measures on Broad Moor, beds with mussels succeed strata with marine fossils (see p. 180). In Chalk Beck 30 to 200 yd upstream from its confluence with Nine Gills the section given below is exposed. The numbering of the beds follows on from that used for the Hensingham Group on p. 185.

	ft	in
(25) Sandstone, purple	10	0
(24) Shales, red, purple and grey with mussels	4	0
(23) Sandstone, purple	4	0
(22) *Not exposed*	4	0
(21) Sandstone, red and purple laminated	6	0

	ft	in
(20) Shale, red	5	0
(19) Ironstone band		2
(18) Shale, red with scattered mussels, and plants ..	1	2
(17) Mussel-band		$\frac{1}{8}$
(16) Shales, red and mottled ..	6	0
(15) Sandstone or ganister, highly siliceous	3	0
(14) Shales, red and green with marine fossils (Hensingham Group)	—	—

From a point [3232 4273], 150 yd upstream (west) of the confluence of Chalk Beck and its tributary Nine Gills, the lower mussel horizon (beds 17 and 18) yielded *Calamites suckowi, Carbonicola* cf. *cristagalli, C.* cf. *oslancis, ?C. rhomboidalis, Geisina arcuata* and fish remains including *Rhizodopsis sp.* Mr. Calver regards this assemblage as Lower Coal Measures and most likely from the basal part of the *A. modiolaris* Zone, i.e. Lickbank to Little Main. The non-sequence or concealed unconformity indicated by this important section in Chalk Beck has been drawn at the base of Bed (15), but as this and Bed (16) contain no fossils they could be placed either above or below the non-sequence, i.e. either in the Hensingham Group or in the Coal Measures.

At a locality [3242 4270], 30 yd upstream from the confluence of Chalk Beck and Nine Gills, the upper mussel horizon (bed 24) yielded *Spirorbis sp., Anthraconaia modiolaris, Anthracosia regularis* [large], *Carbonicola* cf. *bipennis, C.* cf. *cristagalli, C. venusta, Naiadites sp.* intermediate between *productus* and *quadratus*, and *Geisina arcuata*, an assemblage indicating as Mr. Calver points out, the middle of the lower part of the *A. modiolaris* Zone.

Reddened barren Coal Measures are again seen in Chalk Beck east-north-east of Broadmoor and to the north of the Waver–Warnell Fell–Sebergham Fault. The beds dip generally to the north-east at angles varying between 10° and 40°. Here about 100 ft of red sandstones with subordinate red and purple sandy shales are overlain by 7 ft of purple mudstones and fireclay followed by a 4-in ironstone band which [3273 4379], 850 yd E. 25° S. of Broadmoor, yielded *Lingula mytilloides* and hexactinellid sponge spicules. Mr. Calver suggests that

this marine band may represent the Solway Marine Band of the Whitehaven–Workington area. The marine band is succeeded by 10 ft of red mudstone yielding *Spirorbis sp., Anthracosia* aff. *aquilina, A.* cf. *beaniana, A. 'carissima', A.* aff. *disjuncta, A. ovum,* and *Naiadites* aff. *quadratus.* The assemblage indicates the upper part of the *A. modiolaris* Zone. Downstream red shales and red and purple fireclays are succeeded by a mussel-horizon seen in the right bank of Chalk Beck [3283 4396], 900 yd E. 12° S. of Broadmoor, which has yielded through 4 ft of red mudstones *Spirorbis sp., Naiadites angustus, N. obliquus,* and *N.* cf. *productus.* This fauna of small *Naiadites* is difficult to place in the zonal sequence; the mussel-band is higher in the sequence than that which lies a few feet above the marine band mentioned above, and may lie as high as the Lower *A. similis–A. pulchra* Zone.

Overlying measures consisting of about 100 ft of red mudstone with plants including *Neuropteris heterophylla,* and 40 ft of red and purple false-bedded sandstone with hematitic clay pellets occupy the stream for 100 yd S. of the road bridge (Chalk Bridge of 6-in map). The next exposures in Chalk Beck are at Chalk Side and thence downstream for 1000 yd. Here red and purple sandstones, shales, and fireclays dip to the north-east. *Neuropteris heterophylla* occurs in mudstones [3344 4566], 400 yd S. 35° W. of Upper Greenquarries. The beds are much disturbed in the lower part of the section where high dips are associated with two faults trending to the north and east-north-east respectively.

At Sebergham red shales and mudstones with subordinate sandstones and fireclays are exposed in a stream (Warnell Beck of the 6-in maps) that joins the Caldew from the west. Here the north-easterly dip increases upstream from 3° to 30° immediately north of the Waver–Warnell Fell–Sebergham Fault. A mussel-band in red mudstones [3514 4187], 450 yd S. of Lonning Head, includes *Spirorbis sp., ?Anthraconaia modiolaris, Anthracosia regularis, Carbonicola venusta, C.* cf. *oslancis, Naiadites sp.* intermediate between *productus* and *quadratus,* and *Geisina arcuata.* The assemblage indicates a horizon within the *A. modiolaris* Zone and, according to Mr. Calver, probably in its lower part.

The Roe Beck drainage area. Red and purple mudstones, fireclays and sandstones dipping gently eastward are exposed in Roe Beck for 1000 yd north-east of the Waver–Warnell Fell–Sebergham Fault. Fossils collected from mudstones [3947 4157], 730 yd E. 26° S. of Cockleythwaite, include *Alethopteris decurrens, Dactylotheca plumosa, Neuropteris gigantea, N. heterophylla,* with *Naiadites sp.* of the *productus/ quadratus* group. Farther north there is a faulted inlier of the Hensingham Group, and Coal Measures occupy the stream north of this as far as a north-west fault that brings in the Penrith Sandstone. The measures, which dip northwards at 10°, include a 30-ft bed of gritty sandstone and a plant horizon in mudstones [3934 4210], 530 yd E. 25° N. of Cockleythwaite. The flora includes *Alethopteris lonchitica, Mari*

opteris nervosa and *Neuropteris heterophylla.*

Northwards, as far as Gatesgill, Roe Beck crosses Penrith Sandstone except for a faulted inlier of red Coal Measures rocks east of Raughtonhead which are provisionally regarded as Upper Coal Measures (see p. 211).

Barren red Coal Measures are again seen around Gatesgill and dip to the north-north-west. Shales in the left bank of Roe Beck [3863 4662], 40 yd N. of Flat Bank, yield *Lepidodendron sp., Neuropteris heterophylla, Anthraconaia pulchella, Anthracosia subrecta, Naiadites productus* and fish remains. The horizon lies in the Middle Coal Measures. According to Mr. Calver the closest comparison is with the *A. pulchella* fauna from the base of the Lower *A. similis-A. pulchra* Zone of Lancashire and elsewhere.

F.M.T.

UPPER COAL MEASURES

Within the district the Upper Coal Measures consist of red and purple shales, mudstones and sandstones. The sandstones not uncommonly have an ashy appearance due to the presence of kaolinized feldspar. No coal seams have been found in the measures that are definitely Upper Coal Measures. Unfortunately the characteristics just given can be no longer regarded as diagnostic of that formation; the basis of recognition of Upper Coal Measures strata in this area is now wholly palaeontological. Upper Coal Measures of the Zone of *A. phillipsii* have not been found and it remains an open question whether or not the strata of this zone and of the Upper *A. similis-A. pulchra* Zone are absent in this area because of unconformity.

Upper Coal Measures are definitely present in the west beneath New Red Sandstone rocks, notably in two deep boreholes that have been examined by Geological Survey officers, and also at the surface in the east in two small triangular downfaulted areas.

Their presence can be accounted for in the west by a steep north-westerly dip in the measures beneath the unconformity that separates the Coal Measures from the overlying New Red Sandstone. An account to a depth of 2237 ft of one of the western bores, that of Brayton Domain No. 3 [1723 4529] has been published (Smith 1920), and in this account Smith took the base of the Upper Coal Measures at 2186 ft 6 in. From the samples collected by Smith, Mr. Calver has since (1963) recognized *Anthraconaia pruvosti* from reddish purple shales at *circa* 1525 ft. The bore was subsequently deepened to 2910 ft 9 in (given on 6-in Geological Sheet Cumberland 28 S.W. as 2830 ft) without striking any readily identifiable horizons although several thin coal seams were met. No fossils were collected from the deepening, the log of which was supplied by the Brayton Domain Colliery Company. On a copy of their drawn section of the deepening Mr. T. Eastwood has marked, at a depth of 2373 ft, the base of the 'Whitehaven Sandstone Series' (Upper Coal Measures). The placings of the base of the Upper Coal Measures in this bore by Smith, and of the base of the 'Whitehaven Sandstone Series' by Eastwood, were determined essentially by the depth to which reddened strata were found.

The cores of the easternmost deep borehole, that of Crookdake, were examined mainly by the late A. Templeman and the log is given in an abbreviated form on pp. 208–10. The hole passed into Upper Coal Measures at 643 ft 4 in and reddened measures continued to 2018 ft, from about which depth the strata were broken and in places veined and core was missing, probably indicating that the hole crossed a fault. Fossils diagnostic of the *A. tenuis* Zone have been identified by Mr. Calver and include, between the depths of 1399 ft 6 in and 1696 ft, *Anthraconaia pruvosti, Anthraconauta phillipsii* and *A. tenuis*, as well as *Euestheria simoni* and *Leaia bristolensis*. Templeman marked the base of the Upper Coal Measures at a depth of 1926 ft, and at 2020 ft indeterminate lamellibranchs, according to Mr. Calver possibly *Anthracosia*, occur. He states that they are "too poorly preserved for reliable comment, but they do not look Upper Coal Measures lamellibranchs. I should think they are more likely to be from below the Bolton Marine Band horizon." Thus neither of these two boreholes provides satisfactory evidence for fixing a base to the Upper Coal Measures, although Upper Coal Measures are present in both.

The triangular downfaulted outlier of Upper Coal Measures to the south-east of Welton has yielded plants (p. 210) which are referred by Dr. Crookall to either the Staffordian or Lower Radstockian. From the other downfaulted area in the eastern part of the district the evidence of Upper Coal Measures age is suggestive rather than conclusive; it lies near Raughtonhead where an exposure in Roe Beck has yielded *Leaia* cf. *bristolensis*, a form which has not been found elsewhere except in Upper Coal Measures strata.

DETAILS

Aspatria. To the north-east of Aspatria three deep boreholes were drilled in connexion with No. 4 Pit Brayton Domain Colliery. The cores of Brayton Domain No. 3 Bore were examined by B. Smith (1920). The cores of No. 1 and 2 Bores were not seen by a geologist, although the provings of these two bores received brief mention by Smith.

As a satisfactory line cannot be drawn for the base of the Upper Coal Measures in any of the three holes, it is convenient to give details of these boreholes (and of the Crookdake Bore) to the bottom of the hole in each case.

No. 1 Bore was situated [1646 4434] about 1¼ miles E. of Yearngill. The interpretation of the borer's record may be summarized as follows. After passing through 100 ft of boulder clay, New Red Sandstone was encountered to 556 ft. From this depth coloured unproductive measures (with a 7-in hard white limestone

at 588 ft) were encountered to a total depth of 1262 ft 4 in, and it is possible, as Smith suggests, that these coloured measures are Upper Coal Measures, though the essential fossil evidence is lacking.

In No. 2 bore, situated [1718 4453] about ¾ mile S.S.E. of Langrigg, the St. Bees Sandstone appears to be normal to a depth of about 500 ft, but is slaty thence to 613 ft, below which depth brown shales with some gypsum and sporadic thin sandstones were encountered. Some of these shales almost certainly belong to the New Red Sandstone, whereas others are referable to the Coal Measures, but it is difficult from the borer's record to decide where the junction should be placed; the band of pale blue shale at 784 ft and the blue shales with limestone balls 12 ft lower probably belong to the latter group, and the most convenient position for the base of the New Red Sandstone is 742 ft from the surface and not 665 ft as taken by Smith (1920, p. 50). A 7-in limestone at 913 ft is possibly the same bed as that at 588 ft in No. 1 Bore. Grey measures were encountered at 1384 ft 3 in and this depth was taken by Smith as the base of the Upper Coal Measures. The hole passed through the top of a 45-in coal seam (regarded by Smith as the Yard Band) at 1853 ft 11 in, the bottom of the bore being 1870 ft.

A précis of the published account of the Brayton Domain No. 3, situated [1723 4529] about ½ mile S.E. of Langrigg is as follows:

	Thick-ness ft in		Depth ft in	
Glacial Drift	67	2	67	2
New Red Sandstone ..	1002	10	1070	0
Coal Measures [classified by Smith as Upper] Shales and sandstones, red, purple, brown and grey with *Anthraconaia pruvosti* at c. 1525 ft ..	1116	6	2186	6
Coal Measures [classified by Smith as Middle]	51	0	2237	6

The following is an abbreviated account of the underlying strata to the final depth of 2910 ft 9 in, taken from a log that was supplied by the Brayton Domain Colliery Company. There are several depth discrepancies between this and Smith's log, but at 2340 ft these rectify themselves. The intervening strata to that depth are therefore grouped together:

	Thick-ness ft in		Depth ft in	
Shales, dominantly brown, purple and grey, including 2-in dirty coal .. to			2340	0
Coal, poor		4	2340	4
Fireclay and shale ..	5	10	2346	2
Sandstone, brown and grey .. .. .. (Taken by Eastwood as lowest horizon in 'Whitehaven Sandstone Series')	27	1	2373	3
Shales, brown grey and blue	27	9	2401	0
Coal		8	2401	8
Shales, blue	39	7	2441	3
Shales and coal ..	2	3	2443	6
Shales, blue, with iron-stones	30	0	2473	6

	Thick-ness ft in		Depth ft in	
Coal and shale ..		9	2474	3
Shales, blue, with iron-stones	43	10	2518	1
Coal 7 in .. .. Shale, black 2 in .. Coal 13 in	1	10	2519	11
Shales, blue and pale blue	52	6	2572	5
Coal	1	6	2573	11
Shales, blue, with iron-stones	86	11	2760	10
Coal and shale ..		7	2761	5
Shales, blue, with grey sandstones	26	11	2788	4
Sandstones, grey, very broken *? fault* ..	14	10	2803	2
Sandstones, grey with minor bands of dark grey shale	107	7	2910	9

The base of the Upper Coal Measures probably lies between about 1525 ft and 2373 ft. Below the latter depth the dominantly argillaceous measures with thin coal seams are almost certainly Middle Coal Measures to the probable fault at about 2800 ft. It is possible that below that depth the dominantly arenaceous strata encountered may lie within the Hensingham Group.

Allhallows. The easternmost of the deep boreholes sunk through the New Red Sandstone to prove Coal Measures is the most important scientifically, although from the economic viewpoint it was most disappointing, for only one coal, and that only 2 in thick, was struck. Details are as follows:

Crookdake Bore

Cumberland 6-in County Sheet 36 N.E., National Grid 6-in Sheet NY 24 S.W. Grid reference: 2065 4441; 300 yd S. 30° E. of Low Aketon. Ordnance Datum 215 ft above O.D. Sunk 16/2/39 to 14/5/41 for Brayton Domain Collieries and Leconfield Estate Co. by Andrew Kyle Ltd. Cores examined by A. Templeman and (between 2045 and 2102 ft) by F. M. Trotter. Fossil identifications by M. A. Calver. Abbreviated log with borer's terms (fakes, blaes etc.) interpreted:

	Thick-ness ft in		Depth ft in	
DRIFT	11	6	11	6

	Thickness ft in	Depth ft in		Thickness ft in	Depth ft in

NEW RED SANDSTONE SERIES

	Thickness		Depth	
	ft	in	ft	in
NEW RED SANDSTONE SERIES				
Sandstone, dominantly buff-red, with subordinate bands of red shale and marl ..	631	10	643	4
UPPER COAL MEASURES				
Shales, red and grey ..	13	3	656	7
Sandstone, red with shaly beds	53	6	710	1
Shales and marl, red ..	31	0	741	1
Sandstone, reddish grey, shaly	70	10	811	11
Marl, soft red.. ..	8	7	820	6
Sandstone, red, shaly in places with occasional thin impure conglomeratic limestone bands ..	111	8	932	2
Shales and marls, red, with thin bands of impure limestone ..	16	5	948	7
Sandstone, conglomerate and broken marl, red and grey..	5	8	954	3
Shales with marl, red and variegated ..	139	3	1093	6
Sandstone, red, with conglomeratic calcareous bands ..	48	11	1142	5
Shales and marls, red and grey	14	2	1166	7
Sandstone, reddish grey	46	7	1213	2
Shales and marls, red and variegated ..	20	10	1234	0
Sandstone, red ..	4	10	1238	10
Shales and marls, red and variegated; plants	120	7	1359	5
Sandstones, reddish grey	32	7	1392	0
Shales and marls, red; *Anthraconauta phillipsii, Carbonita pungens* and *C. salteriana* at 1399½ ft; *A. phillipsii* at 1406–1406½ ft and 1412–1412½ ft; *Anthraconaia pruvosti* at 1425 ft	54	0	1446	0
Sandstone, reddish and grey	6	6	1452	6
Shales with marls, reddish grey and variegated, with *Anthraconauta sp.* [juv.], *Euestheria simoni*, and *Carbonita sp.* at 1487 ft; *A. phillipsii, A. tenuis, Euestheria simoni, Carbonita wardiana, C. salteriana* at 1493–6 ft	109	6	1562	0
Sandstone, reddish grey	10	0	1572	0
Shales and marls, red and variegated with *Anthraconaia* cf. *pruvosti* and *Anthraconauta phillipsii?* at 1596 ft to 1597 ft ..	40	2	1612	2
Sandstone, reddish grey, gypsum ribs ..	12	6	1624	8
Shales and marls, red and variegated, gypsum ribs; with *Leaia bristolensis* at 1629 to 1630 ft; *A. phillipsii* [juv.], *A. tenuis* [juv.] and *Euestheria?* at 1695 to 1696 ft ..	140	1	1764	9
Sandstone, reddish grey	73	11	1838	8
Shales, red and variegated	5	6	1844	2
Sandstone, reddish grey, hard	1	8	1845	10
Shales, reddish grey	15	8	1861	6
Sandstone, reddish grey, shale band at base	9	9	1871	3
Conglomerate, calcareous, with ironstones	2	0	1873	3
Shales, red, grey and variegated	53	3	1926	6
Fireclay, variegated ..	3	0	1929	6
Coal, dirty		2	1929	8
Fireclay, grey and variegated ..	5	4	1935	0
Sandstone, hard ..		9	1935	9

	Thickness ft in	Depth ft in
Shales, grey and red stained, slightly slickensided, high dip (40° to 53°) (? *faulted beds*) ..	44 0	1979 9
Sandstone, hard, slightly ferruginous	3 3	1983 0
Shales, reddish grey, with thin sandstone band	13 4	1996 4
Sandstone, reddish grey	21 5	2017 9
Ironstone rib, red and grey, broken ..	9	2018 6
(*A note by Templeman reads "Dip uncertain and variable 2016 to 2038 ft and some core lost" and "sparry veins" at c. 2019 ft. A fault is suggested*)		

MIDDLE COAL MEASURES

	Thickness ft in	Depth ft in
Sandstones, shaly, with fireclays and ironstones; indet. lamellibranch (possibly *Anthracosia*) at 2019 to 2020 ft	20 2	2038 8
Sandstone, hard, grey	8 0	2046 8
Sandstone, grey, shaly and micaceous, with sandy mudstone ..	23 10	2070 6
Mudstone, sandy, slickensided ..	2 0	2072 6
Fireclay, grey, broken and slickensided ..	2 0	2074 6
Mudstones, sandy, and shaly sandstones ..	10 0	2084 6
Sandstone, quartzitic and coal traces ..	1 6	2086 0
Sandstones and shales (*no core*)	2 2	2088 2
Fault—breccia of quartzite fragments in matrix of calcite with pyrite	3 0	2091 2

? LOWER COAL MEASURES and/or HENSINGHAM GROUP

	Thickness ft in	Depth ft in
Sandstone, soft (*no core*)	4 4	2095 6
Sandstone, hard, siliceous, grey, white, (*little core*) ..	14 8	2110 2

	Thickness ft in	Depth ft in
Mudstones, grey, sandy and shaly sandstones	6 6	2116 8
Fireclay, with sandy mudstones and shaly sandstones ..	17 10	2134 6
Sandstone, grey ..	8 2	2142 8
Sandstones and shales, grey, broken, with ironstones	52 11	2195 7
Shales, dark grey; *Lingula squamiformis* and *Orbiculoidea* cf. *nitida* at 2198 to 2201 ft	10 6	2206 1
Fireclay, shaly ..	4 4	2210 5
Shales, grey	23 10	2234 3

In this borehole Upper Coal Measures are definitely present between 643 ft and 1695 ft, and it is not unlikely that they continue to the probable fault at about 1979 ft or to the probable fault at about 2019 ft as shown in the above log. The thickness of strata that may be cut out by these probable faults (including beds possibly of Upper Coal Measures age) is unknown. Middle Coal Measures extend to the fault at about 2088 ft. Below this fault the measures are either Lower Coal Measures or Hensingham Group.

River Caldew drainage north of Sebergham. The area is largely drift-covered and exposures of red and purple sandstones and mudstones are confined to the banks of the River Caldew and its tributaries. In one of these, Busta Beck of the 6-in map [3677 4276], 550 yd W. 8° S. of Greens, red mudstones have yielded the following plants: *Aphlebia spinosa, Asterotheca lepidorachis, Cyclopteris sp., Eupecopteris spp., Neuropteris ovata, N. rarinervis.* Dr. R. Crookall reports that the assemblage indicates a horizon high in the Staffordian or low in the Radstockian, that is, near the boundary between Westphalian C and D.

Roe Beck, east of Raughtonhead. In the valley of Roe Beck to the north of Stockdalewath and to the east of Raughtonhead there is an upfaulted section displaying red and purple measures dipping southwards. On fossil evidence they are undoubtedly Coal Measures, and they are indicated on the published One-inch geological map by the symbol d⁵. On the left bank of Roe Beck [3854 4545] 700 yd E. 12° S. of the church in Raughtonhead, 2 ft of red to purple mudstones (under about 12 ft of purple sandy shales and sandstones) have yielded poorly preserved '*Estheria*' and several good specimens of *Leaia*. Recently (1963) the latter were identified by Mr. M. A. Calver as *L.* cf. *bristolensis*. He comments "Recent revision of this group of crustacea has produced several new genera and species, and further work is required to assess their stratigraphical value. However, the identification of these *Leaia* as *L.* cf. *bristolensis* implies an Upper Coal Measures age for the horizon rather than Lower or Middle Coal Measures." The recognition of *L. bristolensis* within strata in the Crookdake bore that are referable to the *A. tenuis* Zone strengthens the suggestion that the measures in the small faulted inlier at Raughtonhead are Upper Coal Measures. T.E., F.M.T.

REFERENCES

CURRIE, ETHEL D., DUNCAN, CATHERINE and MUIR-WOOD, HELEN M. 1937. The fauna of Skipsey's Marine Band. *Trans. geol. Soc. Glasgow*, **19**, 413–452.

EASTWOOD, T. 1929. 'Nips' and 'rock-riders' in the West Cumberland Coalfield. *Summ. Prog. Geol. Surv. Gt Br.* for 1928, Pt. II, 115–9.

——— 1930. The geology of the Maryport District. *Mem. Geol. Surv. Gt Br.*

——— 1931. In *Summ. Prog. Geol. Surv. Gt Br.* for 1930, Pt. I, 55.

——— 1935. British Regional Geology, Northern England. 1st edit. *Geol. Surv. Gt Br.*

——— 1953. British Regional Geology, Northern England. 3rd edit. *Geol. Surv. Gt Br.*

——— DIXON, E. E. L., HOLLINGWORTH, S. E. and SMITH, B. 1931. The Geology of the Whitehaven and Workington District. *Mem. Geol. Surv. Gt Br.*

KITCHIN, F. L. 1932. In *Summ. Prog. Geol. Surv. Gt Br.* for 1931, Pt. I, 65.

MUIR-WOOD, HELEN. 1928. The British Carboniferous Producti. II. *Mem. Geol. Surv. Palaeont.*, **3**.

PEILE, W. 1838. Notes of a singular transformation of the seams of coal into stone, at Crummock Colliery. *Trans. nat. Hist. Soc. Northumb.*, **2**, 178–80.

PRINGLE, J. and JACKSON, J. W. 1928. *Tylonautilus nodiferus* gen. nov., (= *Nautilus (Discites) nodiferus* Armstrong): A Carboniferous guide fossil. *Naturalist*, Hull, 373–8.

SMITH, B. 1920. On a boring for coal at Brayton Domain Colliery, Cumberland. *Summ. Prog. Geol. Surv. Gt Br.* for 1919, 50–6.

——— 1921. On borings for coal near Maryport, Cumberland. *Summ. Prog. Geol. Surv. Gt Br.* for 1920, 85–91.

——— 1927. On the Carboniferous Limestone Series of the northern part of the Isle of Man. *Summ. Prog. Geol. Surv. Gt Br.* for 1926, 108–19.

TAYLOR, B. J., with Palaeontology by CALVER, M. A. 1961. The stratigraphy of exploratory boreholes in the West Cumberland Coalfield. *Bull. Geol. Surv. Gt Br.* No. 17, 1–74.

TROTTER, F. M. and HOLLINGWORTH, S. E. 1927. On the Upper Limestone Group and 'Millstone Grit' of north east Cumberland. *Summ. Prog. Geol. Surv. Gt Br.* for 1926, 98–107.

——— and ——— 1932. The geology of the Brampton District. *Mem. Geol. Surv. Gt Br.*

TRUEMAN, A. E. and WEIR, J. 1947——. A monograph of British Carboniferous non-marine lamellibranchia. *Palaeontogr. Soc.*

Chapter XII

NEW RED SANDSTONE ROCKS

THE NEW RED SANDSTONE occupies a considerable tract of lowland country in the northern part of the district. Comparatively little of it is exposed, however, on account of the thick cover of Glacial deposits, but information concerning it has been obtained from boreholes sunk in connexion with the concealed part of the coalfield.

Considerable confusion once existed as to the sequence and structure of the Solway Basin, of which this region is a part, but on the completion of the resurvey of the Carlisle district it was concluded (Dixon and others 1926) that the order of deposition was as set out below:

> Stanwix Shales
> Kirklinton Sandstone
> St. Bees Sandstone
> St. Bees Shales
> Penrith Sandstone

This sequence persists into the Brampton and Cockermouth districts, though it is not always complete. For instance, the Penrith Sandstone and the Kirklinton Sandstone are absent in the west.

Within the present district the New Red Sandstone rests with marked unconformity on rocks of Carboniferous age varying in horizon from Hensingham Group to Upper Coal Measures. The reddened Carboniferous rocks (see p. 147) indicate that arid conditions prevailed before the onset of New Red Sandstone sedimentation. These conditions also prevailed intermittently during New Red Sandstone times.

The Penrith Sandstone, a deposit largely of aeolian origin, appears to have accumulated in an inland basin of north-westerly trend more or less restricted to Edenside (see p. 213). Then came a widespread submergence which resulted in the deposition of the St. Bees Shales over the site of Edenside, the Solway Basin and other parts of north-western England. Deposition in an inland sea continued with but minor pauses during the formation of the St. Bees and Kirklinton sandstones and the Stanwix Shales. The New Red Sandstone period was brought to a close by a widespread submergence which led to an invasion by the sea, and to the deposition of marine deposits—Rhaetic and Lias—but these two formations are not present in the Cockermouth district.

In age the Penrith Sandstone is considered to be Permian. The St. Bees Shales are regarded as passage beds to the Trias, and are accordingly lettered e-f on the One-inch geological map. On this map the St. Bees and Kirklinton sandstones, regarded mainly as Bunter, are lettered f^{2-3}, while the Stanwix Shales, regarded as equivalent to the Keuper Marl, are indicated as f^6.

PENRITH SANDSTONE

The Penrith Sandstone of the district is the northwestern extremity of an outcrop which stretches many miles to the south-east in Edenside. There, together with the interbedded Upper and Lower Brockrams, it attains an estimated thickness of 1500 ft, and includes the well-known building-stone variety in which the rock is cemented by a secondary crystallization of quartz around the original quartz grains. This variety is absent from the area under review, where the rock is soft, loosely cemented and composed of rounded grains of quartz with some white decomposed feldspar. The sandstone is dominantly red in colour, but orange and brown tints occur as well as grey-white beds. There are two types, medium-grained and coarse-grained sandstones; and both are uniformly graded and strongly false-bedded.

The uniformity of grading, the perfection of rounding of the grains and the prevalence of false-bedding all testify to the accumulation of Penrith Sandstone under desert conditions.

DETAILS

The Roe Beck drainage. Exposures of the Penrith Sandstone are confined to the Roe Beck and its tributaries from High Head Castle downstream to the environs of Gatesgill. The dip is consistently to the north-north-west. The rock is exposed in bluffs and river cliffs up to 30 ft in height. The thickness of the formation is difficult to estimate, but it appears to be several hundred feet thick between Highbridge and Stockdalewath. Farther to the north-north-west the Penrith Sandstone thins and eventually disappears. In two streams to the east of Gatesgill church its thickness is estimated at only 50 ft, and at a point [3869 4701] in Roe Beck, 600 yd W.N.W. of that church, the St. Bees Shales appear to rest directly on reddened Coal Measures with no intervening Penrith Sandstone. The disappearance in a north-north-westerly direction would appear to indicate that the Penrith Sandstone of Edenside, and a similar deposit of apparently the same age (the Dumfries Sandstone) found around Dumfries, are not continuous beneath the Carlisle Plain.

ST. BEES SHALES

This group of red shales and mudstones, usually 150 to 300 ft thick, has long been known in the West Cumberland, Edenside and Carlisle areas, where it is of economic importance on account of its deposits of gypsum. No gypsum of any value, however, has yet been found in the district under description.

To the south and east of Gatesgill the St. Bees Shales fall within the structural unit of Edenside, and there they overlie Penrith Sandstone. Farther to the west, along the main outcrop, they form the southern margin of the Solway Basin and constitute the basal member of the New Red Sandstone. Their base is here marked by gritty marls, or by a breccia or conglomerate up to 6 ft thick, or, exceptionally, by a sandstone up to 30 ft thick.

Where typically developed the beds consist of red and chocolate-coloured shales and mudstones, often containing abundant white mica. Thin interbedded red sandstones and shaly sandstones indistinguishable from the overlying St. Bees Sandstone are commonly present and increase in number in ascending sequence, giving a gradual passage upwards into that formation. The lower beds are calcareous to a varying degree and contain nodules of red and green argillaceous limestone.

DETAILS

Aspatria to Bolton Low Houses. In this area exposures are few and most of our knowledge is derived from boreholes. These indicate a variable series of beds near the base of the New Red Sandstone, which for the most part may be regarded as sandy and shaly, and so may be considered as the broad equivalents of the St. Bees Shales farther east. Nevertheless, locally they are much more arenaceous than typical St. Bees Shales, as may be seen from the following consideration of individual boreholes.

The Lancar Beck Borehole [1300 4275], east of Aiglegill, passed through 50 ft of boulder clay and proved about 500 ft of St. Bees Sandstone; it then passed by intercalations of sandstone and shale into the St. Bees Shales. These are about 150 ft thick, are sandy in places and include thin beds of sandstone. They rest on 26 ft of rough brown sandstone, with rhombs of dolomite, which repose on a very irregular surface of the Hensingham Group at a depth of 629 ft.

In Castlemont (or No. 6) Borehole [1340 4176], west of Aspatria, no shales are recorded though the red sandstones for 100 ft above the 26-ft basal sandstone of the New Red Sandstone are referred to as shaly.

Farther to the north-east, a borehole on the site of the downcast shaft of Brayton No. 4 Pit [1612 4341], near Wellington Farm, commenced in 10 ft of boulder clay and passed through red shales, sandy in part, to a basal sandstone, only 6 ft thick, which rests on Coal Measures at a depth of 133 ft.

The base of the New Red Sandstone is difficult to locate in the log of Brayton Domain No. 2 Borehole [1718 4453] but some St. Bees Shales are present, and over 100 ft of them were passed through in the Little Moss [1590 4402] and Brayton Domain No. 1 boreholes [1646 4434]. Farther north at the Brayton Domain No. 3 Borehole [1723 4529], ½ mile S.E. of Langrigg, the St. Bees Shales are again absent or represented by sandstone. In this hole 4 ft of conglomeratic breccia with a dolomitic matrix were noted by B. Smith at a depth of 1100 ft from the surface and taken as the base of the New Red Sandstone.

Again in the Crookdake Bore [2065 4441] there is no evidence of the St. Bees Shales

at the base of the New Red Sandstone, although between 601½ ft and the base at 643 ft 4 in several beds of red sandy shale are recorded.

There are several sections in both St. Bees Shales and Sandstone in the small streams and quarries about Crookdake. There is considerable variation in dip, the direction varying from north to south-west in the main though in places it is easterly; the amount remains constant between 8° and 10°; and near Low Aketon an anticline of north-north-west trend is discernible.

The absence of St. Bees Shales in the River Waver below Bolton Low Houses is attributed to a fault—possibly of 200 ft throw—since there is an excellent section in them higher upstream [259 445] near Islekirk Hall. There over 30 ft of red mudstones and shales with occasional sandstone bands pass beneath fairly massive St. Bees Sandstone. The dip hereabouts is southerly and towards the large fault.   T.E.

Westward to Gatesgill. Gritty mudstones at the base of the St. Bees Shales occupy the south bank of Wiza Beck [2679 4498] west of the church at Westward, and overlie reddened Coal Measures. The southerly dip hereabouts is attributed to the presence of the small upfold of St. Bees Shales and the older rocks, partly interrupted by a downfaulted wedge of St. Bees Sandstone, extending from Westward to Cowslaw on the River Waver.   W.C.C.R.

Farther east the St. Bees Shales have a double outcrop, being repeated by the Lowling Fault. On both crops they dip northwards but to the south of the fault they rest on Coal Measures and to the north of it on Carboniferous Limestone Series and Hensingham Group. Thus the fault which now throws down to the south has had a post- and a pre-New Red Sandstone movement (see Fig. 17). The basal beds of the St. Bees Shales dipping northwards at 20° to 25° crop out in a stream [3180 4622] 150 yd W. 3° N. of Rosleyrigg. They consist of red marls with thin ribs of sandstone and grit and wisps of fine conglomerate, and rest on gritty sandstone of the Coal Measures. Farther north across the Lowling Fault they crop out with northerly dip in Jacob's Gill to the north-west of Westward Cottage, and although their base is not exposed they presumably rest on beds of the Hensingham Group. They consist of red marls with harder micaceous sandy bands and occasional fine greenish grey dolomitic layers.

Red sandy shales appear beneath the St. Bees Sandstone in Chalk Beck at the ford [3405 4610] 400 yd E.N.E. of Greenquarries and overlie Coal Measures. North of the Lowling Fault they are again seen in Chalk Beck south-east of Barnetrigg in almost continuous exposure, some 300 ft in thickness; the dip is northwards at 12° to 16°. The basal unconformity is seen on the left bank of the stream [3407 4684], 400 yd E. of Kirkstead, and in an old quarry [3418 4715], 600 yd N.E. of Kirkstead, where 3 ft of breccia consisting of fragments of Carboniferous Limestone and sandstone set in a red sandy matrix lie on the First or Great Limestone. Above these basal beds numerous exposures display red and chocolate-coloured micaceous shales and marls with thin ribs of sandstone. The latter increase in thickness in upward succession.

Farther east, in the north-eastern corner of the district, glacial drift obscures the St. Bees Shales, but there are exposures in the Roe Beck drainage area in the vicinity of Gatesgill, which together with information obtained from four boreholes sunk (without success) for gypsum in the vicinity of Raughton, have rendered possible the identification of several distinct outcrops of St. Bees Shales, the repetition of outcrop being due to four faults that trend east-north-eastwards from the Roe Beck East Fault.

The exposure in Roe Beck [3869 4701], 600 yd W.N.W. of the church in Gatesgill, is significant in that it is the easternmost to display St. Bees Shales resting apparently directly upon the Carboniferous. At this exposure the St. Bees Shales, consisting of red marls with red and green calcareous nodules and basal red gritty marls, lie within a few yards of reddened Coal Measures sandstone. Both formations dip northwards without a sign of disturbance and it is clear that the junction is not faulted.

The exposures in the gill (Red Gill of 6-in map) [3971 4680], 900 yd E. 5° S. of the church in Gatesgill, display red sandy shales with ribs of shaly sandstone dipping northwards; and these St. Bees Shales are cut off by an east-north-easterly fault that brings in Penrith Sandstone. A short distance to the north-west in the upper reaches of a gill (Riddings Gill of 6-in map) the St. Bees Shales are exposed [3945 4705] in normal sequence above the Penrith Sandstone. The easterly continuation beneath glacial drift of the latter formation is confirmed by the D 3 Borehole of the British Plaster Board Co., Ltd. situated [3990 4701], 1100 yd E. 12° N. of the church in Gatesgill. This proved, beneath 22 ft of Boulder Clay, 14 ft of Penrith Sandstone and then Carboniferous sandstone to a total depth of 126 ft.

Farther north [3964 4753], 1100 yd N.E. of the church in Gatesgill, the D 1 Borehole proved beneath 10 ft of Boulder Clay, 128 ft of St. Bees Sandstone in an area where St. Bees Shales were to be expected. The St. Bees Sandstone has been brought in by a fault which it is thought trends past Bud Hill in an east-north-easterly direction.

The D 2 Borehole [3878 4805], on the north-east side of the road about 500 yd N.W. of Raughton, proved, under 5 ft of Boulder Clay, St. Bees Sandstone to 35 ft and St. Bees Shales to 160 ft, then Carboniferous sandstones and shales to a total depth of 400 ft. The D 4 Borehole [4002 4849], 850 yd E. 7° S. of Unthank, proved Boulder Clay to 60 ft, St. Bees Shales to 190 ft and Carboniferous sandstone to a total depth of 196 ft.   F.M.T.

St. Bees Sandstone

The St. Bees Shales pass upwards into a thick group of red sandstones containing subordinate bands of shale and shaly sandstone. On account of their even bedding and jointing, and the ease with which they can be worked, these sandstones have been extensively quarried for building stone.

The sandstones are usually compact and even-grained and are made up of sub-angular quartz with some feldspathic material; larger rounded grains of quartz are scattered sparingly throughout. Small flakes of white mica often occur, but are more characteristic of the shaly layers. Examples of minor false-bedding, wedge-bedding, and of ripple-marking are not infrequent. The prevailing colour of the sandstones is dull red, but a development of grey and white beds has been noticed towards the base at several localities. The inter-bedded shales are dull red and chocolate-coloured; as a general rule they are only a foot or two thick, although there is an increase in thickness towards the base where they may be up to 5 ft; exceptionally as in the Brayton Domain No. 3 Borehole and the Crookdake Bore thick beds of shale occur (see below).

The lowest 500 ft of the St. Bees Sandstone are well displayed in Chalk Beck; another good exposure may be seen in the Wiza Beck between Wigton and Red Dial. The thickness of the formation has been estimated at about 1700 ft in the western part of the area.

DETAILS

Westnewton to Bromfield. Apart from exposures in old quarries and natural sections around Aiglegill and to the east of Westnewton in a stream between Warwick Hall and Yearngill, where the sandstones are seen to be dipping at 8° to 10° to the northwest, the outcrop of the St. Bees Sandstone is obscured by glacial drift, and information concerning the formation comes from boreholes. Most of these have been mentioned in the account of the St. Bees Shales, but special reference should be made to the Brayton Domain No. 3 Borehole [1723 4529], about ½ mile S.E. of Langrigg, since this bore proved slightly more than 1000 ft of St. Bees Sandstone, the thickest continuous sequence proved in the area of Sheet 23. From 67 ft to 300 ft red and grey sandstone was proved, and another thick bed of sandstone lay between 310 ft and 384 ft; below this brown shales were proved, separating sandstones up to 23 ft thick, to 685 ft; but from this depth to 837 ft the measures proved to be essentially argillaceous, with in places seams of gypsum; the remainder of the New Red Sandstone to its base at 1100 ft 10 in consisted essentially of red sandstone. The dominantly argillaceous measures (152 ft thick) recall the St. Bees Shales, and they would be so classified but for the fact that B. Smith saw the cores and placed the base of the St. Bees Sandstone at the bottom of a conglomeratic breccia 4 ft thick at the depth already mentioned.

Bromfield to Wigton. The outcrop of the St. Bees Sandstone is almost wholly covered by glacial drift. An important section in the New Red Sandstone is afforded by the

Crookdake Bore [2065 4441] examined by A. Templeman. In this bore under 11½ ft of Drift, the St. Bees Sandstone was proved to a depth of 643 ft. The sequence of red sandstones with subordinate argillaceous bands proved normal except for the dominantly argillaceous measures between 163 ft and 236 ft, which invite comparison with similar measures at approximately the same distance from the base of the formation proved in the Brayton Domain No. 3 Bore.

The best section of the St. Bees Sandstone is at Leegate Quarry [2002 4535], on the railway 600 yd S.W. of Leegate station. This shows about 80 ft of red sandstone with two well-marked shale bands, each about 2 ft thick dipping 10° to the north-west. Both massive and flaggy sandstones occur; the latter are often micaceous, and are occasionally false-bedded and ripple-marked.

There are several exposures of the St. Bees Sandstone to the south and south-east of Wigton; of these, the gorge of Wiza Beck, immediately east of Red Dial, provides a continuous section showing about 500 ft of red sandstones with thin shale bands dipping north at 8° to 20°.   T.E., W.C.C.R.

Greenrigg, Howrigg and Unthank. North of the Lowling Fault a stream (Speetgill of 6-in map), 2 miles S.E. of Wigton, for a quarter of a mile below Studfold exposes red sandstones with dark red to brown shale bands. At Studfold the dip is 20° to 25° to the north-north-west but this decreases downstream to 12°. Farther east another north-westerly flowing stream (Boston Beck of 6-in map) has cut down to the St. Bees

Sandstone. The first massive sandstone seen in passing downstream [3145 4795], 650 yd S.E. of Gillhead, has been taken as the base of the St. Bees Sandstone but there are few exposures in this rock until a point in Boston Beck [3130 4848], 250 yd E.N.E. of Gillhead, is reached. Thence for 300 yd there is much red sandstone with a general dip of 15° to 18° to the north-north-west. Both even-bedded and strongly current-bedded varieties occur.   S.E.H.

Old quarries [328 473], 270 yd S. of Howrigg, show St. Bees Sandstone in massive posts up to 12 ft thick separated by shale partings. At the eastern end of the quarries a fault, throwing down west and trending north, brings up beds that are dominantly grey-white in contrast to the red sandstones of the downthrow side. To the south-east a section south of the Lowling Fault is worthy of note. This is in the old quarries [3398 4628], 300 yd S.E. of Lower Greenquarries, and here near the base of some 30 ft of sandstone with subordinate shale bands there is a well-defined line of contemporaneous erosion, a band of shale being cut out by a 4-ft post of sandstone that contains, in its basal layers, pellets of shale and fragments of sandstone.

In Chalk Beck from a point [3396 4736] east of Barnetrigg, northwards for about half a mile there is a good section in St. Bees Sandstone. Here the beck flows in a gorge and the sandstone cliffs have been quarried from the beck, particularly towards the west. About 500 ft of sandstones with subordinate shale bands are exposed. The dip is to the north-north-west and decreases from 12° near Barnetrigg to 5° west of Greensyke. Separate mention may be made of one quarry, on the left bank of Chalk Beck [3383 4721], 400 yd N.N.E. of Kirkstead, where grey-white sandstones with interbedded chocolate-coloured shales near the base of the St. Bees Sandstone are associated with variegated sandstones displaying grey, yellow, orange and red tints.

At Unthank beds of the St. Bees Sandstone have been quarried on either side of the stream (Pow Beck of 6-in map). The dip of 8° to 10° is steady towards the north-west.   F.M.T.

KIRKLINTON SANDSTONE

The only evidence of the existence of Kirklinton Sandstone in the Cockermouth district comes from boreholes at Wigton in which this formation lay directly below Stanwix Shales. The Kirklinton types of sandstone were seen to be 30 to 40 ft thick. They were red in colour (but in places stained black), markedly false-bedded, soft and cavernous. Although mostly as fine-grained as the St. Bees Sandstone type they nevertheless contained scattered rounded quartz grains of millet seed size.

Compared with its development of 250 to 300 ft in the Carlisle area the Kirklinton Sandstone appears to thin rapidly to the south-west. This may be due to lateral passage into St. Bees Sandstone, but the presence of a shale breccia (p. 218) at the base of the Stanwix Shales suggests that the thinning may be associated with a non-sequence or with overstep by that formation, thus contrasting with the presence of passage beds to the north-east.

Apart from a record (Dixon and others 1926) of at least 75 ft of the Kirklinton Sandstone in the Abbey Town (Kelsick) Borehole on Sheet 17 and 2 miles north of Bromfield, no information is available from the heavily drift-covered ground to the west of Wigton. Under these circumstances, and taking into consideration the fact that Kirklinton Sandstone has not been mapped in West Cumberland, it has been thought inadvisable to continue the sub-drift outcrop to the south-west of Wigton.

STANWIX SHALES

Stanwix Shales have been proved in boreholes for water in Wigton, and it is assumed that they extend beneath the thick Glacial and Recent deposits of the Blencogo and Common Moss area to the west.

From a geological point of view the most important of these bores was that seen by Mr. E. E. L. Dixon in 1928. It was sunk for Nestlés Co., Ltd. and is now owned by British Rayophane, Ltd. It is situated north of the Cockermouth (23) Sheet boundary at Standingstone [2563 4907], and proved 360 ft of Stanwix Shales. The British Rayophane No. 1 Bore [2532 4866] proved Stanwix Shales from 150 to 303 ft.

Typically, the beds proved in the boreholes were red and green marls, often sandy and laminated, with hard calcareous bands and dolomitic nodules. In the boreholes at Wigton there occurs at the base of the formation a breccia, 2 to 4 ft thick, made up of red and green shale fragments. This basal bed has a sharp contact with the underlying Kirklinton Sandstone (p. 217).

In the absence of surface exposures and of other evidence, the actual extent of the formation is unknown, and the line of junction between the Stanwix Shales and the sandstones beneath is necessarily conjectural. From lack of evidence to the contrary this junction is assumed to be affected by the north-west faults which displace the St. Bees Sandstone in the Aspatria region. T.E.

REFERENCES

DIXON, E. E. L., MADEN, J., TROTTER, F. M., HOLLINGWORTH, S. E. and TONKS, L. H. 1926. The geology of the Carlisle, Longtown and Silloth District. *Mem. Geol. Surv. Gt Br.*

Chapter XIII

GLACIAL DEPOSITS

General Account

THE GLACIAL DEPOSITS of the Cockermouth district may be classified as in the adjoining Carlisle district to the north as follows:

4. Upper Sands and Gravels
3. Upper Boulder Clay
2. Middle Sands and Gravels
1. Lower Boulder Clay

In addition to these divisions there are a gravel and a boulder clay beneath the Lower Boulder Clay, but these deposits have been proved only in a few places and nowhere occupy an appreciable outcrop. Furthermore, a borehole at Wigton has proved clays with *Turritella communis* Risso, foraminifera and ostracods at the base of the glacial deposits, and resting on Stanwix Shales. If in place and not a glacial erratic from the Solway the clay may be older than the early glaciations of the region or may represent an inter-glacial phase.

Without unduly anticipating the interpretation of the deposits, it may be pointed out that the boulder clays are considered to represent ground-moraine formed beneath an ice-sheet; the sands, gravels and laminated clays are regarded as having been extra-glacial deposits, mainly frontal, laid down during the recession of the ice-sheet. The limit of the last advance of the ice-sheet (the Scottish Readvance) is defined approximately by the 400-ft contour, and the Upper Sands and Gravels and the Upper Boulder Clay are normally found below that altitude.

Boulder Clay. Deposits of glacial origin consisting of angular and sub-angular boulders set in a clay matrix are classed as boulder clay. The matrix is often composed of material largely of local origin. This clay is red where it has incorporated Permo-Triassic or reddened Carboniferous rocks, but elsewhere it is grey-blue. The texture of the matrix also varies with the underlying solid formations. Thus the boulder clay on the sandstones of the New Red Sandstone rocks is sandy, but heavy boulder clay is found on the wide outcrop of the shales of the Coal Measures near Broadmoor, and on the Skiddaw Slates. On the outcrop of the Borrowdale Volcanic Series the boulder clay is heavily charged with stones from the underlying formation.

On the uplands and in the mountain valleys the boulder clay forms feature-less spreads and the contained erratics consist dominantly of local rocks. Below 800 to 900 ft above O.D. the boulder clay usually lies in smooth elongated hillocks or drumlins that vary considerably in size, and the erratics include many far-travelled boulders. Two suites of erratics may be recognized, derived respectively from Galloway and the Lake District. Among the Galloway rocks, Criffel and Dalbeattie granites, and Silurian grits and greywackes are prominent. The Lake District suite includes andesites, tuffs and various types of lavas from the Borrowdale Volcanic Series, gabbros, granophyres and hybrid rocks from the Carrock Fell complex, the Threlkeld microgranite and the Armboth dyke.

Within the limits of the Scottish Readvance there is a mixture of boulder suites but the Scottish suite becomes more dominant in a northerly and north-westerly direction, and around Bromfield the foreign erratics are almost exclusively of Scottish origin. Galloway erratics also occur beyond the limits of the Upper Boulder Clay, i.e. above the 400-ft contour, but there they are subordinate to the Lake District suite and are of rare occurrence above the 600-ft contour, except in the Gillcambon Beck valley where, at about 1000 ft O.D., there is an exposure of red basal boulder clay that yields erratics of northern derivation.

Sands and Gravels. Bedded sand and pebbly gravel occur above both the Upper and the Lower Boulder Clay. Where they underlie an Upper Boulder Clay they form narrow outcrops running along the sides of the valleys, as for example along the River Caldew and in the glacial channels around Sandybrow to the east of Wigton. Sands and gravels lying above Upper Boulder Clay occupy considerable areas, notably about Cobble Hill to the north of West-newton and around Wigton. They frequently possess definite shapes that provide the clue to their mode of formation. The most frequent form is the delta, characterized by a flat top and lobate fore-set slopes. Three types may be recognized: (a) outwash-deltas deposited at the ice-front by englacial streams and distinguished by a more or less steep and linear ice-contact slope; (b) overflow-deltas found at the mouths of overflow channels where the waters debouched into glacier lakes; (c) land-stream deltas, deposited in glacier-lakes by streams from the land. Examples of outwash-deltas are seen in the mass of sands and gravels around Overby and Ryebottom; Wigton stands on an over-flow-delta; and Sebergham is situated on one of the land-stream deltas of the River Caldew. Other frontal deposits in addition to outwash-deltas include kames and oses—ridges of gravel aligned respectively parallel to and at right angles to the ice-front and deposited from it.

The composition of the Middle Sands and Gravels is very variable. To the east of Wigton they consist dominantly of red sands; farther west in the valley of the River Caldew they include a high percentage of gravel that yields a mixed Lake District–Scottish suite of pebbles in which Lake District pebbles predominate. Deposits of the same age beyond the limits of the Upper Boulder Clay are mostly gravels that yield a Lake District suite, largely derived from the mountainous area that lies within the confines of One-inch Sheet 23. They may vary from gravels, composed exclusively of pebbles of Skiddaw Slate and vein-quartz, as for example near Longlands, to sands and gravels containing pebbles of limestone, sandstone, tuff, lava, gabbro and granophyre, as for example at Sebergham.

The Upper Sands and Gravels consist of red sands and bedded gravels. They yield a far-travelled boulder suite that is dominantly of Scottish origin.

Brickearth. Under this heading are included glacial deposits of stiff red stoneless clay, together with some laminated clay, which accumulated as lake-floor deposits in wide interdrumlin hollows to the west of Bromfield and

Langrigg. They are considered to be of the same age as the Upper Sands and Gravels.

Moraine. Certain deposits do not fall within the categories of either boulder clay or sands and gravels, and are shown on the One-inch map as 'moraine'. They consist of angular and subangular boulders of varying size often with little or no clay matrix, but include subordinate patches of boulder clay and lenticles of bedded sand and gravel that cannot be mapped separately. Where they lie in irregular hillocks and ridges they are almost certainly frontal or sub-frontal deposits. Some more or less featureless spreads of morainic material in some of the high-lying mountain valleys may represent a stony ground moraine.

GLACIAL HISTORY

The district lying on the northern margin of the Lake District falls within a glaciated area that has been described by Trotter (1929) and Hollingworth (1931) and it is not necessary to recapitulate the details previously given. Here a brief outline of the glacial history is given in which the salient events are discussed so far as they affect the present area.

In Cumberland three glaciations have been recognized—the Early Scottish, the Main, and the Scottish Readvance.

During the Early Scottish Glaciation a great ice-sheet from the Southern Uplands of Scotland swept across the Carlisle Plain and split against the mountains of northern Lakeland. One stream flowed up Edenside where it was joined by ice from the Lake District, and the combined stream crossed the Pennines via the Stainmore depression. Another stream flowed southwards into the Irish Sea and this was also joined by ice from the Lake District.

The boulder clay of the Early Scottish Glaciation is buried by, and to a large extent is incorporated in, the deposits of the Main Glaciation. Hence good exposures of the early deposits are rare, but those along Gillcambon Beck (p. 231) and the clays proved in borings in the Wiza Beck (p. 228) may be mentioned. Redistribution of the erratics of this glaciation by a later ice-sheet is the probable explanation of such occurrences as Scottish granites south of Nether Row, and St. Bees Sandstone boulders in the valley of the Cald Beck.

It is probable that the ice evacuated the low ground prior to the oncoming of the Main Glaciation, but within the area under description there is no evidence on this point. The deposits of this Main Glaciation, in the form of boulder clay and sands and gravels, cover large tracts of ground. During the early phases, ice flowed into the low ground and into the Irish Sea from the surrounding mountainous regions of the Southern Uplands, the Lake District, and to a less extent the Pennines. Gradually the general level of the ice in the low-lying areas rose until a height greater than 2200 ft above O.D. was reached in Edenside. In addition Snae Fell (2034 ft O.D.) in the Isle of Man was covered. The surface of the ice-sheet became an area of accumulation and at the maximum of the Main Glaciation the general direction of ice movement became independent of minor surface inequalities. The principal directions of outflow from north-western England were eastwards across the Tyne Gap and the Stainmore depression and westwards and south-westwards along the Solway and into the Irish Sea.

Much of the ice from the north-eastern part of the Lake District passed in an anticlockwise direction around the northern slopes of this mountainous mass to join the stream from Scotland that flowed southwards into the Irish Sea (see Fig. 23). This ice-stream crossed the Cockermouth district. Its course is marked by a magnificent series of drumlins. These are streamlined mounds and ridges elongated in a direction parallel to that of the movement of the ice, their steeper or 'stoss' ends facing the direction from which the ice came. The south-eastern corner of the district lies in western Edenside, and there around Hutton Row the drumlins trend to the north-north-west; but this direction of trend changes progressively so as to describe an arcuate course around the northern end of the Lake District. Thus the trend is to the north-west near Welton, to the west at Westward, and to the south-west near Westnewton.

The direction of the ice movement indicated by the drumlins, though essentially representing the movement of the lower layers of the ice, is confirmed by the distribution of the erratics, as for example the trail of the Threlkeld microgranite from the south of the district and that of the rocks of the Carrock Fell complex.

This ice stream around the northern part of the Lake District was joined by ice nourished in the mountainous country around and to the south of Skiddaw. Ice flowed eastwards down the upper portions of the Glenderamackin and the Caldew valleys to join the main stream, the upper layers of which overrode the summit of Carrock Fell. Ice also passed northwards down the valley of Dale Beck, and across the Uldale Fells, and north-westwards along the valley of Dash Beck and across the western end of Great Cockup to Over Water, whilst another stream flowed north-westwards down Bassenthwaite valley. These movements may be deduced from the distribution of the boulder erratics.

The mountainous area displays numerous examples of ice erosion (see Fig. 23). The head of Bannerdale and Bowscale Tarn may be mentioned as typical corries, the latter with its floor occupied by a moraine-dammed lake; the upper part of Dash Beck is a glacially eroded U-shaped valley flanked by corries.

An amelioration of the climate caused the ice-sheet in the Irish Sea basin to recede northwards, whilst the general surface level of the ice was lowered by ablation. A phase was reached when the mountains emerged from their mantle of ice, and only the intervening valleys harboured glaciers which flowed outwards to join the ice-sheet that still covered the low ground.

A further phase in the recession saw the valley glaciers split off from the main ice-sheet. In our area this severance took place at successive stages as the valley-glaciers split off from the south-west in a clockwise direction around the high ground. The normal drainage of the ice-free valleys was dammed back by the main ice-sheet to form glacier-lakes. These formed an aligned system connected by transverse overflow channels that drained westwards and south-westwards to the open sea. Within the district the Bassenthwaite valley-glacier was the first to split off from the main ice-sheet, and the glacier-lake which then occupied the lower part of the Bassenthwaite and Embleton valleys stood at 340 ft O.D., and later at 300 ft, 280 ft, and 230 ft O.D., these levels being indicated by the flat tops of sand and gravel deltas in the Embleton valley near High Netherscale and in the main valley to the south and south-west of Scarness.

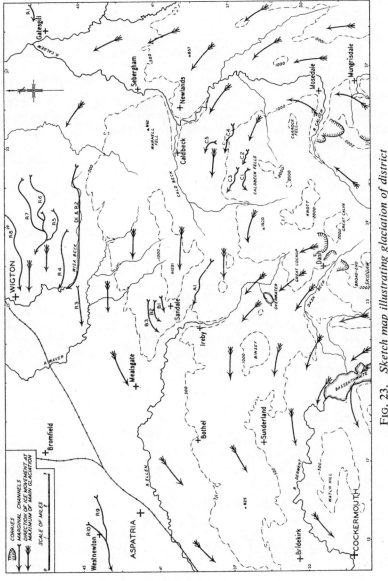

FIG. 23. *Sketch map illustrating glaciation of district*

Glaciers in the valleys of Dash Beck and the River Ellen then became isolated, and their recession may be traced by marginal overflows and frontal deposits of sands and gravels to their corrie-heads around Dash and Burntod. At one stage a glacier-lake in the valley of the Cald Beck at 900 ft O.D. drained by way of a large overflow (A1 of Fig. 23) into a lake in the Ellen valley at 500 ft O.D., where it laid down a sand and gravel delta.

The high ground from Sandale to Warnell Fell appears to have determined the location of the split between the ice occupying the middle reaches of the River Caldew and that of the main ice-sheet to the north. The position of the latter is marked at various stages in its recession northwards by marginal channels (B1 to 3) along the northern side of the Sandale–Warnell Fell ridge.

Pauses in the retreat of the Cald Beck–Caldew valley ice are marked by numerous channels trenching the northern and north-eastern slopes of High Pike and West Fell. A selection of these is shown on Fig. 23 as C1 to C4. Somewhat later stages are indicated by an outwash-delta at Nether Row and kame-belt deposits at Linewath. Subsequently the middle reaches of the River Caldew also harboured a glacier-lake lying between the valley-glacier and the main ice-front to the north; deltas deposited in it by the swollen torrents from the Caldew valley-glacier indicate by their flat tops that the lake stood at the following levels above O.D.: 560 ft, 500 ft, 440 ft, and 400 ft. These are typical examples of land-stream deltas and lie mostly on the right bank of the Caldew between Newlands and Sebergham.

At the 560 ft O.D., and the 500 ft O.D. levels the waters from this glacier-lake drained westwards, but only sharpened features mark the site of the out-flow. During the pause in the general recession when the large deltas at 440 ft O.D. were formed, the Scottish and Lake District ice split off from the ice in Edenside and a glacier-lake came into existence that stretched far beyond the district, and drained by an overflow channel at Gilsland into the drainage system of the River South Tyne. At lower levels the waters again drained westwards probably by the Rosley overflow (D1) which however also functioned as R2 at a later period.

The deltaic deposits in the Caldew valley at lower levels are covered by the Scottish Readvance boulder clay. They may be traced in the banks of the River Caldew as far as Carlisle where they lie at 50 ft above O.D.

At a later stage in the retreat of the Caldew ice the local valley ice west of Mosedale appears to have receded while ice of more southerly origin still occupied the Mungrisdale depression.

Finally, numerous corrie moraines represent the last stages in the decay of the ice within the sheltered recesses of the mountains; although it must be allowed that we have no critical evidence as to whether the Scottish Readvance Glaciation was accompanied by the formation of local glaciers in northern Lakeland.

After an interval the low ground in the northern part of our area was occupied by ice from Scotland up to a height of 400 to 450 ft O.D.—the Scottish Readvance Glaciation. This ice deposited a thin coating of boulder clay on the deposits of the Main Glaciation. An aligned system of glacier-lakes was again dammed back, and drained to the south-west. As the ice retreated the lakes stood at successively lower levels, existing channels were abandoned, and new ones drained the lakes. A glacier-lake in Edenside was connected with a glacier-lake in the neighbourhood of Wigton and channels cut during this phase are shown in Fig. 23 (R1 to R10).

Glacier-lake Wigton was initiated at a height of 260 ft O.D. in the valley of the Wiza Beck near Red Dial, and at this stage drained westwards by a short channel into another lakelet near Crosshill. After a slight recession of the ice-front to the north-west, these two lakes temporarily became confluent at a height of 220 ft O.D. A little later two lakes, connected by another channel, were again in existence—one near Forrester Fold (Dixon and others 1926, p. 59) and another near Low Langthwaite—before finally becoming confluent as Glacier-lake Wigton at a level of about 140 ft O.D. At this period the ice-front had probably receded well to the north-west of the district, and Glacier-lake Wigton then extended northwards and then westwards to Aikshaw, Aldoth, and Highlaws (op. cit. pp. 61–62), west of Bromfield, where the deposition of a large outwash delta commenced. The drainage from Glacier-lake Wigton at the various levels down to 100 ft O.D. appears to have been to the south-west by ill-defined channels some of which were probably marginal to the ice-front.

The lowest lake-level recorded in the area is at 50 ft O.D., shown by strand-lines near Bromfield and along the southern margin of Common Moss, the main lake extending to the north. The overflow at this height was westwards through a channel one mile north of Westnewton and thence in a hollow to the sea near Allanby. The existence of this overflow channel precludes the possibility of the 50 ft level being a sea-level at this time, as has been suggested.

T.E., S.E.H., F.M.T., W.C.C.R.

DETAILS

So far as is practical the Glacial Deposits are described valley by valley in a clockwise order commencing in the extreme south-west with the Embleton valley, followed by the valleys of the Bassenthwaite-Derwent, Ellen, Waver, Wiza, Chalk Beck, Cald Beck and finally the Caldew valley. As a general rule the deposits of each valley are described in a downstream direction.

Embleton Valley. Boulder clay, mostly beneath alluvium, extends along the pre-glacial Embleton valley from the foot of Bassenthwaite Lake westwards to Cocker-mouth. Over the whole of the area the boulder clay is blue-grey in colour; its stones and numerous surface erratics are entirely of Lake District origin and there is no evidence of the presence of Scottish or Irish Sea ice hereabouts. The general direction of ice movement, as shown by numerous glaciated crags and *roches moutonnées* on the Skiddaw Slates of the higher ground, was from E. 10° N. to W. 10° S. This is especially well marked on the fells to the south-east of Routenbeck and indicates movement of the upper part

of the ice across the northerly moving ice-stream occupying Bassenthwaite Lake valley.

A narrow ridge of gravel near Bassenthwaite Lake station may have accumulated at the mouth of an ill-defined channel draining from the Derwent valley near Lowfield through Barkhouse at an earlier stage when a lobe of ice extended westwards from the Uldale Fells across the foot of Bassenthwaite. This gravel forms a natural barrier across the eastern end of the Embleton valley.

A series of small deltas of sand and gravel overlies boulder clay on the floor of the Embleton valley near High Nether-scale. The deltas are believed to have been deposited by a northerly flowing stream in a glacier-lake, part of which occupied this valley during the retreat of the Main Glaciation. W.C.C.R.

The Chapel Beck drainage. Two streams rising in Southerndale and Barkbethdale on Bassenthwaite Common unite at Bark-beth to form Chapel Beck which flows into Bassenthwaite Lake. The two dales are glaciated valleys with corries at their heads.

A narrow ridge, arête-like in character, separates Southerndale from the Bassenthwaite valley, and a somewhat similar ridge lies between Southerndale and Barkbethdale. The dales are floored by a gravelly moraine, consisting of fragments of normal and metamorphosed Skiddaw Slates, vein-quartz and, in Southerndale, blocks of picrite up to 4 ft in diameter; this deposit weathers into a stony clay soil. On both sides of Chapel Beck the ground is covered by thin boulder clay mainly derived from Skiddaw Slates. South of Scarness there are flat-topped deltas of gravel deposited into Glacier-lake Bassenthwaite when that lake stood at 280 ft and later at 230 ft above O.D. The gravel includes many pebbles of Borrowdale Volcanic lavas from Borrowdale, as well as local rocks.

The Dash Beck drainage. Dash Beck rises on the northern slopes of Skiddaw (Broad End) and joins Chapel Beck near the outfall of that stream into Bassenthwaite Lake. Above Brocklecrag the valley of Dash Beck is glacially eroded, being U-shaped and flanked by corries at Dead Crag, and Black Nettle Hause [273 314], ½ mile S.S.E. of Dash, whilst Whitewater Dash [271 314] lying between the corries is a waterfall over a glacially eroded step in the valley floor.

A trail of picrite boulders stretches north-westwards from its source near Dash to cross Great Cockup at altitudes up to 400 ft above the outcrop of the parent rock. The direction of ice movement thus indicated is confirmed by the trend of the ice-eroded U-shaped dry valley [279 334] that cuts across the eastern end of Great Cockup north-west of Burn Tod.

A spread of moraine varying in composition from stony clay to clean gravel composed chiefly of slate pebbles lies to the south of Brocklecrag, and there is clean slate gravel at Mirkholme. The northern slopes of the Dash Beck valley in its lower reaches are free from drift, but the southern slopes are covered by boulder clay derived from Skiddaw Slates which gives rise to a medium to heavy clay soil.   F.M.T.

Derwent Valley drainage from Setmurthy to Cockermouth. Broad irregular mounds of boulder clay flank the River Derwent at the foot of Bassenthwaite Lake and pass northwards in a gently rising but featureless expanse of drift-covered ground in the neighbourhood of Hawgill Wood. Downstream from here the lower slopes of the valley are covered with a blue-grey boulder clay, but higher up the slopes, particularly on the southern side of the valley, the Skiddaw Slates rise from beneath the mantle of drift. Overlying the boulder clay and generally falling in level with the thalweg of the River Derwent are a number of spreads of loamy sand and earthy gravel. They extend from north of Lowfield downstream as far as Cockermouth. Both the Boulder Clay and the Sands and Gravels contain stones that are exclusively of Lake District origin. The most common are slates, sandstones and grits of the Skiddaw Slates, but Borrowdale Volcanic rocks and diorites also occur as boulders or pebbles.

On the northern slopes of the Derwent valley and across the divide between it and the valley of the River Ellen to the north there are large drift-free areas and where there is boulder clay present it is thin. The erratics are exclusively of Lake District origin similar to those already mentioned, but to the north picrite boulders appear and as the Ellen valley is approached boulders of Carrock Fell gabbro are to be found.   T.E.

River Ellen drainage. Ridges of gravel composed almost entirely of pebbles of Skiddaw Slate lie to the north of Great Cockup at the headwaters of the River Ellen. Downstream from here as far as Over Water the southern slopes of the Ellen valley are covered by a medium to heavy boulder clay that contrasts with the light and stony boulder clay found on the outcrop of the Borrowdale Volcanic rocks to the north of the river. The moraine lying to the west of Longlands Fell consists chiefly of angular and sub-angular Borrowdale Volcanic lavas derived from the underlying and nearby outcrops of these rocks, but to the north of it, east of Longlands, there is a small deposit of water-worn gravel in which at least 80 per cent of the pebbles are Skiddaw Slates. The south-western slopes of the River Ellen valley downstream from Stanthwaite are plastered with featureless boulder clay; on the opposite side of the valley the boulder clay is patchy and there are several deposits of gravel. Gravel ridges between Uldale and Aughertree are composed of pebbles of lava, tuff, vein-quartz and Carboniferous Limestone. Similar suites of pebbles are found in the two flat-topped deltas, situated respectively at Uldale Mill and to the south of Guards, that were deposited when a glacier-lake occupied the valley at a level of 500 ft O.D. A glacial overflow channel, dry in its upper reaches, trenches the divide between the Ellen and the Cald Beck drainage north-east of Aughertree Fell.

Farther downstream mounds of sand and gravel lie at heights not greatly in excess of 200 ft O.D. To the north of the River Ellen they stretch from Baggrow westwards past Brayton Hall to the neighbourhood of Aspatria. They have been dug on a small scale for gravel as well as for sand. Their contained suite of pebbles is of both Scottish and Lake District origin.

To the north in the neighbourhood of Mealsgate, Crookdake, Heathfield and as far west as Westnewton there are many well-defined drumlins of west-south-westerly trend. They are composed of boulder clay, and yield a mixed suite of erratics that includes Eycott lavas, Carrock Fell gabbro and granophyre from the northern part of the Lake District, and Criffel and Dalbeattie granite from Southern Scotland.

T.E., F.M.T.

River Waver and Wiza Beck (lower) drainage, Westnewton to Wigton. At Wigton thick glacial deposits have been proved by water-bores now controlled by British Rayophane Ltd. The thickest glacial drift was proved in their No. 2 Bore [2515 4875], about 200 yd S.W. of Wigton station, but the most interesting is their nearby No. 1 Bore [2532 4866], about 650 yd S. of Wigton station, the cores of which were examined by S. E. Hollingworth. Gravel extended to 60 ft and drab boulder clay to about 90 ft. Both deposits contained a suite of stones from Southern Scotland. There was little core between 90 ft and about 150 ft, but the clays recovered contained foreign erratics and the base of the Drift was taken at about 150 ft, at which level pieces of red clay with lenses of drab clay were recovered and these have yielded a marine fauna including several specimens of *Turritella communis*, foraminifera and ostracods. This marine clay appeared to rest directly upon

Stanwix Shales but core recovery was deficient down to 286 ft; from that depth to 303 ft red, brown and green shales of the Stanwix Shales were proved. The surface levels of British Rayophane No. 1 and No. 2 bores are at about 80 ft O.D., so that the pre-glacial hollow, now infilled with drift proved by these bores, descends well below present sea-level.   S.E.H.

In this area Upper Boulder Clay covers the greater part of the ground and gives rise to well-developed drumlins. By their alignment and steeper 'upstream' ends, the drumlins indicate an ice-movement in a direction from east to west near Wigton, but swinging from north-east to south-west towards Bromfield and Westnewton. The boulder clay varies from a stiff, red to purple stony clay to a sandy, incoherent, stony loam with included patches of sand and gravel. To the south-west of Wigton the boulder content in the clay, apart from a certain amount of Triassic and Carboniferous material, is predominantly of Scottish origin, and includes Criffel and Dalbeattie granites, and Lower Palaeozoic grits. Lake District rocks are usually few, but locally may become abundant, as for instance, near High Scales. To the south-east of Wigton the proportion of Lake District stones exceeds that of Scottish stones, boulders from Carrock Fell and of the Borrowdale Volcanic Series being especially characteristic. Large boulders of Carboniferous Limestone are common in the valley of the Wiza Beck near Red Dial.

Lower Boulder Clay, possibly representing a phase of the Main Glaciation, has been recognized near Waverton, and is separated from Upper Boulder Clay by a thin bed of sand. These subdivisions may be seen in a railway cutting [215 462] south of Parkgate, Waverton. The lower clay is stiffer, and of a rather darker colour than that above, but each yields a predominantly Scottish suite of erratics. The intervening sand, about 10 ft thick, has been traced northwards towards Parkgate and southwards as far as Aikbank.

Several large deltaic masses of sand and gravel with well-preserved flat tops and lobate fronts, overlie the Upper Boulder Clay near Wigton and Red Dial, and provide a marked contrast to the surrounding drumlin topography. They represent material accumulated in Glacier-lake Wigton (see

p. 225) chiefly at the mouths of overflow channels draining from the east and south-east. The highest and oldest of these sand and gravel deltas is that at 260 ft O.D. flanking the Wiza Beck (which, higher upstream, probably served as an overflow channel) immediately south-east of Red Dial; later deltas at successively lower levels, down to that on which stands Wigton at 100 ft O.D., indicate rest-levels of the lake as the ice barrier receded towards the north-west. The large delta near Gerrard House has two well-marked terraces, at 220 ft and 200 ft O.D., showing that the lake-level dropped during its formation. Similarly the Forrester Fold delta (Dixon and others 1926) has a 170 ft and a 140 ft O.D. terrace. The Low Houses delta has a flat top at 140 ft O.D. at its north-western and south-eastern ends, with a lower, 120 ft O.D. terrace forming the central portion. Much of the sand and gravel comprising these deltas is earthy and in places is only roughly bedded. Scottish granites and grits form the bulk of the pebbles, but some Triassic sandstone and Lake District rocks are usually present. The gravels in the neighbourhood of Red Hall and Greenhill House, however, contain many Coal Measures rocks, including much coal, and were probably transported by a land-stream from the south. The hummocky nature of much of the gravel near Crosshill and High Crosshill suggests that this delta was never built up to lake-level.

The positions of overflow channels (R2 to R8) are indicated on Fig. 23. In many cases, as for instance the fine channel draining from east to west between Intake House and Greenhill, they are merely interdrumlin hollows which have been widened and deepened. The present Wiza Beck occupies an overflow channel south-east of Red Dial, and again from Tiffinthwaite to Low Longthwaite; the intervening portion of the valley north of Red Dial is of post-glacial date.

The large outwash delta which occupies the north-west corner of Sheet 23, has been dug in several places for sand and gravel. A more detailed reference to this delta is given in the Carlisle Memoir (Dixon and others 1926, pp. 61–62), and the Mary-port Memoir (Eastwood 1930, p. 112). An old gravel pit [1256 4640], 200 yd N.E.

of Aikshaw, in the foreset beds, shows about 14 ft of alternating beds of fine and coarse sand and gravel.

To the west of Langrigg a dull red, plastic and stoneless clay, formerly dug for tile-making, occupies the floor of a wide inter-drumlin hollow, and extends in a south-westerly direction between Greenah and Beechill for about a mile. A similar stoneless clay, for the most part obscured by a thin growth of peat, is visible along the southern margin of Common Moss, and along the edges of peaty hollows between Langrigg and Mealrigg. A small exposure in a stream bed north-west of Clappers shows the clay to be laminated, and it is probable that the deposit accumulated between drumlins in the backwaters of a large glacial lake (p. 220). Features at 50 ft, 75 ft and 100 ft O.D. between Langrigg and Mealrigg may represent strand-lines of this lake.   W.C.C.R.

The Chalk Beck and Wiza Beck drainage above Westward. The drainage areas of Chalk Beck and the headwaters of Wiza Beck are related, and the glacial deposits in them may be conveniently described under one heading. The whole area contains drumlins aligned generally from east to west. Above the 500 ft contour the drumlins normally have solid cores and in several cases their eastern ('stoss') ends are drift free. In this higher-lying area the composition of the boulder clay reflects the lithological character of the underlying solid rocks to a marked degree. In particular around Broad-moor red Coal Measures shales are overlain by a stiff heavy red boulder clay.

To the north the pre-glacial valley of the Wiza Beck, infilled to a depth of 50 ft by glacial and superficial deposits, has been proved along the site of a proposed reservoir dam [2958 4486], ½ mile E. of Westward Park. In the centre of the valley there are three boulder clays separated by gravels. The lowest boulder clay was proved only by chisel borings but the remainder of the sequence was seen in trial pits. Criffel granite and Silurian greywackes from the south of Scotland, but no boulders of definite Lake District origin were recognized in the material from the lowest boulder clay. The lower gravel contained a Scottish and Lake District suite of pebbles including Criffel and Dalbeattie granites, Silurian greywackes, Borrowdale lavas and tuffs and Carrock Fell gabbro. In the middle boulder clay there was a predominance of Lake District boulders, with rare Scottish erratics. A similar suite was found in the upper bed of gravels. The highest boulder clay contained a much higher percentage of Scottish rocks, but on the whole Lake District rocks predominated.

This part of the valley of the Wiza Beck functioned as a glacial overflow channel during the retreat phase of the Scottish Readvance Glaciation, and the two beds of gravel are interpreted as indicating deposition by overflow waters when the valley functioned in like manner during two earlier phases of the glaciation. Too much reliance cannot be placed on the exclusively Scottish nature of the boulder suite from the lowest boulder clay because of the limited amount of material available for examination, but it is suggested that this boulder clay may represent the ground moraine of the Early Scottish Glaciation. The middle and highest boulder clays are undoubtedly deposits of the Main and Scottish Readvance glaciations respectively and the relatively high percentage of Lake District rocks in the upper clay is accounted for by the fact that Scottish Readvance ice overrode Main Glaciation deposits of Lake District origin which here directly underlie the highest clay.

To the north of the Wiza Beck there is a system of well-developed overflow channels (of which Wiza Beck is the highest) that drained westwards at successively lower levels from Lake Carlisle into Lake Wigton during the retreat stage of the Scottish Readvance Glaciation. Several channels (R6, 7 and 8 of Fig. 23) cut through the Scottish Readvance clay to expose sands on their valley sides, and it is probable that the areas between them are underlain by sands and gravels at shallow depth. The junction of the boulder clay and sands was seen in a sand pit at Sandybrow, where 6 ft of alternations of fine red and coarse grey sand are directly overlain by 2 ft of red sandy boulder clay.

The Cald Beck drainage. The Cald Beck flows eastwards past Parkend, Whelpo and Caldbeck to the River Caldew, but is not named on the One-inch map. It occupies a wide pre-glacial valley to the south of the Carboniferous Limestone escarpment formed by Snowhill, Seat, Faulds Brow and Warnell Fell. There is little drift on the northern side of the valley. Large areas of boulder clay cover the southern side; and scattered over the relatively small drift-free areas, as far west as Mickle Rigg, are many erratics of Carrock Fell gabbro. Their presence indicates westward ice movement from Carrock Fell around the northern margin of the Lake District. The boulder clay is thick around Intack and Clay Gap where it gives rise to a heavy loamy soil. Where the boulder clay is thin, as between Caldbeck and Hesket Newmarket, there is a gravelly soil charged with numerous boulders of limestone. Kames of clean sand and gravel occur at Whelpo and near Biggards, west of Hesket Newmarket. Their pebble-content consists mainly of Borrowdale Volcanic lavas, including the Eycott type, and Carrock Fell gabbro and granophyre. The hummocky moraine to the south of Hesket Newmarket consists chiefly of pebbles and boulders of limestone with some lavas, gabbro and granophyre set in a clay matrix.   F.M.T.

The Northern Fells (Brae Fell to West Fell). This high ground is drained by northward flowing tributaries of the Cald Beck and River Caldew. The broad sheet of boulder clay that floors the Cald Beck valley south of Faulds Brow (see above) passes southwards up the rising ground of Lower Palaeozoic rocks into a more loose-textured and gravelly deposit consisting largely of angular and subangular fragments of local rocks. This material eventually grades up into resorted hill-wash, as on the northern slope of Brae Fell, where this wash is channelled to a depth of 6 to 8 ft. The upper 10 ft of the 30 ft deep trench of Ramps Gill [296 300], ¾ mile N.E. of Brae Fell, is cut through material of this type.

Typical local boulder clay on the sides of the Dale Beck valley and its tributaries represents a partial infilling of ground moraine that in places is overlain by a more stony drift. Here and there the latter develops a hummocky surface and in part was probably deposited during the valley-glacier stage, as for example on the floor and sides of the amphitheatre [305 345] surrounding the old Roughton Gill Lead Mine. Beyond the walls of this corrie-like hollow, high-level boulder clay occupies shallow depressions in the feebly dissected upland to at least 1900 ft O.D. and is visible where streams have cut through the widespread peat cover, e.g. east of Great Sca Fell.

Between Dale Beck and Potts Gill a skin of stony drift forms oval mounds up to 100 yd long and elongated east–west, the intervening hollows being accentuated by a series of shallow anastomosing glacial drainage channels. Boulders from Carrock Fell in places form an almost unbroken surface layer. To the east of Fellside Brow this moundy drift passes into the deltaic mass of gravel east of Branthwaite, and it seems possible that the hummocky drift is itself of frontal or subfrontal origin.

Traces of marginal channels are recognizable up to 1600 ft O.D. and above the limit of mappable drift west of the Potts Gill valley, and similar features are more strongly developed east of that valley on the northern slope of High Pike, and high on the eastern and northern flanks of West Fell. A prominent later stage in the northward recession of the ice-front from this high ground is represented by the great mile-long overflow channel south-east of Nether Row with ice-front deltas south of Woodhall at 970 ft O.D. at its eastern end, and at Nether Row at 850 ft O.D. at its western end. Rocks from Carrock Fell make up 70 per cent of the material of the latter delta; the remainder includes volcanic rocks notably Eycott lavas, Skiddaw Slates, occasional Threlkeld microgranite, and rare Scottish granite. Ose-ridges trending west-south-west would appear to indicate deposition hereabouts from an ice-front of north-north-westerly trend.

Upper Caldew and Glenderamackin drainage west of Mungrisdale. The drifts here are predominantly of local origin; the principal items of interest arise from the invasion of the area by external ice. The boulder distribution indicates that during the Main Glaciation ice from the south crossed the eastern spur of Saddleback up to 2000 ft O.D., overrode Souther Fell, west of Mungrisdale (1600 to 1700 ft O.D.), and sent a strong stream of ice-borne boulders down the Glenderamackin valley west of Mungrisdale. Here the boulder clay includes many Borrowdale rocks with a fair sprinkling of Armboth quartz-porphyry. There is an abundance of unmetamorphosed slate associated with some blocks of hornfels on the south-eastern spur of Carrock Fell

(1500 ft O.D.), and gabbro boulders that have been carried uphill by northerly moving ice are fairly common on and beyond the summit ridge of Carrock Fell.

In the Caldew valley, drift appears here and there beneath the widespread peat of the broad hollow centred about the main outcrop of the Skiddaw Granite. A section [2967 2969] on the west bank of the River Caldew 80 yd below the stream junction 1 mile S.S.E. of Great Calva is as follows:

		ft
(4) Drab grey, loose-textured, stony drift with clayey matrix, wholly Skiddaw slate	up to	9
(3) Reddish brown gritty clay with boulders of hornfelsed slate and Borrowdale lavas; the matrix includes much local granitic material and unaltered slate		3–4
(2) Ochreous coloured boulder deposit passing up into (3). Boulders up to 3 ft include Borrowdale rocks with a friable weathered ochreous skin up to 1 in thick. Boulders of hornfels are also deeply weathered and often rotted throughout		2–4
(1) Reddish clayey granitic sand, only top seen		

The deposit (1) may be compared with that on the west side of Blackhazel Beck [3127 3116] 200 yd above its outfall, where 2 to 3 ft of granitic sand with scattered fragments of hornfels overlie decomposed and streaked-out granite. It is not clear here whether the weathering is post-glacial or of some earlier date. A somewhat analogous boulder deposit 6 ft thick is exposed in the west bank of the Caldew [3130 3134], 100 yd below the outfall of Blackhazel Beck. It includes granite and Borrowdale tuffs and is overlain by a purely local accumulation of micacized hornfels and aplitic granitite. The likelihood of a northward dispersal of Borrowdale rocks up the Glenderaterra valley into the Caldew drainage during the Main Glaciation is problematical. The deeply weathered character of deposit (2) is suggestive of an older deposit which could well have been preserved in the sheltered situation where it is now found. The validity of such an interpretation is partially dependent upon the significance of the weathering of the boulders and the granitic material below, and on the origin of the local drift (3) above.

Among the late-glacial deposits may be mentioned the great morainic mound which dams up Bowscale Tarn and the crescentic triple ridge of moraine across the head of the Bannerdale valley, south-east of Bowscale Fell. Many considerable accumulations of boulders, e.g. north-east of the Caldew–Grainsgill junction and north of Grainsgill and east of Carrock Fell, are also referable to the late-glacial period.

Gravels half a mile west of Mosedale include many pebbles of Borrowdale Volcanic lavas and other rocks of southern origin, and are considered to be a frontal deposit from a lobe of ice which projected westwards from ice in the Mungrisdale–Mosedale depression into the ice-free part of the Caldew valley.

River Caldew drainage, Mosedale to Newlands. The broad pre-glacial valley that extends past Mosedale southwards to Mungrisdale is bottomed by post-glacial deposits which however are considered to overlie boulder clay. Drumlin-form boulder clay prevails on the eastern slopes of this pre-glacial valley and eastwards and north-eastwards outside the valley on higher ground drumlin topography persists over thinly veneered 'solid'.

On the western side of the Caldew valley a number of east-facing features, trending and falling gently northwards between the crags at the eastern end of Carrock Fell and Carrock Beck, are thickly strewn with boulders from those crags, and appear to represent lateral ice-contact slopes in morainic material on the western margin of ice in the Caldew valley. It was only after the main ice in that valley had disappeared that the local wall-glacier on the eastern face of Carrock Fell was able to spread its load of boulders eastwards over the shelf at its foot. On the same side of the valley farther north drift extends westwards into the valley of Carrock Beck. Hereabouts the proportion of Carrock Fell complex boulders is high, e.g. 70 per cent in the boulder clay cliff [3499 3502] beside the ford across Carrock Beck at 900 ft O.D. On the other hand a count of pebbles from roadside gravel-pits in the somewhat kettle-holed outwash gravels west

of Linewath reveals a bare 5 per cent from Carrock Fell, with volcanic rocks and associated intrusives from farther south as the dominant element. The contrast between the boulder-content here and that of the boulder clay from Carrock Beck, provides a good illustration of the difference which is frequently found to exist between the ground moraine of largely local origin, and the dominantly foreign character of the overlying englacial material as indicated by deposits at the ice-front.

The high ground between the Caldew and its tributary from the south-east, the Gillcambon Beck, lies in the main track of the northward dispersal of boulders of Threlkeld microgranite, Armboth quartz-porphyry and lavas from Eycott Hill, all of which are found in the glacial drift of this area.

In the west bank of Gillcambon Beck [3888 3474], 300 yd above the road-bridge 3 miles E.N.E. of Carrock Fell, sections show a grey boulder clay overlying a red boulder clay with a distinctive boulder-suite. At the junction the grey clay has incorporated rafts and lenses of the red clay. Up to 10 ft of the latter are exposed. The boulders include, in addition to Lake District volcanic rocks and Carboniferous material, a few Scottish granites, some St. Bees Sandstone and rare Penrith Sandstone. In the upper grey clay Borrowdale rocks greatly predominate, the only other notable constituent being Carboniferous Limestone and a few fragments derived from Mell Fell. The proportion of Carboniferous sandstone is much higher in the lower than in the upper clay. The assemblage of the lower clay is most readily accounted for as a northern suite, carried by southerly moving ice that has incorporated much Lake District material of some problematical earlier dispersal. It is probably to be correlated with the Early Scottish ice-sheet of Edenside. The volcanics-limestone assemblage of the grey clay represents the ground moraine of the Main Glaciation ice that has moved from the Ullswater area across the intervening limestone terrain.   S.E.H.

River Caldew drainage, north of Newlands. The area is almost completely covered by drift; only in the River Caldew and in Roe Beck and their tributaries has denudation reached the solid rocks. Outside the valleys of these streams the boulder clay lies in the form of drumlins. Their trend changes progressively from north-north-west in the south and east, to west-north-west in the north and west. They vary in length from 100 yd to half a mile, and in height from a few to 50 ft.

A series of well-defined gravel deltas lies in the Caldew valley, from a point a quarter of a mile north of Newlands to Newhouse, half a mile north of Sebergham. They yield a suite of pebbles that is exclusively Lake District in origin. The deltas were deposited into a glacier-lake during the Main Glaciation by a stream that occupied the upper reaches of the Caldew valley.

The heights of their flat tops (500, 440 and 400 ft O.D.) mark the levels at which the lake stood. Two large sand and gravel deltas, at Sebergham and north-west of Welton, with flat tops at 440 ft O.D., indicate that the glacier-lake stood at this level for a considerable period and it is probable that it formed part of Lake Eden, for numerous deltas at 440 ft O.D. were deposited into that lake outside the Cockermouth district (Trotter 1929). The 400 ft O.D. delta at Newhouse is partly covered by a thin upper boulder clay, and downstream from here in both banks of the River Caldew there are intermittent outcrops of gravels and sands overlain by boulder clay.   F.M.T.

REFERENCES

DIXON, E. E. L., MADEN J., TROTTER, F. M., HOLLINGWORTH, S. E. and TONKS, L. H. 1926. The geology of the Carlisle, Longtown and Silloth District. *Mem. Geol. Sury. Gt Br.*

EASTWOOD, T. 1930. The geology of the Maryport District. *Mem. Geol. Surv. Gt Br.*

HOLLINGWORTH, S. E. 1931. The glaciation of western Edenside and adjoining areas and the drumlins of Edenside and the Solway Basin. *Quart. Jl geol. Soc. Lond.,* **87**, 281–359.

TROTTER, F. M. 1929. The glaciation of eastern Edenside, the Alston Block and the Carlisle Plain. *Quart. Jl geol. Soc. Lond.,* **85**, 549–612.

Chapter XIV

POST-GLACIAL AND RECENT

UNDER THIS HEADING are included all deposits younger than the last local glacial deposits. Thus it may happen that outside the mountains the higher terraces of the rivers may be as old as, or older than, the latest morainic deposits of the valley- and corrie-glaciers in the hills.

Compared with more southerly regions in Britain post-glacial changes have been comparatively slight owing, no doubt, to the comparatively late disappearance of the ice-sheets from the north. In the hill country many of the most noticeable changes are readjustments of surface-form to subaerial conditions following on the effects of ice-erosion and deposition. Among these may be mentioned the partial burial of steep ice-plucked crags of the corrie and U-valley walls by a blanketing scree of weathered rock, the formation of steep alluvial fans where local oversteepened slopes or overdeepened valleys lie in the paths of streams, and the breaching of morainic barriers or the cutting of new stream courses following on local diversion by glacial agency.

Beyond the mountains there has been little post-glacial change except erosion in the stream and river valleys, some silting up of hollows, and the accumulation of alluvium in the lower inter-drumlin reaches of the rivers.

Post-glacial deposits are of two kinds, those that have been transported, such as valley deposits and screes, and those that have grown *in situ*, of which Peat is the only representative.

River Terraces. Within the mountainous areas the streams seldom possess more than one terrace, situated not far above the level of the gravelly flood-plain alluvium. Outside the mountainous areas a series of terraces of gravel with beds of sand and loam is developed in the principal rivers, but only in certain reaches. Thus the River Caldew possesses two terraces in its middle course south of Hesket Newmarket, but downstream terraces are absent along much of the gorge to the north of Newlands, and farther north beyond Sebergham three major terraces are present.

Individual terraces grade into one another and vary considerably in their height above the alluvium. On the One-inch map they are grouped for convenience into three; labelled first, second and third terraces: but terraces bearing the same symbol in different streams are not necessarily correlatives, and this also applies to widely separated terraces of the same stream. As the terraces appear to have been formed by progressive downcutting of the rivers rather than as a result of elevation their development varies greatly in different river systems. Thus, by contrast with the River Caldew mentioned above, the middle reaches of the rivers Derwent and Ellen have only one major terrace, whereas the River Waver shows three well-developed terraces between Bolton

Low Houses and Waverton. These terraces change from narrow gravel strips near Woodrow to broader stretches of sand and loam near Waverton and Parkgate.

Alluvial Fans. Among the more conspicuous alluvial fans may be mentioned that deposited by the River Ellen on entering at Stockdale the pre-glacial valley which meanders northwards from the Dash Beck valley near Orthwaite to the valley of the River Ellen. This old valley, which is a former course of Dash Beck, has been dammed by the alluvial fan to form Over Water.

Another large fan is situated at Mungrisdale. It has been deposited by a stream from the west (River Glenderamackin of 6-in map), where that stream enters the pre-glacial north-south through valley that hereabouts crosses the watershed. The Glenderamackin, with a steep fall southwards from Mungrisdale through Skiddaw Slates, has now lowered its bed some 15 ft below the level of the fan.

Alluvium. Recent alluvium of varying width depending on the size, velocity and situation of the river, floors most of the river valleys except in certain narrow rock gorges, and calls for little comment.

In the south-west the anomalous Embleton valley, with the present watershed near Stanley Hall, is floored by a broad spread of grey clay and loam. To the north-east of Bassenthwaite there is approximately a square mile of alluvium representing a former extension of the lake, now silted up. Along a line west-south-west from Wigton narrow valleys, cut in a plateau at 300 ft to 400 ft O.D., open out as they emerge on to the lowland, and broad spreads of alluvium have been laid down. Among these may be noted those formed by Langrigg Beck and Crummock Beck at the eastern end of Common Moss, by the River Waver north of Waverton, and by the Wiza Beck west of Wigton. At Mosedale, where the River Caldew enters the north-south pre-glacial valley (mentioned above) to flow northwards, there is a broad alluvial spread which stretches as far north as Linewath.

Peat. Peat deposits are divided on the Drift Edition of the One-inch map into two groups. Those formed at low or intermediate altitudes under conditions of impeded drainage (sometimes termed Basin Peat) have been shown as peat; and those which form a blanket over much of the mountainous uplands where the climatic, topographical and drainage conditions are or have been favourable to its accumulation, have been termed Hill Peat. Deposits that are transitional in character exist.

By analogy with other areas it is probable that peat-formation commenced in the depressions in that phase of early post-glacial time referred to as the Boreal and reached its maximum development during the relatively moist Atlantic and sub-Atlantic climatic phases. Although peat is still being formed in situations favourable to the growth of sphagnum moss, it is undoubtedly wasting away under present climatic conditions (Hollingworth 1934) over much of the ground, and drainage and cultivation have restrained its development or favoured its decay elsewhere.

Several patches of basin peat occur near Bromfield in the north-western part of the map, but it is in all cases a black variety and unsuitable for burning.

An extensive growth of peat floors the low-lying marshy ground to the west of Bromfield known as Common Moss. The peat rests largely on alluvium, but near the margins of the moss extends on to boulder clay and laminated clay. Up to 5 ft of peat may be observed on the banks of Holme Dub. Oak, hazel and thorn are common constituents.

The thick peat deposits known as Mungrisdale, Bowscale, and Mosedale mosses occupy much of the floor of the broad pre-glacial north–south trending valley east of Carrock Fell. This hollow was probably the site of a shallow lake basin in early post-glacial time; the mosses occupy the spaces between the alluvial deposits poured into the hollow by the Glenderamackin, Caldew, and Carrock Beck streams. Peat has been dug for fuel to a considerable extent on these mosses in the past and is still worked to a limited degree. The uppermost 2 ft or so of brown fibrous peat are of little use. It is absent in a section at the northern end of Bowscale Moss where a compact black peat of good quality up to 5 ft thick is overlain by 2 to 3 ft of alluvial clay loam deposited by the River Caldew. At the base of this peat a woody layer underlain by 2 or 3 ft of soft peaty 'muck' is reported.

The thicker developments of hill peat are found on undissected portions of the upland surface and on flat-lying cols or saddles such as Miller Moss at the head of Grainsgill and Birk Moss west of High Pike. In such situations it attains a thickness of 5 to 6 ft. In many places it is channelled by numerous stream courses giving rise to a much broken surface ('haggy peat' or 'peat hags') that is difficult to traverse. Alternation of dry and wet weather favours crumbling, undercutting, and rapid removal of peat in the drier parts of such mosses.

In moister situations as for example the open upper part of the Caldew valley south of Great Calva the peat shows no sign of diminution and some growth is probably still in progress.   S.E.H., W.C.C.R., F.M.T.

REFERENCES

HOLLINGWORTH, S. E. 1934. Some solifluction phenomena in the northern part of the Lake District. *Proc. Geol. Ass.*, **45**, 167–88.

Chapter XV

MINERAL PRODUCTS AND WATER SUPPLY

COAL

VIEWED BROADLY there is a north-easterly deterioration of the coal seams in the Coal Measures from the main part of the West Cumberland Coalfield into the present district. The Yard Band and to a less extent the Ten-quarters Seam are exceptions to this generalization. In the past it was essentially these two seams which supported a thriving mining industry extending from Oughterside eastwards to Bolton Low Houses but mainly centred upon Aspatria and Allhallows. Particulars appear in the Details of the Coal Measures. The collieries now have all ceased production. They mined general purpose coals.

On the question of possible future development northwards an over-riding consideration is the proved presence of pre-Triassic folds beneath the cover of northerly dipping New Red Sandstone rocks, and the knowledge that coal seams are likely to occur only in the pre-Triassic synclines. In assessing the potentialities of this concealed field the Regional Survey of the Ministry of Fuel and Power reported as follows (1945, p. 27 para 140):

"The northern concealed area does not appear particularly attractive as a whole when viewed in relation to the general deterioration of coals in that direction in the known coalfield and in the two boreholes between Maryport and Allonby; in explorations between say Wigton and Allonby it should be borne in mind that any colliery in that area is likely to have to depend on one or at most three seams. Farther north in the Abbey Town area the thickness of New Red cover is likely to be of the order of 3000 feet, to this may be added a possible thickness of 2000 ft of Whitehaven Sandstone [= Upper Coal Measures] in the synclines. Exploration, therefore should proceed cautiously along north-westerly lines from the exposed field."

In considering this question in an industrial survey of Cumberland, F. M. Trotter (*in* Daysh and Watson 1951, pp. 56–8) arrived at a similar conclusion. Additionally, however, the area to the east of Wigton was considered as follows: "In the neighbourhood of Lowling there is a faulted pre-Triassic anticline with Hensingham Beds on the northern limb dipping to the north-west at 20°. If this dip persists Productive Coal Measures may be brought in beneath New Red Sandstone within a mile of the outcrop of the base of that formation." On this basis Productive Coal Measures would be at workable depth (say 1000 to 2000 ft) about two miles due east of Wigton.

T.E., F.M.T.

MINERALS OTHER THAN COAL

There are three metalliferous fields in the Lake District, and that falling within Sheet 23 is usually referred to as the Caldbeck Fells field, although strictly speaking Ruthwaite and Carrock mines lie respectively to the west and to the south of these Fells. The Caldbeck Fells are famed for their variety of minerals and extensive lists have been recorded, of which that of Goodchild (1885) is the most important. Many are merely mineral curiosities, but others exist on a scale which has warranted exploitation for the ores of lead, zinc, copper and tungsten, as well as for umber and barytes. The Caldbeck Fells field was active chiefly for copper in Elizabethan times and intermittently afterwards until the 19th Century. The peak of mining activity was reached during that century when copper and lead ores were principally in demand. In the latter part of the 19th Century there was also some demand for barytes and umber (an ochreous iron-manganese mixture). In the 20th Century mining has been principally for barytes with some production of tungsten. All of the more important mining undertakings have been described previously. Special mention should be made of Postlethwaite's (1913) account of the mines which gives much historical data and includes plans and sections of many of the mines. Special Reports on the Mineral Resources of Great Britain (Eastwood 1921; Wilson and others 1922; Dewey and Dines 1923; and Dewey and Eastwood 1925) give accounts of the mining of particular minerals—lead, zinc, tungsten, copper and barytes. The workings for barytes are also described by S. E. Hollingworth in a Wartime Pamphlet (Dunham and Dines 1945, p. 93), Hitchen (1934) has dealt with the mineralization associated with the Skiddaw Granite and Eastwood (1959) has dealt with all of the more important mines. No metalliferous mine is working, but the barytes mine at Potts Ghyll works intermittently. The following account is intended mainly to supplement published records.   S.E.H.

There has been considerable discussion on the age of the mineralization of the veins found in the Lower Palaeozoic rocks of the Lake District and new light on this question is afforded by recent work. First there have been absolute age determinations of the Skiddaw Granite by A. J. Miller (1962) using the potassium-argon method. The average of five determinations gives an age of 399 ± 6 million years and as the north to south wolfram-bearing veins worked from Grainsgill (p. 115) have been related conclusively to the end stages of the intrusion of the Skiddaw Granite, these veins may be assigned with confidence to that date, in other words to a Lower Devonian stage of the Caledonian orogeny.

Secondly Moorbath (1962) has conducted lead-isotope abundance studies on samples from mineral veins of Great Britain, including samples from veins lying within Sheet 23. To the south some veins containing lead ore that are associated with the Shap Granite have an estimated mean model age of 370 ± 50 million years, and this estimation compares closely with the absolute age determinations for this granite which are 391 ± 7 million years by the potassium-argon method, and 381 ± 7 million years by the rubidium-strontium method. Clearly there is no significant time-interval between the intrusion of the Shap Granite and the emplacement of the nearby associated mineral veins. Surprisingly, however, no similar correspondence exists between the intrusion of the Skiddaw Granite and a lead-bearing vein found within the granite and proved in Carrock Mine, Grainsgill. There is however correspondence between the age estimates of this galena vein and other galena-carrying veins to the north. The relevant model age determinations are as follows:

(a) East–west vein in Skiddaw Granite, Carrock Mine 210 ± 70 m.y.

(b) Roughton Gill South Vein 220 ± 40 „

(c) Driggith Main Vein, ? eastward extension of (b) 260 ± 90 „

These determinations from the Carrock Fell mineral field, as Moorbath points out (*op. cit.* p. 335) fall within the group allocated to his Period 5, and this group embraces determinations from widely scattered districts in the United Kingdom all of which give comparable determinations and have a mean model age of 220 ± 30 m.y. It should be noted, however, that the model ages of these (and other) determinations give the estimated date at which the lead separated from the uranium and thorium. It does not necessarily give the date of emplacement of the lead into the veins. This may be much later and in the case of those lead ores grouped as Period 5 it would appear to be later. The date of the original formation of lead (220 ± 30 m.y.) indicates the Triassic period. But Period 5 includes determinations of the Alderley Edge, Cheshire, mineralization where veins carrying lead and copper ores occupy faults that cut the Keuper rocks thereby indicating a post-Triassic age for the mineralization.

To sum up, the determinations from the lead ores of the Carrock Fell field indicate a mineralization that is not older than Triassic, and by analogy with Alderley Edge it would appear probable that the emplacement of the lead ore in the veins is post-Triassic. A post-Triassic mineralization is found in the West Cumberland hematite field which carries, peripherally, lead and copper ores in small quantities.   F.M.T.

Veins in Grainsgill Beck. These comprise a number of mineralized quartz-veins trending northwards that cross the lower part of the valley of the Grainsgill Beck where they have been worked from Carrock Mine [322 329]. Here they traverse the northernmost outcrop of the Skiddaw Granite, where the granite is mostly converted to greisen, and also the adjacent hornfels and gabbroic rocks to the north. This upper surface of the granite in the greisenized area about Grainsgill has the form of a cupola or dome, which attains its greatest surface elevation beneath the eastern spur of Coomb Height between the Caldew and Grainsgill valleys. This roof-contact falls fairly steeply in all directions to pass beneath the metamorphosed Skiddaw Slates. The principal veins are given from west to east followed by grid references indicating where they cross Grainsgill Beck: Smith Vein [3211 3296]; 70 yd to east Harding Vein [3217 3294]; and 200 yd to east-south-east Emmerson Vein [3233 3289].

The principal workings have been on the Harding Vein. This is essentially a quartz-vein hading steeply to the west and maintaining a width of 2 to 3 ft for much of its explored extent. It carries notable quantities of wolfram, with subordinate scheelite and a variable amount of arsenopyrite with some sphalerite. Pyrite and chalcopyrite are also present with minor quantities of tetradymite and molybdenite. The vein infilling is a complex one.

Exploitation was by levels driven from the vein into the hillsides to the north and south of Grainsgill Beck, the principal production being in the first decade of this century and in the 1914–1918 period. During 1942–3 the Government-sponsored Non-Ferrous Minerals Development Ltd. carried out considerable exploration of the wolfram potentialities of this area by means of a cross-cut driven west from the stream level to intersect the Harding and Smith veins some 70 feet below the level of previous workings. Levels were driven on the Harding Vein southwards and northwards and it is estimated that some 21000 tons of ore, carrying 1·29% WO_3 were proved. Towards the southern limit of exploration, the vein passed from granite into greisen and tended to split into strings. To the north it passed from greisen into micacized hornfelses (microschists of earlier accounts) and then into a varied suite of rocks grouped under the term 'gabbro' belonging to the Carrock Fell complex. Wolfram mineralization remained strong for some distance in the gabbro, but with the vein tending to split in a northerly direction. Small mineralized east to west cross-fractures are occupied by quartz and ankerite carrying a little galena and sphalerite; one of these displaces the Harding Vein some 20 ft to the west on the northern side.

A little exploration has been carried out on the Smith Vein at surface, where it contained arsenopyrite and scheelite. The 1942–3 cross-cut to the Harding Vein mentioned above was extended to the Smith Vein, but it was explored for a short distance to north and south with not very satisfactory results.

The Emmerson Vein has a long history of sporadic working by a number of levels on the northern slopes of Grainsgill valley, but efforts to establish its worth to the south and to the north of the stream have not been successful. The wolfram content is said to have been quite rich in places, but with very patchy distribution. A strong vein of ankerite flanks the quartz-vein on the west: this appears to leave the Emmerson in a northerly direction and eventually crosses Brandygill near the head of that stream.

There are indications of the continuation of some wolfram mineralization in quartz-veins in the middle reaches of Brandygill and again on the southern slope of Coomb Height.

In quartz-veins at the head of Brandygill [322 340] that are possibly a northward continuation of Grainsgill veins, the principal ore minerals are manganese oxides. In Blackhazel Beck also, a manganese-bearing quartz-vein trending a few degrees east of south occurs; this is possibly the southern continuation of one of the Grainsgill belt of fractures. It is possible, therefore, that along this belt of fractures there is a rough zonal distribution of ores outwards from a centre in the Grainsgill neighbourhood. Manganese-bearing quartz-veins also occur in the upper part of Burdell Gill.

In the higher part of Brandygill [3226 3386], about midway between Grainsgill and Drygill, there is an east–west vein on which a level was driven many years ago in a westerly direction for lead ore. Dumps from these exploratory trials are of interest because of the suite of rare minerals such as wolfenite and stolzite which they have yielded in recent years.

Roughton Gill Veins. The old Roughtongill Mine [304 345] has worked a group of mineralized fractures in the valley of Roughton Gill, collectively known as the Roughton Gill Veins, which trend to the north-east across the western end of the Carrock Fell complex and displace the main rock groups of that complex in a north-easterly direction along the north-western side. The considerable lateral displacements of the steeply inclined junctions are suggestive of a horizontal component in the dislocations. The effects of the faulting are less evident to the north-east where the fractures lie wholly within the Borrowdale

Volcanic Series in an area where the paucity of exposures has made detailed sub-division of the succession impracticable. Crossing the headstreams of Roughton Gill there are two principal mineralized fractures known as the North and South Roughton Gill veins. The North Vein crosses Roughton Gill at a point [3020 3433] about 400 yd S. of the old mine buildings, and the South Vein crosses the Gill some 235 yd upstream [3022 3402]. The intervening belt of rocks some 200 yd wide has suffered intense rotting by hydrothermal solutions and is traversed by numerous fractures, some of which are occupied by quartz and barytes. The ores in order of importance were galena, chalcopyrite, malachite and other oxidized copper minerals, and sphalerite with cerussite: manganese is present as psilomelane incrustations, and umber also occurs.

The South Vein, which was the more productive, hades to the north-west at about 20°. The gangue is largely quartz with a good deal of broken country rock. The vein was subject to local swells up to, in one case, 30 ft, where a substantial lens of calcite was present—a gangue mineral which is not usually prominent in this district.

Early workings were on the vein at high altitudes and from short cross-cuts. Deeper workings were by longer cross-cuts driven south-east to the vein, the deepest being the 90-fathom level driven from the east side of Roughton Gill [3025 3440] some 240 yd to the vein, and then south-west along the vein for a distance of 500 yd. To the south-west the mineralization appears to have decreased towards the overthrust mass of Skiddaw Slates west of the Carrock Fell complex (p. 14), and the fractures as such have not been traced within the Skiddaw Slates although there appear to be one or two trials along the conjectured lines of continuation of the veins. To the north-east, although there is extensive alteration of the country rocks—granophyre, felsite and andesites—in the vicinity of the veins, the workable deposits of ore appear to have petered out as the intersection of the Drygill Vein is approached. Some china clay has been got where the vein traverses altered Harestones Felsite.

Several small north-westerly trending mineralized fractures in the Borrowdale Volcanic Series have been explored in the vicinity of Red Gill (a tributary to Roughton Gill), including Red Gill Vein which crosses Red Gill [2935 3467]. These have yielded some lead and copper ores but the total output does not appear to have been considerable. The locality is perhaps best known as a source of the rare mineral linarite.

Sandbed—Driggith Vein. This vein trending to the north-east high on the east flank of High Pike may be considered as a northern continuation of the South Roughton Gill Vein, although continuity as a single mineralized fissure over the intervening obscure ground at the head of Drygill has not been established.

The vein was first worked from the old Driggith Mine [328 352] at the head of Driggith Beck, a tributary of Carrock Beck, on the south-eastern side of High Pike, by cross-cuts driven north-west to the vein and, at a later date, from levels of the Sandbed Mine [332 362] on the north-eastern side of High Pike.

The vein is said to have averaged 4 ft wide with local swellings up to 8 ft, and good exposures can still be seen at the old workings and the caved-in stopes, as for example on the eastern slope of High Pike [3235 3534] where the complex vein consisting of strings of quartz and barytes with ribs of decomposed country rock has a slight hade to the north-west. Quartz and barytes appear to have been the gangue minerals, the principal ore extracted being galena with a considerable amount of sphalerite. Chalcopyrite, bornite and malachite are also present. There has been little activity since 1870 although a little blende was obtained in 1906–7 and some barytes was obtained from Driggith in 1944–5. The ore content seems to decrease south-westwards towards the head of Drygill in an area where there has been extensive hydrothermal rotting of the country rock in a broad belt extending some hundreds of yards from the vein.

The Low Pike Vein is a feebly mineralized fracture carrying quartz and some barytes traceable for a few hundred yards on the northern side of High Pike. It may represent some continuation of the Roughton Gill North Vein.

The Potts Ghyll Veins. These comprise two east to west veins across the upper part of the Potts Gill valley, in the Borrowdale Volcanic Series on the northern slope of High Pike, and they have been worked from the Potts Ghyll Mine [319 365] some two miles south by west of Caldbeck. The mine and the veins retain the older form of the name, though the stream is named "Pott's Gill" on the Ordnance Survey maps. The veins were intermittently worked for barytes in the second part of the 19th Century and during the periods 1915–20, 1926–31 and from 1938 onwards. The two main veins are known as the North or Main Vein and the South Vein. The North Vein crosses Potts Gill [3196 3611], and the South Vein crosses this stream valley some 50 yards farther south [3196 3606]. Their trends are respectively N. 82° W. and N. 70° W. and they intersect at an acute angle some 180 yd west of the stream. Both veins hade south at variable angles from 20° to 35°. To the east the North Vein splits into three.

The veins are principally massive barytes up to 6 ft and exceptionally 10 ft wide, with subordinate quartz. The ore is liable to frequent pinchings and swellings, and where not well developed the fracture may be a single one or be represented by a zone of broken andesitic rock up to 15 ft wide. There is considerable decomposition of the country rock.

Early exploitation was from adits driven on the vein from the sides of the valley of Potts Gill and from short cross-cuts driven from the north to encounter the veins at lower levels. In 1935 a cross-cut was commenced from the valley bottom [3191 3600], 750 yd upstream from Potts Gill Farm. From 1940 for some years the principal output was from that portion of the ore-shoot lying between this level and the old workings 165 ft above. The North Vein was the more productive, the chief mineral output of the South Vein being restricted to the area lying within 200 ft of its intersection with the North Vein. About 1944 there was renewed exploration by adits driven both on the North and South veins. The North Vein was found to split into three, 100 to 150 yd west of the stream. All three branches have been productive. The more northerly branch, known as the Back Lode, was worked only from an adit (the Gill Adit) on the vein; it dies out to the east and at depth. Considerable exploitation of the middle branch, known as the New North Lode, and the southerly branch, known as the Main Lode, has taken place, in the first place by adits driven on the vein from the west and at a later date by a cross-cut approximately in a south-easterly direction from the dressing plant alongside Potts Gill.

An interesting feature of these workings in the east of Potts Gill is the presence of a number of cross-courses which in some places displace the vein to the north on the eastern side. At the eastern limit of the workings on the Main Lode mineralization follows a fracture known as the Blockley Vein trending in a direction N. 30° E. with an easterly hade. This eventually links up with the New North Lode to the north. In the extreme east, beyond the point at which these two veins meet, mineralization deteriorates and the barytes is replaced by a massive sideritic carbonate rock.

Recently the Potts Ghyll barytes mill has been mainly supplied from another east–west vein situated at the northern flank of Westfell some ¾ to 1 mile E. of Calebrack. This lies east of the Sandbed–Driggith Vein and is approximately in line with the Potts Ghyll veins, but is known as the Sandbed Barytes Vein. It hades 10° to the south and is over much of the developed area a strong vein 4 to 10 ft wide in very decomposed volcanic rocks. It has been worked over a maximum vertical height of about 180 ft, principally from a cross-cut driven south to the vein [3316 3618] at about 1300 ft O.D., 100 yd from the upper part of How Beck. From exploration westwards on the vein it appears to be terminated by a northerly fault near to its anticipated intersection with the north-easterly Sandbed–Driggith Lead Vein. To the east it has been explored from a short cross-cut driven from the valley of Bleagill on the north-west slope of Westfell. Here the vein is less productive than farther west. An exploratory level has been driven into the hillside from a point [342 357] about 400 yd S.W. of Calebrack on a vein trending a few degrees north of west and in alignment with the Sandbed Barytes Vein. Quartz is dominant over barytes and the vein has not proved workable.

Ruthwaite Vein. This vein has been worked for barytes from the old Ruthwaite Mine by an adit [2400 3675] situated 1¼ miles S. of Ireby. The barytes occupies a fault (Boundary Fault), which here trends to the north-west and shifts the Carboniferous Limestone Series. The vein is of interest because it is the only one of the Caldbeck Fell suite of veins to indicate on purely geological evidence a post-Carboniferous age.

BUILDING STONE

The use of natural stone for building purposes has been superseded locally by bricks and by concrete, and no quarries for building stone are in operation today within the district. Although other stones have had limited use for buildings and stone walls, the only building stone of real importance is the St. Bees Sandstone. This has been extensively wrought and some of it, from Chalk Beck, was exported. There are innumerable small excavations, and large quarries in this sandstone were worked between Aspatria and Westnewton and farther east near Howrigg and Greenquarries. The most important quarries, however, lie on both sides of Chalk Beck for half a mile northwards from Barnetrigg to Curthwaite. These extensive quarries are probably to be accounted for by the presence of massive grey-white sandstone interbedded with the normal dull red sandstone. Prior to the Second World War there was a good demand for the grey-white stone, the selling price of which was 50 per cent higher than the red stone. Both types of stone are easily worked, and dressed stones of various sizes were produced. Many large buildings are built of St. Bees Sandstone, including Carlisle Cathedral.

ROADSTONE

The harder rocks of the older Palaeozoic formations have all been used for roadstone to a greater or less extent, particularly the lavas of the Borrowdale Volcanic Series. The intrusive igneous rock near Embleton provides an excellent roadstone which has been quarried on a large scale by the Keswick Granite Co. Ltd. There are ample reserves in other igneous intrusions, as for example in the gabbro along the eastern side of Carrock Fell, where recently the above named company has opened a quarry. Also there are ample reserves in the Carboniferous Limestone as is indicated by the numerous quarries that are worked as the need for local roadstone arises, for example the quarry in the Scar Limestone on Faulds Brow formerly worked by the Cumberland County Council and now by Messrs. Strickland and Hill, Uldale.

LIMESTONE

There is a large number of old quarries scattered over the outcrop of the Carboniferous Limestone. Though some provided road-metal the bulk of the quarried stone was formerly burnt for agricultural lime. This branch of the industry has largely died although there is some lime-burning at Bothel.

Limestone is a necessary flux in the conversion of hematite to metallic iron, and the large quarries at Threapland and Ward Hall at one time supplied the iron works of Maryport; but with the closing of this works the quarries were abandoned. Limestone for this purpose, however, is or has been supplied from some of the modern quarries, including Moota Quarry [1485 3615] worked by the Bothel Lime and Limestone Co. Ltd. Also by this company chippings suitable for tarmacadam and concrete aggregates are produced. Adam Lythgoe Ltd. produce roadstone, concrete aggregates and ground lime at Clintz Quarry [1585 3640], Moota, and until recently Thomas Armstrong Ltd., Cockermouth, worked a limestone quarry at High Close for ground limestone, road-metal and flux for blast furnaces. Other companies with limestone quarries in this area are Gilcrux Lime and Limestone Co. Ltd., and Gilcrux, Aspatria, and Hodgsons Quarries, Prospect, near Aspatria. The former Company works Old Bothel Quarry on a small scale to burn lime. All the large modern quarries lie near the main Cockermouth–Carlisle road between Bridekirk and Bothel, in an area where the Fourth to Seventh Limestone crops out mainly as massive limestone up to 500 ft thick and where the drift is thin or absent. Ample reserves exist.

Of the smaller quarries that in the Great Limestone [2835 4010] east of Seat is being worked for roadstone by P. Greggains of Maryport.

WATER SUPPLY

The considerable area of mountainous and moorland ground with fairly high rainfall has permitted the development of gravitational schemes, so that in spite of a scattered population practically all of the villages and hamlets have piped supplies, some of which extend beyond Sheet 23.

These schemes fall into two main groups according to source of supply, and the character of the water differs accordingly. In the first group are supplies derived from surface water or springs (often old mine adits) on the Lower Palaeozoic rocks. These are essentially soft waters; they may be sub-divided into two classes according to their origin as 'very soft' from surface waters and 'moderately soft' from springs and mine adits. The second group comprises springs arising from the Carboniferous Limestone Series and these are 'moderately hard' to 'hard'.

Also on the low ground underlain by Triassic rocks on the northern side of the sheet there is a potential source of underground water in the St. Bees Sandstone that has been tapped to a limited extent at Wigton for industrial purposes.

Since April 1st 1961 the supplies for Cockermouth and the Cockermouth U.D.C. have been taken over by the West Cumberland Water Board. The Cockermouth supply comes from Crummock Water on Sheet 29 (Keswick). The main source for the villages in the Cockermouth R.D.C. is the Hause Gill scheme. The intake is from Hause Gill just above its junction with Dash Beck and about $\frac{3}{4}$ mile N.W. of Dash. It supplies the parishes of Bassenthwaite, Bothel and Threapland, Blindcrake, Gilcrux and Bridekirk, Oughterside and Plumbland. Supplies for Caldbeck come from a spring $\frac{3}{4}$ mile S.W. of Caldbeck church, and for Hesket Newmarket from springs from the Old Sandbed Mine about $1\frac{1}{2}$ mile S.W. of the village. Among smaller schemes, Embleton, Setmurthy and Wythop take from Tom Rudd Beck (on Sheet 29).

The greater part of the central and northern parts of Sheet 23 falls within Wigton Rural District and of several schemes the largest is that of the old Aspatria and Silloth Joint Water Board, now incorporated in the West Cumberland Water Board, which derives its supply from the upper reaches of the River Ellen and from Over Water, augmented by a piped supply from Dash Beck. These supplies drain into Chapel House Reservoir to the north-east of Over Water. The villages supplied from this scheme include Aspatria, Boltongate, Mealsgate, Bolton Low Houses, Fletchertown, Blennerhasset, Baggrow and Westnewton.

Another important source for Wigton Rural District operated by the West Cumberland Water Board, is a series of springs rising on the northern side of the Carboniferous Limestone outcrop that stretches eastwards from Sandbeds to Faulds Brow at an elevation of 1000 ft O.D. or more. The Carboniferous Limestone of this ridge is cut off to the north by the Thornthwaite Fault which brings in relatively impervious beds of the Hensingham Group to the north. Numerous springs rise along or near to the Thornthwaite Fault, and for distributive purposes they have been bunched into groups which carry distinctive names (e.g. Thornthwaite spring is a grouping of seven separate springs). From west to east, they are known as Wellrash, Greenfoot, Boiling, Keld and Thornthwaite springs. These supplies are now augmented by a piped supply from the upper reaches of Hay Gill, an eastern tributary of Dale Beck, in the Caldbeck Fells. From the combined scheme are supplied Wigton and the villages of Westward, Blencogo, Waverton, Langrigg and Bromfield on Sheet 23 as well as several parishes to the north on Sheet 17 (Carlisle). Of other small supplies in the Wigton Rural District may be noted the Aughertree spring from the Carboniferous Limestone to the north of Ireby, and also the water from an old adit about $\frac{1}{4}$ mile W. of Longlands Fell. This last scheme supplies high-lying hamlets in the parish of Ireby.

The north-eastern part of Sheet 23 was supplied by the Border Rural District from the old Ninety Fathom level of Roughton Gill Mine, now abandoned;

but since April 1st 1961 the Border undertaking has been transferred to the Carlisle County Borough Council, and supplies the parish of Dalston.

In the south-eastern part of the sheet, water is supplied by the Eden Water Board. Springs near the head of Bullfell Beck, 1½ miles W. of Mungrisdale, supply Berrier and Murrah. The scheme is now linked up with the larger Aira Beck scheme and the combined scheme supplies the villages of Mungrisdale, Bowscale, Mosedale and Castle Sowerby.

On account of the abundance of surface supplies and springs, underground water from wells and boreholes is of minor importance. At Wigton, however, boreholes to depths of about 700 ft have produced good supplies of water from the St. Bees Sandstone for industrial purposes. These bores are now under the control of British Rayophane Co. Ltd; in 1959 and 1961 that company sank two additional and adjoining bores into St. Bees Sandstone on the southern margins of the town, one mile north of Red Dial which have considerably augmented its supplies. The St. Bees Sandstone is considered to be capable of yielding additional water in other parts of the low-lying ground where it crops out or where it is concealed by younger formations.

T.E., S.E.H., F.M.T.

REFERENCES

DAYSH, G. H. T. and WATSON, E., 1951. *Cumberland, with special reference to West Cumberland. A survey of Industrial Facilities.* Whitehaven.

DEWEY, H. and DINES, H. G. 1923. Tungsten and Manganese Ores. (Edn. 3). *Mem. Geol. Surv. Gt Br. Spec. Rep. Miner. Resour.*, **1**.

————— and EASTWOOD, T. 1925. Copper Ores of the Midlands, Wales, the Lake District and the Isle of Man. *Mem. Geol. Surv. Gt Br. Spec. Rep. Miner. Resour.*, **30**.

DUNHAM, K. C. and DINES, H. G. 1945. Barium Minerals in England and Wales. *Wartime Pamph. Geol. Surv. Gt Br.* No. 46.

EASTWOOD, T. 1921. Lead and Zinc Ores of the Lake District. *Mem. Geol. Surv. Gt Br. Spec. Rep. Miner. Resour.*, **22**.

————— 1959. The Lake District Mining Field in *The Future of Non-Ferrous Mining in Great Britain and Ireland. A symposium.* London.

GOODCHILD, J. G. 1885. Contributions towards a list of minerals occurring in Cumberland and Westmorland. *Trans. Cumb. and Westm. Ass.*, **9**, 175–99.

HITCHEN, C. S. 1934. The Skiddaw Granite and its residual products. *Quart. Jl geol. Soc. Lond.*, **90**, 158–200.

MILLER, A. J. 1962. The Potassium-Argon ages of the Skiddaw and Eskdale Granites. *Geophys. J. R. Astr. Soc.*, **6**, 391–3.

MINISTRY OF FUEL AND POWER. 1945. *Northumberland and Cumberland Coalfields, Regional Survey Report.* London.

MOORBATH, S. 1962. Lead isotope abundance studies on mineral occurrences in the British Isles and their geological significance. *Phil. Trans. R. Soc.* Series A, **254**, 295–360.

POSTLETHWAITE, J. 1913. *Mines and Mining in the Lake District (Edn. 3)*, Whitehaven.

WILSON, G. V., EASTWOOD, T., POCOCK, R. W., WRAY, D. A. and ROBERTSON, T. 1922. Barytes and Witherite (Edn. 3). *Mem. Geol. Surv. Gt Br. Spec. Rep. Miner. Resour.* **2**.

Appendix I

LIST OF FOSSILS FROM THE LOWER
CARBONIFEROUS ROCKS

The names of the fossils in the following lists are those of specimens mainly collected by Mr. S. W. Hester and Mr. W. Dewar during the course of the resurvey. The original determinations (except the corals) were by Sir James Stubblefield; they were revised (1962) where necessary by Dr. W. H. C. Ramsbottom. The corals were originally identified by the late Dr. S. Smith; recently (1963) Mr. M. Mitchell has revised some of the names and these modifications are indicated in brackets under his initials. The fossil lists have been prepared by Miss E. M. Pyatt.

The localities are listed numerically and wherever practicable eight-figure National Grid References of the 100 kilometre square NY are given within square brackets for each locality; exceptionally six-figure references are given. The description of the locality is followed by the Geological Survey registered number(s) of the specimen(s), e.g. Ht 269–82.

The ranges of the fossils are given by symbols which are abbreviations for the names of the horizons. These abbreviations are as follows: 7L = Seventh Limestone; 6–7L = Sixth to Seventh Limestone, undivided; 5–7L = Fifth to Seventh Limestone, undivided; 4–7L = Fourth to Seventh Limestone, undivided; 6L = Sixth Limestone; 5–6L = Fifth to Sixth Limestone, undivided; 5L = Fifth Limestone; 4–5L = Fourth to Fifth Limestone, undivided; 4L = Fourth Limestone; WL = White Limestone; RL = Rough Limestone; JL = Jew Limestone; TBL = Tyne Bottom Limestone; SPL = Single Post Limestone; ScL = Scar Limestone; 5YL = Five Yard Limestone; 3YL = Three Yard Limestone; 4FL = Four Fathom Limestone; GL = Great Limestone.

Fossil Localities

Locality
1. Blindcrake, quarry [1421 3429], 850 yd W. 29° S. of Inn; 7L; TE 722–4.
2. Gill Beck [1494 3456], 110 yd S. of Inn, Blindcrake; 7L; TE 698–710.
3. Gill Beck [1495 3452], 150 yd S. of Inn, Blindcrake; 7L; TE 711–3.
4. Isel Park, springheads [1585 3454], 600 yd N. of Isel Mill; 7L; Ht 337–42.
5. Isel Park, crags and quarries extending E.N.E. for 800 yd from a point [1584 3456] 620 yd N. of Isel Mill; 7L; Ht 299–336.
6. Isel Park, crag [1586 3461] 670 yd N. of Isel Mill; 7L; Ht 283–92.
7. Isel Park, crags extending E.N.E. for 700 yd from a point [1578 3474] 800 yd N. by W. of Isel Mill; 7L; Ht 293–8.
8. Thackray Wood, crags extending E.N.E. for 400 yd from a point [1594 3482] 920 yd N. of Isel Mill; 7L; Ht 269–82, TE 751–2.
9. Isel Mill, crags [160 349] about 1000 yd N. by E. of; 7L; Ht 235–51.

10. Isel Mill, crags [161 350] about 1100 yd N. by E. of; 7L; Ht 234.
11. Blindcrake, small quarry [1605 3469] on 500 ft contour, 1200 yd E. of Inn; 7L; TE 755.
12. Stinkeld Quarry [180 364], 700 yd E.S.E. of Threapland Moss; 7L; TE 565-6.
13. Dobby Quarry [1805 3672], 800 yd E.N.E. of Threapland Moss; 7L; TE 570.
14. Uldale church, quarry [2524 3689] 200 yd S.E. of; 7L; Hs 1132-70.
15. Longlands, crag [2664 3633] crossing track 450 yd N.N.W. of; 7L; Hs 1041-42A.
16. Moor House, quarry [3090 3816] ¼ mile N.W. of; 7L; Hs 3741-7.
17. Murrah Hall, old quarry [3864 3084] 1250 yd S.E. of; 7L; De 2874-903.
18. Murrah Hall, quarry [3876 3060] 1430 yd S.E. of; 7L; De 3099-100.
19. Greenah Crag, N. and S. trench [3946 2994] extending for 100 yd, 1 mile N. 10° W. of; 7L; Hs 491-502.
20. Parkend Beck, left bank [2976 3853], 500 yd S.W. of Parkend; Bryozoa Band at top of 7L; Hs 820-39.
21. Wharrels Hill, quarry [1711 3781] 200 yd S.S.W. of milestone 'Wigton 9' on; 6-7L; Hs 1222-35.
22. Wharrels Hill, quarry [1761 3797] 480 yd E. of milestone 'Wigton 9' on; 6-7L; Hs 1309-18, TE 572-4, TE 734.
23. Bothel School, quarry [1778 3840] on E. side of Cockermouth road, 900 yd S.W. of; 6-7L; Hs 1305-8.
24. Bothel Beck [1829 3934], 100 yd N. of Limekiln Bridge; ?6-7L (see p. 166); TE 696.
25. Bothel Beck [1827 3937], 150 yd N. by W. of Limekiln Bridge; ?6-7L (see p. 166); Ht 101-15.
26. Gillands Quarry [1833 3946], 500 yd N. of Bothel School; 6-7L; Hs 1296-1304, TE 571.
27. Bank House, old quarry [3709 3363] 300 yd N.W. of; 6-7L; De 2724-57.
28. Hutton Roof School, 200 yd S.W. of [3708 3400]; 6-7L; SEH 141.
29. Murrah Hall, old quarry [3808 3194] ¼ mile N.E. of; 6-7L; De 2819-68, SEH 162-74.
30. Murrah Hall, 460 yd N. 50° E. of [3816 3189]; 6-7L; SEH 157-8.
31. Blindcrake, scar [1562 3479] on 600 ft contour, 800 yd E. 10° N. of Inn; 5-7L; TE 753-4.
32. Isel Park, crag extending N.E. for 150 yd from a point [1562 3479] 920 yd N. by W. of Isel Mill; 5-7L; Ht 252-68.
33. Isel Park, crag extending N.E. for 450 yd from a point [1556 3490] 1050 yd N.N.W. of Isel Mill; 5-7L; Ht 221-33.
34. Isel Park, crag extending N.E. for 150 yd from a point [1555 3500] 1150yd N.N.W. of Isel Mill; 5-7L; Ht 220.
35. Thackray Cottage, crag [1587 3521] 600 yd W. of; 5-7L; TE 568-9, Ht 211.
36. Thackray Cottage, crag [1581 3523] 700 yd W. of; 5-7L; Ht 212-9.
37. Thackray Cottage, old quarries [1599 3521] 500 yd W. of; 5-7L; Ht 191-210.
38. Salkeld Close [1623 3640], 900 yd S. of Threapland Gill Bridge; 5-7L; TE 567.
39. Clints Crags [164 354], immediately N. of Thackray Cottage; 5-7L; Ht 170-90.
40. Salkeld Close Crags [1643 3570], 500 yd N. of Thackray Cottage; 5-7L; Ht 167-9.
41. Threapland Moss, quarry [1696 3711] 800 yd N. 30° W. of; 5-7L; Hs 1257-73, TE 564.
42. Sunderland Heads [1721 3573], about ½ mile W.N.W. of Sunderland; 5-7L; TE 561.
43. Borrowscale Quarries, small old quarry [1977 3871] 1000 yd S. 10° W. of West House, Torpenhow; 5-7L; Hs 3555-8, TE 726-7.

44. Borrowscale Quarries [1967 3855], 1200 yd S. 15° W. of West House, Torpenhow; 5–7L; TE 741–2.
45. Borrowscale Quarries, main quarry [1967 3880] 900 yd S.S.W. of West House, Torpenhow; 5–7L; Hs 3540–54, TE 738–40.
46. Snittlegarth, quarry [2165 3809] on E. bank of stream, 400 yd N.W. of; 5–7L; Hs 3691–5.
47. Stottgill, quarry [3387 3766] 500 yd W.S.W. of; 5–7L; Hs 967–83.
48. Normancrag, quarry [3681 3432] 350 yd E. of; 5–7L; Hs 1010–21.
49. Howhill, quarry [3952 3569] ¼ mile E.S.E. of; 5–7L; De 2430–79, SEH 137–9.
50. Howhill, quarry and crags [3980 3555] 700–800 yd S.E. of; 5–7L; De 2483–500.
51. Howhill, quarry [3962 3563] 600 yd S.E. of; 5–7L; De 2480–2.
52. Whypot Crags [3972 3435], 1 mile S. of Howhill; 5–7L; De 3113–30.
53. Whypot Crags, small crag [3958 3418] 250 yd S.W. of; 5–7L; De 3131–5.
54. Whypot Crags, crags [4031 3436] 650 yd E. of; 5–7L; De 2582–611.
55. Blindcrake, quarry and scar [1426 3451] 750 yd W. 13° S. of Inn; 4–7L; TE 714–5.
56. Blindcrake, [1443 3410] 900 yd S.W. of Inn and 100 yd S.E. of Redmain road; 4–7L; TE 681.
57. Blindcrake, quarry [1443 3452] 550 yd W. 15° S. of Inn and 200 yd N.E. of Redmain road; 4–7L; TE 682–95.
58. Blindcrake, quarry [1445 3430] 650 yd W. 40° S. of Inn; 4–7L; TE 716–21.
59. Threapland Gill [1582 3824], 850 yd N.E. of Plumbland Cottage; 4–7L; TE 558.
60. Threaplandgill Bridge [1616 3716] on W. side of Cockermouth-Bothel road; 4–7L; Hs 1204–15, TE 560.
61. Threapland Moss, quarry [1725 3641] 100 yd S.W. of; 4–7L; Hs 1236–56, TE 562–3.
62. Wharrels Hill, quarry [1743 3807] 300 yd E.N.E. of milestone 'Wigton 9' on; 6L; Hs 1319–25.
63. Stangerhill Quarry [204 382] 200 yd W. of Stangerhill; 6L; TE 728–30, Hs 3522–39.
64. Stanger Hill, quarry [2055 3815] on S. side of road, 1 mile S.S.E. of Torpenhow; 6L; Hs 3510–21.
65. Uldale Mill, quarries [2324 3770] 800 yd W.S.W. of; 6L; Hs 1179–1203.
66. Uldale Church, quarries [2540 3720] 350 yd N.E. of; 6L; Hs 1114–31 A.
67. Uldale church, quarry [2560 3700] 550 yd E. of; 6L; Hs 1171–8.
68. Gill Beck [3219 3947], 600 yd S.W. of Caldbeck church; 6L; FMT 119–20.
69. Gill Beck [3221 3950], 560 yd S.W. of Caldbeck church; 6L; Hs 3794–820, FMT 129–30.
70. Whelpo Beck [319 397], gorge upstream from point 600 yd W.S.W. of Caldbeck church to Fairy Bridge; 6L; Hs 3999–4014, FMT 135.
71. Murrah Hall, 650 yd E. 12° S. of [3841 3148]; 6L; SEH 176–8.
72. Highbanks Wood, scarp [3887 3091] 220 yd E.S.E. of N.W. corner of; 6L; De 3029–69.
73. Snowhill, crag [2817 3857] 200 yd E. of; 5–6L; FMT 118.
74. Thistlebottom, crag [2848 3875] 500 yd S.W. of; 5–6L; FMT 113–4.
75. Thistlebottom, 200 yd W. of [2859 3812]; 5–6L; FMT 132–3.
76. Thistlebottom, stream [2845 3917] 300 yd W.N.W. of; 5–6L; Hs 964–6.
77. Parsonby Brow, old quarry [143 381] ½ mile S. of Parsonby; 5L; De 2224–30.
78. Lower Scar [1477 3576], 100 yd W. of Moota House; 5L; TE 522.
79. Moota Hill Beacon, small quarry [1459 3709] 800 yd N. 10° E. of; 5L; TE 521.
80. Moota Hill Beacon, quarry [1464 3745] ¾ mile N. of; 5L; TE 523–4.
81. Moota Hill Beacon, 750 yd E. 5° N. of [1514 3641]; 5L; TE 520.
82. Moota Hill Beacon, 800 yd E.N.E. of [1512 3663]; 5L; TE 526–35.

83. High Close, quarry [147 382] ½ mile S.E. of Parsonby; 5L; De 2214–23, Hs 1326–8, TE 549–50.

84. Roadside Quarry [1560 3712], 1000 yd S.S.E. of Plumbland Cottage; 5L; Hs 1274–87.

85. Threaplandgill Bridge, quarry [1587 3694] 500 yd S.W. of; 5L; Hs 1216–21.

86. Wharrels Quarry [171 382], Wharrels Hill; 5L; TE 488–502, 731–3.

87. Baggra Yeat, quarry [2645 3720] 650 yd N.N.W. of; 5L; Hs 875–92.

88. Snowhill, quarry [2796 3879] 250 yd N. of; 5L; Hs 794–809, FMT 79–82, 102–5.

89. Nether Row, 700 yd N.W. of [3185 3829]; 5L; FMT 131.

90. Nether Row, 650 yd N.W. of [3186 3817]; 5L; FMT 136.

91. Townhead, quarry [3205 3913] 180 yd W.S.W. of; 5L; Hs 3757–67, FMT 123–7.

92. Hesket Bridge, quarry [3407 3879] 300 yd W. 15° S. of; 5L; Hs 4015–28, FMT 189.

93. Hutton Roof, quarry [3719 3403] 180 yd W.S.W. of Inn; 5L; Hs 1022–31.

94. Hegglehead, dump [3713 3480] 100 yd W.N.W. of; from 5L; De 2537–42, SEH 135.

95. Hegglehead, scarp [3719 3473] immediately S.W. of; 5L; De 2528–36.

96. Thwaite Hall, scarp [3732 3501] 120 yd W. of; 5L; De 2646–51.

97. Bank House, quarry [3752 3355] 300 yd E.N.E. of; 5L; Hs 1032–9, SEH 142–3.

98. River Caldew, right bank [3677 3663] 200 yd N. of Haltcliff Bridge; 5L; De 2523–7.

99. Murrah Hall, quarry [3815 3210] 650 yd N.E. of; 5L; De 2784–818, SEH 151–6.

100. Murrah Hall, quarry [3824 3190] 560 yd N. 58° E. of; 5L; SEH 159–61.

101. Highbanks Wood, scarp [3894 3097] 270 yd E. of N.W. corner of; 5L; De 3010–28.

102. Highbanks Wood, 300 yd E. 17° S. of N.W. corner of [3897 3092]; 5L; De 2998–3009, SEH 179–81.

103. Highbanks Wood, 380 yd E. 26° S. of N.W. corner of [3899 3082]; 5L; SEH 183.

104. Highbanks Wood, scarp [3909 3083] ¼ mile E.S.E. of N.W. corner of; 5L; De 2956–97, SEH 180.

105. Highbanks Wood, 470 yd E. 20° S. of N.W. corner of [3908 3081]; 5L; SEH 182.

106. Bothel Limeworks Quarry [176 391], 800 yd W.N.W. of Bothel School; 4–5L; TE 545–8.

107. Arkleby church, quarry [1398 3867] by roadside, 600 yd S.S.W. of; 4L; De 2322–8.

108. Threapland Gill [1554 3897], 400 yd S.S.W. of Threapland Hall; 4L; TE 556–7.

109. Thrushgill Quarries, N.W. Quarry [155 392] on W. side of road immediately S.W. of Threapland; 4L; De 2357–64, TE 551–2.

110. Thrushgill Quarries, S.E. Quarry [1555 3915], on E. side of road immediately S.W. of Threapland; 4L; De 2329–54, TE 553–5.

111. Millstonemoor, 750 yd E. of [1436 3583]; 4L; TE 518–9.

112. Moota Hill, quarry [1438 3624] 850 yd E.N.E. of Millstonemoor; 4L; TE 503–8.

113. Moota House, 500 yd W.S.W. of [1443 3565]; 4L; TE 525.

114. Moota Quarry [148 362], ¼ mile N. of Moota House; 4L; TE 509–17.

115. Threaplandgill Bridge, 950 yd S.W. of [1563 3663]; 4L; TE 559.

116. Wardhall Quarries, Main Quarry [138 380], ¼ to ⅜ mile S.S.E. of Wardhall Guards; 4L; De 2255–68.

117.   Wardhall Quarries, Middle Quarry [1393 3803], 900 yd S.E. of Wardhall
        Guards; 4L; TE 539–44, De 2269–70.
118.   Wardhall Quarries, Eastern Quarry [139 382], 800 yd S.E. of Wardhall
        Guards; 4L; De 2271–321.
119.   Plumbland Cottage, 520 yd N.E. of [1542 3825]; 4L; TE 575–80.
120.   Plumbland Cottage, scar [1584 3652] 1 mile S.S.E. of; WL; Hs 1288–95.
121.   Snowhill, quarry [2767 3865] 300 yd W.N.W. of; WL; Hs 792–3.
122.   Paddigill, quarry [3029 3987] 400 yd S.S.E. of; WL; Hs 634–50, FMT
        98–101.
123.   Biggards, 470 yd W. 10° S. of [3158 3862]; WL; FMT 121–7.
124.   Biggards, quarry [3161 3877] 450 yd W. 10° N. of; WL; Hs 3700–19.
125.   Biggards, quarry [3173 3887] 350 yd W. 35° N. of; WL; FMT 137.
126.   River Caldew, left bank [3419 3907], 250 yd N.N.W. of Hesket Bridge;
        WL; Hs 4029–44, FMT 178–81.
127.   River Caldew, left bank [3424 3923], 400 yd N. by W. of Hesket Bridge;
        WL; FMT 184.
128.   Hesket Bridge, crag [3460 3907] 350 yd N.E. of; WL; FMT 187.
129.   Hudscales, quarry [3296 3773] 300 yd N.N.W. of; WL; Hs 984–98, SEH
        125, 133–4.
130.   Thwaite Hall, scarp [3735 3513] 200 yd long, to the N.W. of; WL; De
        2612–45, SEH 136.
131.   Thwaite Hall, quarry [3764 3478] 250 yd S.E. of; WL; De 2545–52.
132.   Thwaite Hall, roadside quarry [3745 3487] 120 yd S. of; WL; De 2543–4.
133.   Highbanks Wood, scarp [3918 3098] 520 yd E. of N.W. end of; WL; De
        2931–55.
134.   Highbanks Wood, scarp [3923 3105] 570 yd E. by N. of N.W. end of;
        WL; De 2904–30.
135.   River Caldew, right bank [3480 4009], 660 yd N.W. of Newlands; RL;
        Hs 4211–51.
136.   Banks, quarry [3538 3818] 240 yd S.S.W. of; RL; Hs 3825.
137.   Hudscales, old quarry [3303 3784] 350 yd N.W. of; RL; Hs 999–1009.
        SEH 126–32.
138.   Scale Quarry [3809 3344], just E. of Scale Farm; RL; De 3101–12.
139.   Berrier Hill, 700 yd S.W. of summit of [3999 3045]; RL; SEH 175.
140.   Uldale church, quarry [2576 3734] 800 yd E. 25° N. of; JL; Hs 1096–1113.
        FMT 237–8.
141.   Faulds, quarry [2978 3992] 500 yd N. of; JL; Hs 651–83, FMT 91–6.
142.   Biggards, quarry [3280 3823] 1000 yd E. 30° S. of; JL; Hs 3748–56.
143.   Parkhead, 850 yd S. of [3379 3979]; JL; FMT 191.
144.   Hudscales, 700 yd N. of [3322 3818]; JL; FMT 186.
145.   Banks, roadside quarry [3539 3822] 200 yd S.S.W. of; JL; Hs 3821–4.
        FMT 182.
146.   Banks, quarry [3546 3813] 300 yd S. of; JL; Hs 3826–9.
147.   River Caldew, left bank [3415 3952], 750 yd N. 12° W. of Hesket Bridge;
        JL; FMT 183.
148.   Howhill, quarry [3882 3577] ¼ mile W.S.W. of; JL; De 2558–75.
149.   Murrah Hall, quarry [3855 3240] 1200 yd N.E. of; JL; De 2758–83,
        2869–73, SEH 147.
150.   Lamonby Quarries [4007 3588], 1000 yd E. of Howhill; JL; De 2501–22,
        SEH 140.
151.   Highbanks Wood, scarp [3996 3100] 950 yd N.E. by E. of S.E. corner of;
        JL; De 3092–8.
152.   New Park, quarry [2310 3836] 750 yd S.E. of; JL and TBL; Hs 3688–90.
153.   Cleamire, quarry [2704 4127] 800 yd W.S.W. of; TBL; Hs 810–9.
154.   Thistlebottom, quarry [2926 3971] 800 yd N.E. of; TBL; Hs 866–74.

155. Cald Beck, left bank [3413 3980], 250 yd upstream from its junction with River Caldew; TBL; Hs 4169–87.

156. River Caldew, right bank [3502 4022], 800 yd N. 5° E. of Newlands; TBL; Hs 4198–203.

157. Gillcambon Beck, old quarry [3782 3627] on E. bank, 250 yd N.W. of St. Kentigern's Church; TBL; De 2368–91.

158. Howhill, old quarry [3885 3579] ¼ mile W.S.W. of; TBL; De 2576–81.

159. Howhill, old quarry [3913 3546] 550 yd S.W. by S. of; TBL; De 2553–7.

160. Howhill, quarry [3934 3605] 200 yd E.N.E. of; TBL; De 2411–29.

161. River Caldew, right bank [3436 3978], 50 yd S.S.E. of confluence with Cald Beck; between TBL and SPL; FMT 188.

162. Seat, crag [2844 3996] crossing parish boundary 1000 yd N.N.W. of Thistlebottom; SPL; Hs 864–5.

163. River Caldew, right bank [3537 4028], 400 yd W.S.W. of Starnmire; SPL; Hs 4188–97.

164. Gillcambon Beck, small crag [3774 3638] near E. bank, ¼ mile N.W. of church, Sowerby Hall; ? SPL; De 2351–67.

165. Wardhall Quarries, Main Quarry in old tramway [1357 3819], 50 yd from quarry entrance, 500 yd S.S.E. of Wardhall Guards; Junceum and Chert Beds (top of 4L); De 2231–54, TE 536–8.

166. Banks, crags [3561 3814] 300 yd S. of; ScL; Hs 3831–52.

167. Seat, quarry [2839 4010], ⅔ mile N.N.W. of Thistlebottom; ScL; Hs 840–63.

168. Paddigill, line of quarries [304 409] about 800 yd N.N.E. of; ScL; Hs 921–7, FMT 107–9, 239.

169. Whelpo Beck [3252 3991], 20 yd N.W. of N.W. corner of Caldbeck church; ? ScL; FMT 134.

170. Gillcambon Beck, right bank of tributary [3703 3733], 500 yd W.S.W. of Low Moordike; ScL; De 2312–8.

171. Howhill, quarry [3883 3649] 700 yd N.N.W. of; ScL; De 2392–408.

172. Kirkland Guards, quarry [1873 3950] 600 yd S. 10° E. of; ? 5 YL; Hs 3559–64.

173. West House, Torpenhow, section in stream [1963 3945], 400 yd W.S.W. of; 5YL; Hs 3583–8.

174. West House, Torpenhow, section in stream [1960 3934], 500 yd S.W. of; ?5YL; Hs 3580–2.

175. Cockshot Beck [218 391], 500 yd S.W. of Cockshot Bridge to S. end of wood; 5YL; Hs 3633–64.

176. Paddigill, quarry [3019 4107] 900 yd N. of; 5YL; Hs 893–920.

177. Aughertree Fell, quarry [2617 3761] ¾ mile E.N.E. of Uldale church; 5YL; Hs 723–71.

178. West House, Torpenhow, section in stream [1962 3950], 375 yd W.S.W. of; shales above 5YL; Hs 3589–613.

179. Cockshot Beck [2207 3937], 150 yd W.S.W. of Cockshot Bridge; shales above 5YL; Hs 3614–32.

180. Paddigill, crag [2965 4072] 800 yd N.W. of; 3YL; Hs 944–9.

181. Parkhead, 300 yd S. of [3390 4011]; 3YL; Hs 3768–75, FMT 192.

182. Castle How [3601 3837], 600 yd E. of Banks; 3YL; FMT 185.

183. How Hill, quarry [3933 3643] 75 yd E. of summit of; 3YL; De 2409–10.

184. Parkhead, 150 yd S. of [3391 4027]; 4 FL; Hs 3737–40, FMT 190.

185. Gillcambon Beck, section [3708 3735] in tributary, 450 yd W.S.W. of Low Moordike; ? 4FL; De 2319–41.

186. Gillcambon Beck, section [3761 3703] in tributary, 20 yd downstream from Wharton House; ?4FL; De 2342–50.

187. Newbiggin Grange, quarry [2168 4066] 300 yd E. of; GL; Hs 3696–9.

188. Close, quarry [2343 4160] 350 yd S. of; GL; TE 646–8.

189. Daleside, north quarry [2706 3941], 1000 yd E. 30° N. of; GL; Hs 700–20.

190. Daleside, south quarry [2705 3934], 1000 yd E. 20° N. of; GL; Hs 721–2.
191. Townthwaite Beck [2898 4210], 700 yd W. 35° S. of Hilltop; GL; Hs 4045–61.
192. Brocklebank, quarry [3054 4292], 1250 yd E. 25° N. of Hilltop; GL; Hs 4252–73, FMT 138–43, 235.
193. Wellrash, quarry [2402 4132] 500 yd S.W. of; GL; FMT 128.
194. Sandale, 350 yd N. of northern end of [2471 4077]; GL; FMT 116–7.
195. Headend Quarry [250 408], ¼ mile S.S.W. of Angerton Bank; GL; Hs 950–63, FMT 110.
196. Angerton Bank, quarry [252 411] 50 yd S. of; GL; FMT 83–9.
197. Daleside, crags [2645 3858] on either side of gorge, 500 yd S.S.E. of; GL; Hs 779–91.
198. Seat, quarry [2908 4048] in swallow-hole, 1250 yd W. 12° N. of Paddigill; GL; Hs 684–99, FMT 115.
199. Snowhill, quarry [268 381] 1400 yd W.S.W. of; GL; Hs 772–8.
200. Parkhead, quarry [3371 4037] 350 yd S.W. of; GL; Hs 3720–36, FMT 195.
201. Parkhead, quarry [3393 4044] 200 yd S. of; GL; FMT 193–4.
202. Ryelands, quarry [3331 4071] 300 yd S.E. of; GL; FMT 196–7.
203. Chalk Beck, old quarry on right bank [3417 4714], 700 yd E.S.E. of Barnetrigg; GL; Hs 4901–12.
204. Lowling Borehole No. 5 [3143 4646], 350 yd S. 17° W. of S.W. corner of Lowling; In GL at 1050 ft; FMT 966.

LIST OF FOSSILS

The symbols denoting fossil horizons are given on p. 246.

The numbers which follow the symbols refer to the fossil localities listed above. Thus for example: 5L to GL. 82, 192 indicates that the range of the fossil is from the 5th Limestone to the Great Limestone and that the localities from which it was collected are numbers 82 and 192.

PLANTAE

ALGAE

Cf. *Aphralysia sp.* 5–7L. 39, 40.
Calcisphaera? 5L to GL. 82, 192.
Girvanella? 5L to JL. 85, 139, 148.
Spongiostroma? 7L. 18.
Algae? TBL to SPL. 158, 163.

ANIMÀLIA

FORAMINIFERA

Endothyra sp. 5L. 77.
Saccamminopsis fusulinaformis (McCoy). RL to GL. 136, 140–1, 143, 151–3, 163, 166, 168, 172, 174, 181, 200.
Saccamminopsis cf. *fusulinaformis.* 5–7L. 43.
?Saccamminopsis fusulinaformis. 3 YL to GL. 182, 203.
Saccamminopsis? 6–7L to GL. 26, 109, 158, 192.
Textularia sp. 6L to ? 5YL. 65, 104–5, 129, 133, 143, 172, 174.
Foraminifera indet. 7L to 5YL. 16–7, 25, 29, 49, 52, 54, 63, 65, 72, 76–7, 85, 87, 91, 99, 101, 104–5, 112, 122, 124, 129–33, 138, 142, 145, 148, 151, 153–4, 165–6, 175.

PORIFERA

Erythrospongia ?? 6–7L. 25.
Sponge spicules indet. 7L. 2.

ANTHOZOA

Aulophyllum fungites (Fleming). 6L to GL. 62, 112, 117, 140, 154, 166–8, 192, 195, 198, 200.

Caninia juddi (Thomson) emend. Lewis. 7L to GL. 9, 29, 50, 56, 61, 92, 100, 110, 117–8, 133, 140, 147, 154, 181, 192, 197, 200–1.

Caninia cf. *juddi* (Thomson) emend. Lewis. 5–7L to GL. 48, 84, 87, 189.

? Caninia juddi (Thomson) emend. Lewis. 5–7L. 33.

Caninia subibicina McCoy. WL. 130.

Caninia sp. [= *Campophyllum* aff. *murchisoni* Milne Edwards and Haime]. 6–7L. 29.

Caninia sp. [early stage possibly *C. juddi* (Thomson) emend. Lewis]. 5–7L. 49.

Caninia sp. 4–7L. 61.

Caninia? 5–7L. 39.

Carcinophyllum vaughani Salée. 6L to WL. 43, 101, 130.

Cf. *Carcinophyllum vaughani.* 6L. 49, 71.

Carcinophyllum cf. *vaughani:* 5L to WL. 99, 104, 134.

? Carcinophyllum cf. *vaughani.* 6L. 63.

Carcinophyllum sp. WL. 129.

Carcinophyllum? 5–7L. 54, 61, 104.

Chaetetes depressus (Fleming). 6–7L to JL. 25, 33, 39, 40, 148.

Chaetetes septosus (Fleming). 7L to GL. 5, 13, 65, 87–8, 97, 193.

Chaetetes sp. 5–7L. 48.

Cf. *Clisiophyllum multiseptatum* Garwood. 5–7L. 32.

Clisiophyllum cf. *multiseptatum.* 6–7L. 25.

Clisiophyllum? 5–7L. 54.

Clisiophyllid [new form]. 5–7L. 5, 32.

Clisiophyllid coral. 5–7L. 33.

Clisiophyllid indet. 5–7L to Shales above 5YL. 49, 179.

Corwenia rugosa (McCoy). 4L. 118.

? Corwenia rugosa. 5L. 92.

Cf. *Cyathaxonia costata* McCoy. TBL. 155.

Densiphyllum sp. 5L. 101.

Dibunophyllum cf. *bourtonense* Garwood and Goodyear. 5–7L to GL. 35, 200.

Dibunophyllum cf. *bristolense* Garwood and Goodyear [≡ *D. bipartitum bipartitum* (McCoy). M. M.]. 4–7L to GL. 61, 140, 200.

Dibunophyllum turbinatum (McCoy) [≡ *D. bipartitum bipartitum* (McCoy). M. M.]. 6L to GL. 72, 93, 104, 130, 138, 141, 180, 189–90, 192, 195–7.

Dibunophyllum turbinatum [near *D. bristolense* Garwood and Goodyear] [≡ *D. bipartitum bipartitum* (McCoy). M. M.]. 5–7L to GL. 36–7, 192, 195.

Dibunophyllum turbinatum [*D. matlockense* Sibly]. [≡ *D. bipartitum bipartitum* (McCoy). M. M.]. GL. 197.

Dibunophyllum turbinatum [near *D. matlockense* Sibly] [≡ *D. bipartitum bipartitum* (McCoy). M. M.]. 5–7L to GL. 32, 47, 84, 192, 195–6, 199.

Dibunophyllum turbinatum [with large central column] [≡ *D. bipartitum bipartitum* (McCoy). M. M.]. JL. 140.

Dibunophyllum turbinatum [near *D. rhodophylloides* Garwood and Goodyear] [≡ Cf. *Slimoniphyllum slimonianum* (Thomson). M. M.]. 3YL. 180.

Dibunophyllum turbinatum [cf. *D. rhodophylloides* Garwood and Goodyear] [≡ Cf. *Slimoniphyllum slimonianum* (Thomson). M. M.]. 5L to GL. 104, 197.

Dibunophyllum sp. [*Aspidophyllum* type]. 4L. 118.

Dibunophyllum sp. 7L to GL. 9, 27, 29, 32, 35–7, 39, 45, 48, 54, 61, 64, 69, 77, 92, 97, 99, 101, 104, 107, 109–10, 117, 130, 148, 166–7, 171, 173, 184, 187, 192, 194, 196–7, 199, 201.

Dibunophyllum? 5–7L to 4FL. 52, 54, 57, 155, 167, 176, 184.

? Dibunophyllum [traces only]. 7L. 16.

Diphyphyllum gracile McCoy. JL. 150.

Diphyphyllum lateseptatum McCoy. 5–7L to GL. 35, 37, 39, 146, 188, 192, 195–6, 198.

Diphyphyllum sp. TBL. 156.

Fasciculophyllum cf. *densum* (Carruthers) [but a small and slender form. S.S.]. *junceum* and Chert Beds (Top of 4L). 165.

Fasciculophyllum cf. *omaliusi* (Milne Edwards and Haime). 5YL to GL. 177, 189.

Heterophyllia grandis McCoy. 6L. 70, 72.

Heterophyllia cf. *grandis*. 5YL. 177.

Heterophyllia ornata McCoy. 5L. 92.

Heterophyllia sp. 6–7L. 29.

Hexaphyllia maccoyi (Duncan). 5YL. 177.

Hexaphyllia mirabilis (Duncan). 6–7L. 25.

Koninckophyllum cf. *dianthoides* (McCoy). Between TBL and SPL. 161.

Koninckophyllum magnificum Thomson and Nicholson. 5–6L to GL. 73, 202.

Koninckophyllum cf. *magnificum*. WL. 120.

Koninckophyllum sp. 5L to 3YL. 99, 110, 180.

Koninckophyllum? 7L. 12.

Lithostrotion arachnoideum (McCoy). 6L. 27.

Lithostrotion irregulare (Phillips) [≡ *L. pauciradiale* (McCoy). M. M.]. 7L to ScL. 4, 5, 9, 12, 19, 21, 23, 25, 27–9, 32–3, 37, 39, 41, 45–9, 54–5, 57, 61, 63–7, 69, 71–2, 78–9, 83–4, 92–3, 97–9, 104, 106, 110–2, 118, 120, 124, 129–30, 135, 137, 140–1, 146, 148, 150–1, 163, 166.

Lithostrotion irregulare [var. approaching *L. junceum*] [≡ *L. pauciradiale* (McCoy). M. M.]. ? 5YL. 172.

Lithostrotion irregulare [approaching *L. martini* Milne Edwards and Haime] [≡ *L. pauciradiale* (McCoy). M. M.]. 6–7L to ScL. 23, 51, 55, 166.

Lithostrotion irregulare [passing to *Diphyphyllum*] [≡ *L. pauciradiale* (diphymorphic). M. M.]. 6–7L. 26.

Lithostrotion cf. *irregulare* [≡ *L.* cf. *pauciradiale* (McCoy). M. M.]. RL. 137–8.

Lithostrotion junceum (Fleming). 7L to 3YL. 9, 21, 33–4, 37, 39, 41, 45–6, 49, 52, 54, 60–2, 65–6, 68–70, 72, 77, 80, 83–4, 86–8, 91–3, 95, 97, 99–101, 106, 109–10, 114, 116–7, 120, 122, 124, 126, 129, 135, 141–2, 146, 150, 155, 163, 165–8, 175, 177, 181.

Lithostrotion junceum [approaching *L. irregulare* Phillips] [≡ *L. pauciradiale* (McCoy). M. M.]. JL. 150.

Lithostrotion junceum [large var.]. 6L to JL. 63, 149.

Lithostrotion maccoyanum Milne Edwards and Haime. 6–7L to TBL. 26–7, 29–30, 40, 45, 49, 60, 63, 97, 99, 102, 122, 129, 135, 145, 155.

Lithostrotion cf. *maccoyanum*. 5L. 92.

? Lithostrotion cf. *maccoyanum*. 7L. 10.

Lithostrotion martini Milne Edwards and Haime. 7L to ScL. 5, 17, 29, 48–9, 61, 72, 89, 101, 129, 131, 133, 144, 166.

Lithostrotion martini [passing into *Diphyphyllum lateseptatum* McCoy]. 7L. 15.

Lithostrotion martini [tending to become cerioid]. 5L. 102.

Lithostrotion cf. *martini*. 7L to WL. 16, 29, 41, 43, 47, 57, 64, 97, 113, 129.

Lithostrotion cf. *martini* [small var.]. ?ScL. 169.

Lithostrotion cf. *martini* [small var. showing *Nemistium* trend]. 5L. 91.

Lithostrotion [*Nematophyllum*] *minus* (McCoy). 6–7L to WL. 21, 60, 74–5, 83, 88, 91, 96, 122, 126.

Lithostrotion [*Nematophyllum*] cf. *minus*. 7L to 4L. 9, 38, 83, 106, 114.

Lithostrotion portlocki (Bronn). 7L to 4L. 4, 37, 80, 85–8, 109–10, 114, 117.

Lithostrotion portlocki [large form]. 6L. 70.

Lithostrotion portlocki [approaching *L. maccoyanum* Milne Edwards and Haime]. 5L to JL. 86, 142.

Lithostrotion cf. *portlocki*. 6–7L to RL. 30, 129, 137.

Lithostrotion cf. *portlocki* [a form intermediate between a cerioid and a phaceloid *Lithostrotion*]. 5L. 87.

Lithostrotion sp. [*Diphyphyllum lateseptatum* McCoy]. JL. 141.
Lithostrotion sp. [between *L. maccoyanum* Milne Edwards and Haime and *L. portlocki* (Bronn)]. WL. 129.
Lithostrotion sp. 5–7L. 32.
Lithostrotion? 5–7L. 50.
Lonsdaleia duplicata (Martin). 7L to GL. 19, 29, 88, 100, 104, 106, 110, 118, 195.
? Lonsdaleia duplicata. 7L. 9, 17.
Lonsdaleia floriformis (Martin). 6–7L to GL. 21, 42, 65, 84, 88, 112, 118, 121, 129–30, 140, 142, 198, 203.
Lonsdaleia floriformis floriformis (Martin). 5–7L to WL. 44, 86, 122.
Lonsdaleia floriformis laticlavia S. Smith. GL. 192, 195, 197–8, 204.
Lonsdaleia floriformis cf. *laticlavia.* 5L to GL. 87, 191.
Lonsdaleia? 5L. 99.
Nemistium edmondsi S. Smith. 4–7L (probably 4L) and JL. 59, 110, 111, 140.
Orionastraea phillipsi (McCoy). ? 6–7L. 25.
Orionastraea cf. *phillipsi.* JL. 145.
Orionastraea placenta (McCoy). ? 6–7L. 24.
Palaeosmilia murchisoni Milne Edwards and Haime. 6–7L to JL. 23, 27, 29, 61, 84, 87–8, 92, 97, 99, 102, 129, 137, 142.
Palaeosmilia murchisoni [early var. near *Cyathophyllum* φ Vaughan]. JL. 141.
Palaeosmilia sp. 7L to 5L. 9, 49, 65, 93, 99.
Palaeosmilia sp. nov.? 5–7L. 44.
Palaeosmilia? 4–7L. 61.
Syringopora catenata (Martin). 4L. 112, 118, 124.
Syringopora cf. *catenata.* 5L to JL. 84, 129, 140.
Syringopora geniculata Phillips. 6L. 72.
Syringopora ramulosa Goldfuss. Bryozoa Band at top of 7L to JL. 20–1, 23, 41, 62, 65, 66, 84, 122, 137, 141.
Syringopora cf. *ramulosa.* WL. 125, 129.
Syringopora reticulata Goldfuss. 7L to SPL. 5, 19, 21, 29, 32, 48, 60, 63, 65, 72, 86, 88, 91–3, 99, 101, 114, 116–8, 124, 130, 163.
Syringopora cf. *reticulata.* 7L to RL. 5, 13, 37, 66–7, 83, 135.
Syringopora sp. 7L to GL. 9, 14, 17, 33, 39, 41, 77, 99, 104, 129, 132, 141, 171, 192, 195.
Zaphrentites delanouei (Milne Edwards and Haime). ScL. 168.
Zaphrentites disjunctus (Carruthers). 5YL. 176.
Zaphrentites cf. *disjunctus.* ScL. 168.
'*Zaphrentis' enniskilleni* Milne Edwards and Haime. 5–7L. 39.
'*Zaphrentis' enniskilleni* var. 6L. 69.
'*Zaphrentis'* cf. *enniskilleni.* 5–7L. 52.
Zaphrentid. 4L. 116, 165, 176.
Zaphrentid? 5–7L to GL. 39, 45, 148, 171, 197.
Zaphrentid indet. 5L to 3YL. 91, 126, 173, 179, 181.
New coral [S. Smith]. 4–7L. 57.

CRINOIDEA

Platycrinites cf. *laevis* Miller. 5YL. 177.
Platycrinites sp. WL to 5YL. 126, 177.
Crinoid fragments. 7L to GL. 8, 14, 20–2, 25, 29, 43, 45, 47, 72, 84, 99, 107, 109, 116, 118, 122, 124, 126, 129, 135–6, 141–2, 145, 148, 152, 159, 162, 165, 170–5, 177–9, 184, 187, 192, 195–6, 198, 200–1.

ECHINOIDEA

Archaeocidaris sp. 7L to GL. 2, 108, 175, 200.
Cf. *Melonechinus etheridgii* (Keeping). GL. 188.

ANNELIDA

Serpula sp. RL. 138.
Campylites [*Serpulites*] *sp.* Bryozoa Band at top of 7L. 20.

POLYZOA

Batostomellid polyzoans. 7L to 5L. 14, 20, 58, 88.
Fenestella membranacea (Phillips). WL to 5YL. 126, 177.
Fenestella cf. *membranacea.* 5YL. 175.
Fenestella nodulosa (Phillips). 7L to 5YL. 5, 8, 20, 29, 67, 117, 126, 135, 176–7.
Fenestella cf. *nodulosa.* 5YL. 177–8.
Fenestella plebeia McCoy. 7L to 5YL. 8, 176, 178.
Fenestella cf. *plebeia.* 6–7L. 22.
Fenestella polyporata (Phillips). RL to 5YL. 135, 176–7.
Fenestella sp. 7L to Shales above 5YL. 8, 14, 135, 155, 178.
Fistulipora minor McCoy. 7L. 8.
Fistulipora sp. 7L. 8.
Hemitrypa cf. *hibernica* McCoy. 6–7L. 8, 14, 29.
Penniretepora gracilis (McCoy), 5YL. 175.
Penniretepora aff. *grandis* (McCoy). 5YL. 177.
Penniretepora cf. *grandis.* RL. 135.
Penniretepora sp. 6–7L to 5YL. 22, 29, 126, 135, 176.
Polypora papillata McCoy. 5–7L. 47.
Polypora? RL. 135.
Ptylopora sp. 7L. 8, 14.
Rhabdomeson sp. 7L to 5YL. 8, 29, 135, 177.
Rhabdomeson? 7L. 14.
Stenodiscus compactus (Munro). 7L. 14.
Stenodiscus sp. JL. 148.
Stenodiscus? 7L to 5L. 14, 61, 83.
Polyzoa [encrusting]. 6L. 69.
Polyzoa indet. 6–7L to GL. 29, 36, 47, 49–50, 52, 54, 56, 63, 104, 118, 123, 129, 148, 153–5, 177, 198.

BRACHIOPODA

Acanthoplecta mesoloba (Phillips). Shales above 5YL. 178.
Actinoconchus planosulcatus (Phillips). 7L to GL. 5, 14, 49, 58, 142, 148, 150, 164, 167, 171–3, 178, 184, 191, 198.
? *Actinoconchus planosulcatus.* TBL to Shales above 5YL. 154, 179.
Cf. *Actinoconchus planosulcatus.* 6L to 5L. 69, 92.
Actinoconchus cf. *planosulcatus.* 5–7L. 36.
Actinoconchus? 7L to GL. 4, 133, 160, 183, 192.
Alifera cf. *panderi* Muir-Wood and Cooper. ScL. 167.
Antiquatonia cf. *insculpta* (Muir-Wood). GL. 189.
Antiquatonia sulcata (J. Sowerby). GL. 203.
Antiquatonia sp. 6L to JL. 66, 75, 148.
Athyris expansa (Phillips). 7L to GL. 17, 50, 72, 104, 149, 191.
? *Athyris expansa.* 6L. 70.
Cf. *Athyris expansa.* 5–7L to ? 4 FL. 36, 185.
Athyris cf. *expansa.* 7L. 16.
Athyrid indet. 5L to TBL. 83, 156.
Avonia davidsoni (Jarosz). 6–7L to 4L. 25, 117.
Avonia youngiana (Davidson). *junceum* and Chert Beds (Top of 4L) to GL. 165, 175, 178, 189, 195.
Avonia cf. *youngiana.* TBL to Shales above 5YL. 155, 162, 164, 178.
Avonia sp. 7L to TBL. 5, 64, 148, 157.
Avonia? TBL to *junceum* and Chert Beds (Top of 4L). 160, 165.

Brachythyris cf. *decora* (Phillips). GL. 198.

Brachythyris integricosta (Phillips). TBL. 155.

Brachythyris sexradialis (Phillips). TBL. 158.

Brachythyris sp. [*B. integricosta* group]. ScL. 167.

Brachythyris sp. WL to JL. 122, 141.

Brachythyris? 5YL and Shales above 5YL. 175, 178.

Buxtonia sp. 6L to GL. 69, 118, 191.

Buxtonia? JL. 141.

'*Camarotoechia*' *sp.* 7L to GL. 8, 20, 118, 135, 178, 192.

'*Camarotoechia*' ? ? 4FL. 185.

Chonetes sp. s.l. 5–7L to GL. 27, 45, 52, 72, 124, 141, 200.

Chonetes? s.l. ? 4FL. 185.

Cleiothyridina cf. *glabristria* (Phillips). 5–7L. 14, 48.

Cleiothyridina royssii (Davidson). 4L to Shales above 5YL. 110, 177, 179.

Composita ambigua (J. Sowerby). JL to GL. 148–9, 178–9, 188, 195.

Composita aff. *ficoidea* (Vaughan). 7L. 5.

Composita? WL. 133.

Davidsonina carbonaria (McCoy). 7L.5–6.

Davidsonina septosa (Phillips). WL. 129–30.

Davidsonina aff. *septosa*. 5L. 50, 88, 104.

? Davidsonina aff. *septosa*. JL. 148.

Davidsonina cf. *septosa*. 5L. 85–6.

Davidsonina? 5–7L. 36.

Daviesiella cf. *llangollensis* (Davidson). WL. 133.

Delepinea aff. *comoides* (J. Sowerby). 5–6L to WL. 53, 65, 83, 85, 88, 104, 123, 130, 134.

? Delepinea aff. *comoides*. 5L. 104.

Cf. *Delepinea* aff. *comoides*. 5L to WL. 50, 120.

Delepinea sp. 6L. 65.

Derbyia? TBL. 156.

Dictyoclostus cf. *semireticulatus* (Martin). 6L. 69.

Dielasma hastatum (J. de C. Sowerby). Bryozoa Band at top of 7L to GL. 20, 198.

Dielasma cf. *hastatum*. 5–7L to Shales above 5YL. 48–9, 99, 133, 148–9, 155, 164, 167, 178.

Dielasma sacculum (J. de C. Sowerby). 5–7L to GL. 48, 137, 155, 175, 189, 192.

? Dielasma sacculum. 6L. 72.

Dielasma cf. *sacculum*. 4–7L to GL. 60, 69, 77, 167, 198.

Dielasma sp. 7L to GL. 8, 20, 25, 39, 54, 63, 91–3, 117, 138, 149, 154, 157, 160, 164–5, 167, 179, 188, 192, 195.

Dielasma sp. [wide form]. 5–7L. 52.

Dielasma? 4L to ScL. 107, 134, 171.

Echinoconchus elegans (McCoy). 7L to GL. 8, 14, 25, 47, 117, 135, 155, 165, 176, 196.

Echinoconchus cf. *elegans*. 7L to JL. 4–5, 148.

Echinoconchus punctatus (J. Sowerby). 7L to GL. 14, 29, 118, 138, 166, 173, 175, 191, 200.

Echinoconchus cf. *punctatus*. 5L to Shales above 5YL. 83, 177–8.

Echinoconchus sp. 7L to Shales above 5YL. 5, 72, 119, 150, 157, 178.

Eomarginifera cf. *derbiensis* (Muir-Wood). GL. 192.

Eomarginifera cf. *lobata* (J. Sowerby). 5YL. 173.

Eomarginifera longispina (J. Sowerby). 5–7L to GL. 54, 175, 198.

Eomarginifera cf. *longispina*. GL. 196–7.

Eomarginifera cf. *praecursor* (Muir-Wood). JL. 150.

Eomarginifera setosa (Phillips). 5YL to GL. 175, 189.

Eomarginifera cf. *setosa*. JL to GL. 141, 149, 151, 191.

Eomarginifera cf. *tissingtonensis* (Sibly). Shales above 5YL. 179.

Eomarginifera sp. Bryozoa Band at top of 7L to GL. 20, 64, 135, 152, 156, 163, 166–7, 178, 190–2.

Eomarginifera? 4L. 110.

Fluctuaria cf. *undata* (Defrance). 7L to 5YL. 14, 126, 176.

Cf. *Gigantoproductus bisati* (Paeckelmann). 6L. 69.

Gigantoproductus cf. *bisati.* 6L. 66.

Gigantoproductus cf. *bisati* [a slightly inflated, fine ribbed, thin shelled form. C. J. S.]. 5L. 93.

Gigantoproductus aff. *crassus* (Fleming). JL. 140.

Gigantoproductus edelburgensis (Phillips). JL. 141, 150.

Gigantoproductus cf. *edelburgensis.* 5–7L to SPL. 52, 83, 91, 118, 124, 129, 141, 163.

Gigantoproductus giganteus (J. Sowerby). RL. 138.

Gigantoproductus aff. *giganteus.* TBL. 155.

Gigantoproductus cf. *giganteus.* ?SPL. 164.

Gigantoproductus gigantoides aequalicostatus (Paeckelmann). 5–7L. 33.

Gigantoproductus latissimus (J. Sowerby). 6L to GL. 63, 116, 118, 160, 180, 192, 198.

Gigantoproductus latissimus var. [with folded trail]. GL. 191.

Gigantoproductus latissimus cf. var. GL. 196.

Gigantoproductus latissimus subsp. nov. 7L. 9.

Cf. *Gigantoproductus latissimus.* 4L. 109.

Gigantoproductus aff. *latissimus.* JL. 140.

Gigantoproductus aff. *latissimus* [thick shelled form]. JL. 140.

Gigantoproductus cf. *latissimus.* 5L to GL. 83, 107, 110, 118, 141, 155, 163, 165, 178–9, 187, 189.

Gigantoproductus cf. *latissimus* var. [with folded trail]. GL. 189.

Gigantoproductus maximus (McCoy). 5–7L to Shales above 5YL. 49, 63–4, 66–7, 92, 126, 129, 137, 178.

Gigantoproductus aff. *maximus* [large transverse form]. 5–7L. 37.

Gigantoproductus cf. *maximus.* 7L to WL. 1, 5, 27, 45, 48–50, 57, 60–1, 63, 65–6, 69–70, 72, 82, 86, 88, 99, 102, 104, 123, 134.

Gigantoproductus sp. 7L to GL. 2, 9, 11, 22, 33, 36–7, 39, 41, 46, 52, 54, 57, 61–2, 65, 67, 83–4, 86–7, 114, 116, 133–4, 140, 157, 160, 164, 166, 197–8, 200, 203.

Gigantoproductus sp. [thick shelled domed form]. 5–7L. 49.

Gigantoproductus sp. [high vaulted, thick shelled species]. 5L. 91.

Gigantoproductus sp. [large thin shelled geniculated form]. 5–7L. 50.

Gigantoproductus sp. [folded trail]. GL. 199.

Gigantoproductus sp. nov. [wide, thick shelled slightly inflated form, fine ribs posteriorly (18 in 1 cm), which laterally thicken and end in spines on hinge line. C. J. S.]. 5L. 97.

Gigantoproductus sp. nov.? [large spinose form with median sinus]. GL. 192.

Gigantoproductus? 5–7L to WL. 37, 39, 47, 123–4.

Krotovia spinulosa (J. Sowerby). ScL. 171.

Krotovia cf. *spinulosa.* 5YL. 175.

Krotovia sp. 7L to TBL. 14, 29, 93, 157.

Krotovia? TBL. 160.

Leptagonia analoga (Phillips). 6–7L. 29.

Lingula cf. *squamiformis* Phillips. 6–7L. 22.

'*Linoproductus*' *corrugatohemisphericus* (Vaughan). 7L. 5–7.

'*Linoproductus*' cf. *corrugatohemisphericus.* 5–7L to WL. 41, 52, 71–2, 102, 134.

'*Linoproductus*' cf. *corrugatus* (McCoy). 5–7L. 33, 49.

'*Linoproductus*' aff. *globosus* (Garwood). 7L. 14, 20.

'*Linoproductus*' aff. *hemisphaericus* (J. Sowerby). 7L. 7.

'*Linoproductus*' cf. *hemisphaericus.* 5–7L. 29, 49.

'*Linoproductus*' *sp.* 7L to GL. 19–20, 31–2, 36–7, 41, 45, 52, 63, 72, 86, 88, 92, 104, 115, 122, 134, 185, 190.

'*Linoproductus*' *spp.* [including a convex species with a spreading trail]. 7L. 6.

'*Linoproductus*' *spp*. [including geniculate form with spreading trail]. 7L. 5, 7.
'*Linoproductus*' *sp*. [thick shelled form]. WL. 130.
'*Linoproductus?*' [form with spreading trail]. 5–7L. 41.
'*Linoproductus?*' [large expansive trail with flattish visceral disc]. 5–7L. 32.
'*Linoproductus?*' [large thick shelled form with spreading trail]. 5L. 85.
'*Linoproductus?*' 5–7L to 5YL. 54, 175.
Martinia? 3YL. 180.
Megachonetes dalmanianus (de Koninck). 6L. 69.
Megachonetes cf. *dalmanianus*. 7L. 19.
Megachonetes papilionaceus (Phillips). 6L. 69–70, 72.
Megachonetes aff. *papilionaceus*. 5–7L to WL. 50, 104, 134.
Megachonetes cf. *papilionaceus*. 5–7L to RL. 41, 53, 82–3, 105, 122, 128, 135, 138
Megachonetes siblyi (I. Thomas). 5–7L to RL. 45, 66, 76, 122, 137.
Cf. *Megachonetes siblyi*. 5L. 90.
Megachonetes cf. *siblyi*. 6–7L to WL. 29, 43, 63, 70, 75, 87, 89, 114, 131.
Megachonetes sp. 6–7L to 5L. 21, 39, 64, 86.
Orbiculoidea sp. 5YL. 177.
Overtonia fimbriata (J. de C. Sowerby). RL. 135.
  ? Overtonia fimbriata. WL. 122.
Phricodothyris lineata (J. Sowerby). GL. 198.
Phricodothyris cf. *lineata*. WL to GL. 122, 141, 151, 189, 192.
Phricodothyris cf. *verecunda* George. WL. 120.
Phricodothyris sp. 6–7L to 4L. 25, 117.
Pleuropugnoides [*Camarotoechia*] cf. *pleurodon* (Phillips). 7L to JL. 14, 20, 61, 149.
Plicatifera? TBL. 160.
Plicochonetes buchianus (de Koninck). TBL. 158.
Plicochonetes cf. *buchianus*. JL to *junceum* and Chert Beds (Top of 4L). 150, 157,
  160, 164–5.
Plicochonetes cf. *crassistria* (McCoy). WL. 134.
Plicochonetes sp. 7L to 5YL. 15, 22, 43, 69, 110, 164, 175.
Productina margaritacea (Phillips). RL to TBL. 137, 154.
Productina sp. 7L to WL. 9, 29, 131.
Productina? 7L to 6L. 14, 27, 65.
Productids indet. Bryozoa Band at top of 7L to GL. 20, 26, 53, 69, 81, 89, 91, 130,
  141–2, 146, 167, 175, 188.
Productids indet., costate. 6–7L to TBL. 22, 40, 58, 60–1, 63, 82, 86, 114, 155.
Productus concinnus. J. Sowerby. 5L. 103.
Productus cf. *concinnus*. 6–7L to RL. 22, 135.
Productus garwoodi Muir-Wood. 7L. 14.
Productus cf. *garwoodi*. 7L. 5–6, 20.
Productus cf. *productus* (Martin). WL. 133.
Productus cf. *redesdalensis* Muir-Wood. 7L to 5YL. 2, 177.
Productus sp. 7L. 1.
Pugilis pugilis (Phillips). 5YL. 175.
Pugilis cf. *pugilis*. 7L to ScL. 14, 23, 66, 116, 141, 168.
Pugilis cf. *scoticus* (J. Sowerby). WL to 5YL. 126, 137, 177.
Pugnax pugnus (Martin). ScL. 167.
Pugnax sp. 4L. 165, 177.
Pugnax? WL. 130.
Punctospirifer redesdalensis North. Bryozoa Band at top of 7L. 20.
Punctospirifer scabricosta North. Bryozoa Band at top of 7L. 20.
Punctospirifer sp. RL to Shales above 5YL. 135, 179.
Punctospirifer? 4L, 116.
Pustula pustulosa (Phillips). 5L to 5YL. 93, 138, 173.
Pustula cf. *pustulosa*. *junceum* and Chert Beds (Top of 4L). 165.
Pustula sp. 5YL. 177.

Pustula? 6L to 5YL. 70, 177.
Quasiavonia aculatea (J. Sowerby). 5–7L to GL. 52, 104, 155, 157, 164, 173, 175, 177, 189, 191–2, 195–6, 198–200.
Reticularia sp. 5–7L to ScL. 41, 49, 69, 135, 137, 141, 150, 155, 157, 160, 167.
Reticularia? 5L to 5YL. 82, 124, 175.
Rhipidomella michelini (Léveillé). GL. 200.
Rhipidomella michelini (Davidson *non* Léveillé). 4L. 165, 177.
Rhipidomella cf. *michelini.* 5YL. 177.
Rugosochonetes cf. *hardrensis* (Phillips). 5YL to GL. 175, 176, 178–9, 189.
Rugosochonetes sp. 5–7L to Shales above 5YL. 36, 64–5, 87, 117, 178.
Schellwienella crenistria (Phillips). 6L to 5L. 68, 92.
Cf. *Schellwienella crenistria,* ? 4FL to GL. 186, 200.
Schellwienella cf. *crenistria.* 6L. 69.
Schellwienella aff. *rotundata* I. Thomas [dental plates too long to be typical of *S. rotundata*]. GL. 191.
Schellwienella sp. 5–7L to 5YL. 32, 117, 141, 153, 177.
Schellwienella? 5L to 5YL. 101, 110, 135, 162, 168, 175.
Schizophoria resupinata (Martin). 5YL and Shales above 5YL. 175, 178–9.
Schizophoria cf. *resupinata.* RL to GL. 135, 192.
Schuchertella? 4L. 118.
Sinuatella sinuata (de Koninck). GL. 191.
Spirifer bisulcatus J. de C. Sowerby. JL. 149.
Spirifer aff. *bisulcatus.* 5YL. 176.
Spirifer cf. *bisulcatus.* 7L to TBL. 14, 26, 157.
Spirifer cf. *distans* J. de C. Sowerby. 7L. 5.
Spirifer cf. *duplicicosta* Phillips. 7L to 5YL. 5, 41, 82, 118, 177.
Spirifer cf. *furcatus* McCoy. Bryozoa Band at top of 7L. 20.
Spirifer cf. *trigonalis* (Martin). 4L to GL. 118, 177, 199.
Spirifer (*Fusella*) cf. *triangularis* J. de C. Sowerby. GL. 196.
Spirifer (*Fusella*) *sp.* GL. 198.
Spirifer sp. 7L to GL. 5, 92, 110, 116, 118, 135, 165, 176, 189, 192.
Spirifer? Bryozoa Band at top of 7L to JL. 20, 133, 142.
Spiriferellina octoplicata (J. de C. Sowerby). GL. 200.
Spiriferellina octoplicata (J. de C. Sowerby) 'mut'. D. North. RL. 135.
Spiriferellina cf. *perplicata* (North). 6–7L. 29.
Striatifera striata Auctt. 7L to 5L. 8, 88.
Striatifera sp. 7L. 19.
Striatifera? 7L to WL. 17, 72, 134.
Tornquistia polita (McCoy). JL to 5YL. 148, 157, 160, 176.
Tornquistia sp. JL. 140.

GASTROPODA

Bellerophon sp. 7L to GL. 5, 15–6, 21, 29, 41, 47, 50, 88, 93, 95, 99, 122, 124, 133, 140–1, 148–9, 154, 189, 192.
Bellerophon sp. [large]. 6L. 62.
Bellerophon? Bryozoa Band at top of 7L to Shales above 5YL. 20, 96, 179.
Bucanopsis cf. *exilis* (de Koninck). 6L. 63.
Donaldina sp. 7L to 5YL. 8, 177.
Eoptychia sp. 5–7L. 49.
Eoptychia? 5–7L. 49.
Euomphalus cf. *carbonarius* J. Sowerby. 4L. 119.
Euphemites sp. 5YL. 177.
Euphemites? 4–7L. 60.
Glabrocingulum atomaria (Phillips). WL. 126.
Hypergonia nana (de Koninck). JL. 141.
Hypergonia sp. 5–7L to 5YL. 49, 65, 177.

'*Loxonema*' *sp.* 6–7L to JL. 27, 66, 141, 149.
Mourlonia sp. 5L to JL. 95, 149.
Mourlonia? 7L. 14.
Naticopsis ampliata (Phillips). 5–7L to WL. 49, 130.
Naticopsis cf. *mammillaris* de Koninck. WL. 124.
Naticopsis cf. *plicistria* (Phillips). 6L. 70.
Naticopsis sp. 6–7L to JL. 29, 32, 49, 52, 65–6, 123, 133, 150.
Naticopsis? 5L. 77, 92.
Phymatifer cf. *pugilis* (Phillips). 5–7L. 37.
Platyceras sp. nov? GL. 198.
Soleniscus cf. *obesa* (de Koninck). 5YL. 177.
Sphaerodoma sp. 6L to WL. 66, 69, 99, 126.
Sphaerodoma? GL. 195.
Straparollus aequalis (J. Sowerby). 5–7L. 50.
Straparollus cf. *convolutus* de Koninck. 5L. 87.
Straparollus cf. *jamesi* (McCoy). 6L. 72.
Straparollus cf. *mammula* de Koninck. WL. 124.
Straparollus sp. 6–7L to JL. 29, 52, 64–5, 69, 88, 104, 118, 131, 133–4, 137–8, 141, 150.
Straparollus sp. [with high spire]. 6L. 70.
Straparollus? 5–7L. 37.
Strobeus ventricosus de Koninck. 5–7L. 41.
Zygopleura rugifera (Phillips). 5YL. 177.
Indet. gastropods. 5–7L to 4L. 39, 66, 82, 112.
Small indet. gastropods. 5–7L to GL. 37, 85, 91, 137, 200.

LAMELLIBRANCHIA

Acanthopecten? cf. *nobilis* (de Koninck). 4L. 110.
Acanthopecten cf. *stellaris* (Phillips). 5YL to GL. 175, 191, 198.
Cf. *Actinopteria persulcata* (McCoy). 5–7L. 31.
Aviculopecten cf. *eskdalensis* Hind. 7L. 2.
Aviculopecten cf. *knockonniensis* McCoy. 5YL. 176–7.
Aviculopecten cf. *murchisoni* (McCoy). 5YL. 177.
Aviculopecten sp. 5–7L to Shales above 5YL. 39, 108, 112, 118, 126, 135, 171, 176, 178.
Aviculopecten? 5–7L. 43, 64.
Conocardium alaeforme (J. de C. Sowerby). 4L. 107.
Conocardium rostratum (Martin). 4L. 117.
Conocardium cf. *rostratum.* 6L to 5YL. 66, 116, 173.
Conocardium sp. nov. [has weak radial ornament]. 5YL. 175.
Conocardium? 6L. 72.
Edmondia senilis (Phillips). 7L. 2.
Edmondia aff. *senilis.* JL. 141.
Edmondia sulcata (Phillips). 6–7L to GL. 27, 29, 176, 192, 200.
Edmondia cf. *sulcata.* JL. 141.
Edmondia sp. RL. 137.
Edmondia? 5L. 82.
Euchondria? *clathrata* (McCoy *emend.* Hind.) WL. 126.
Euchondria? cf. *clathrata.* 7L. 14.
Leiopteria cf. *thomsoni* (Portlock). 6L. 64.
Leiopteria? GL. 189.
Limipecten dissimilis (Fleming). 5–7L to RL. 49, 119, 135.
Limipecten cf. *dissimilis.* 7L to Shales above 5YL. 2, 8, 33, 135, 178.
Nuculopsis gibbosa (Fleming). 5YL. 177.
Palaeolima simplex (Phillips). 5YL. 176.
Palaeolima cf. *simplex.* 5YL. 175.
Palaeoneilo cf. *laevirostris* (Portlock). 5YL. 177.

Parallelodon bistriatus (Portlock). 7L. 8.
Parallelodon sp. 5–7L. 32, GL. 189.
Cf. *Pernopecten concentricus* (Hind). 5YL. 176.
Polidevcia attenuata (Fleming). 4L. 108.
Posidonia cf. *becheri* Bronn. RL. 135.
Posidonia sp. 5YL. 177.
Posidonia? 5YL. 176.
Promytilus cf. *emaciatus* (Hind). 7L. 3.
Promytilus sp. 7L. 3.
Promytilus? 5L. 87.
'*Pseudamussium*' *ellipticum* (Phillips). 5YL. 176.
'*Pseudamussium*' cf. *ellipticum*. 7L. 8.
'*Pseudamussium*' *sp.* 7L to Shales above 5YL. 8, 14, 29, 126, 134, 157, 175, 178.
'*Pseudamussium*'? TBL to ? SPL. 159, 164.
Sanguinolites cf. *plicatus* (Portlock). 7L to JL. 2, 140.
Sanguinolites cf. *variabilis* (McCoy). 7L. 2.
Sanguinolites? 5–7L to 4L. 41, 112.
Schizodus cf. *subaequalis* (de Koninck). *junceum* and Chert Beds (Top of 4L). 165.
Schizodus sp. 7L to ? 4FL. 14, 176, 186.
Solemya excisa (Hind *non* de Koninck). 6L to GL. 69, 189.
Solenomorpha cf. *minor* (McCoy). 6L. 69.
Streblochondria anisota (Phillips). 6–7L. 22.
? *Streblopteria laevigata* McCoy. TBL. 155.
Streblopteria? 5YL. 177.
Sulcatopinna flabelliformis (Martin). JL. 141.
Sulcatopinna mutica (McCoy). 7L. 2.
Wilkingia elliptica (Phillips). 4L to GL. 118, 189.
Cf. *Wilkingia elliptica*. 7L. 2.
Wilkingia cf. *variabilis* (McCoy). WL. 134.

NAUTILOIDEA

Epistroboceras aff. *sulcatum* (J. Sowerby). 6L. 69.
Cf. *Nautilus discus* (J. Sowerby). 7L. 2.
Reticycloceras sp. 5YL. 177.
Solenocheilus? 5YL. 176. Bryozoa Band at top of 7L, 20.
Stroboceras? s.l. 6L to 5YL. 66, 177.
Orthocone nautiloids. 7L to 6L. 7, 29, 69.

CRUSTACEA

Bairdia sp. 6–7L to ? 4FL. 23, 29, 49, 130, 133, 153–4, 160, 164, 185.
Beyrichiopsis? 5–7L. 49.
Bythocypris? WL. 131.
Cypridina primaeva (McCoy). WL. 122.
Cypridina sp. Shales above 5YL. 178.
Cytherella sp. 7L to WL. 16, 69, 122.
Cytherella? 5–7L. 48.
Hollinella cf. *radiata* (Jones and Kirkby). 5–7L. 47.
Hollinella? JL. 148.
Paraparchites cf. *armstrongianus* (Jones and Kirkby). 5L. 84.
Paraparchites sp. 7L. 3, 17.
Rhombina sp. ? 5YL. 172.
Ostracods indet. 7L to ? 4FL. 2, 7–9, 14, 17, 22, 25, 27, 29, 32, 37, 39, 41, 43, 47, 54, 56, 58, 61, 65, 82, 88–9, 91, 99, 116, 120, 124, 133, 137, 141–2, 145, 153–7, 164–7, 171, 175, 178, 185.

TRILOBITA

Griffithides cf. *acanthiceps* H. Woodward. RL. 137.
Griffithides cf. *longiceps* Portlock. JL. 141.
Griffithides longispinus Portlock. ? 4FL. 185.
Weberides mucronatus (McCoy). 5YL. 176–7.
Weberides? 7L to GL. 8, 82, 118, 148, 160, 177–8, 200.
Trilobite fragments. 6L to Shales above 5YL. 72, 88, 127, 178.

PISCES

Petalodont tooth. GL. 200.
Psephodus sp. 5YL. 177.
Psephodus sp. [lateral tooth]. GL. 197.
Xystrodus sp. TBL. 153.
Fish fragments indet. 4–7L to 3YL. 58, 170, 179–80.

Appendix II

LIST OF FOSSILS FROM THE
UPPER CARBONIFEROUS ROCKS

The names of the fossils in the following two lists are those of specimens mainly collected by Mr. S. W. Hester and Mr. W. Dewar during the course of the resurvey. The original determinations of fossils from the Hensingham Group were by Sir James Stubblefield and they were revised (1962) where necessary by Dr. W. H. C. Ramsbottom. The original determinations of the fauna from the Coal Measures were by the late Sir A. Trueman; they were revised by Mr. M. A. Calver in 1962. The identifications of the fossil plants are by Dr. R. Crookall. Both lists have been prepared by Miss E. M. Pyatt.

The localities for the Hensingham Group and for the Coal Measures are given separately and eight figure National Grid References are used wherever practicable. The descriptions of localities are followed by the Geological Survey registered numbers of the specimens.

No faunal sub-divisions are indicated in the list for the Hensingham Group, and this also applies to the Coal Measures list, except that the fossils from the Bolton Marine Band and ? Solway Marine Band are respectively indicated by the abbreviations B.M.B. and ? S.M.B. after the locality numbers.

FOSSIL LOCALITIES: HENSINGHAM GROUP

Locality
1. Leathes Gill [1312 3703], near Grange Grassings, Gilcrux; TM 449–62.
2. Leathes Gill [1245 3790], 60–100 yd below High Flat Farm, near Gilcrux; TM 442–8.
3. Crabtree Beck [1609 3959], 550 yd N.E. of Threapland Hall; TE 736.
4. Gillgooden Beck [1681 4031], by cattle bridge, 350 yd E. by S. of Gillgooden; Ht 151–66.
5. Gillgooden Beck [1698 4032], by cattle bridge, 550 yd E. of Gillgooden; Ht 145–50.
6. Bothel Beck [1808 3988], 750 yd N.N.W. of Limekiln Bridge; Ht 116–8, 119–27.
7. Bothel Beck [1798 4004], 900 yd N.N.W. of Limekiln Bridge; Ht 128–37, TE 737.
8. Bothel Beck [1791 4013], 1050 yd N.N.W. of Limekiln Bridge; Ht 138–9.
9. Bothel Beck [1787 4018], 1100 yd N.N.W. of Limekiln Bridge; Ht 140–4.
10. Towtops Wood, stream [2097 3988], 300 yd S.W. of Park House; Hs 3665.
11. Towtops Wood, stream [2098 3997], 220 yd S.W. of Park House; Hs 3666–7.
12. Cockshot Beck, S. bank [2147 4005], 350 yd E. of Park House; Hs 3668–87, TE 725.
13. Greenspot Spring [2488 4155], 800 yd E.S.E. of Hallbank; TE 649–51.
14. Pow Gill [2537 4216], 30 yd S. of bridge at Powbank; TE 629–30, 749–50.

15. Pow Gill [2537 4218], 10 yd S. of bridge at Powbank; Hs 3419–500.
16. Pow Gill [2536 4226], 80 yd N. of bridge at Powbank; Hs 3411–8.
17. Pow Gill [2536 4227], 90 yd N. of bridge at Powbank; Hs 3408–10.
18. Pow Gill [2537 4230], 130 yd N. of bridge at Powbank; Ht 765–93, Hs 3366–407, TE 634–40, 643–4.
19. Pow Gill [2536 4235], 180 yd N. of bridge at Powbank; Hs 3302–65, TE 626–8.
20. Pow Gill [2538 4238], 220 yd N. of bridge at Powbank; TE 641–2.
21. Pow Gill [2541 4248], waterfall 330 yd N. by E. of bridge at Powbank; TE 652.
22. Low Loughing Beck [2630 4172], 300 yd N.E. of Bolton Park; TE 645.
23. Thackwaite Beck [2654 4381], 350 yd N.N.E. of Thackwaite Hall; Hs 4913–54.
24. Townthwaite Beck [2676 4396], S. bank, 350 yd W. of High Hall Bridge; Hs 3567–75.
25. Townthwaite Beck [2674 4398], N. bank, 370 yd W. of High Hall Bridge; Hs 3576–9.
26. Townthwaite Beck [2674 4398], S. bank, 370 yd W. of High Hall Bridge; Hs 4955–8.
27. Townthwaite Beck [2834 4286], 700 yd W. 25° S. of Hazelspring; Hs 4274–321
28. Townthwaite Beck [2840 4254], 900 yd S.W. of Hazelspring; Hs 4322–42.
29. Chalk Beck [3227 4271], 200–240 yd W. of junction with Nine Gills; Hs 3853–99, 4405–33, 4568–621.
30. Chalk Beck [3275 4328], 570 yd N. 13° E. of Chalk Plains; Hs 3944–59.
31. Chalk Beck [3255 4352], 900 yd S.E. of Broadmoor; FMT 222–31.
32. Chalk Beck [3263 4366], 850 yd E. 37° S. of Broadmoor; Hs 3937–43.
33. Caldbeck church, stream 600 yd N. of [3256 4040]; Hs 3776–93.
34. Cald Beck [3346 3989], right bank, 1000 yd E. of Caldbeck church; Hs 4393.
35. Cockley Beck [3889 4142], 500 yd S. of Cockleythwaite; Hs 4763–91, FMT 203–4.
36. Whale Gill [3938 3920], 650 yd W. 35° N. of Roe House; Hs 4155–68, FMT 170–2.
37. Roe Beck [3972 4075], left bank, 300 yd W. 15° N. of Longlands; Hs 4112–37, 4792–809, FMT 173–7.
38. Roe Beck [3966 4089], left bank, 400 yd W. 35° N. of Longlands; Hs 4138–54, 4810–22, FMT 166–9.
39. Roe Beck [3931 4191], left bank, 470 yd E. 7° N. of Cockleythwaite; Hs 4075–98, 4746–62, FMT 201–2.
40. Crookdake Borehole [2065 4441], 300 yd S. 30° E. of Low Aketon; ? Hensingham Group; Bg 498–9 from 2198–2210 ft.

LIST OF FOSSILS: HENSINGHAM GROUP

The numbers which follow the fossil names refer to the localities listed above.

PLANTAE

Calamites sp. 23, 37.
Plant indet. 8, 10.
? Plant remains indet. 21.

ANIMALIA

ANTHOZOA

Koninckophyllum?. 22.
Zaphrentid indet. 12.

CRINOIDEA

Crinoid fragments. 4, 6–7, 9, 14–5, 18–9, 23–5, 29–31, 33, 35, 38.

ECHINOIDEA

Archaeocidaris sp. 14, 18–9.

ANNELIDA

Cornulitella cf. *carbonaria* (Young). 15.

POLYZOA

Fenestella cf. *nodulosa* Phillips. 33.
Fenestella plebeia McCoy. 15.
Fenestella cf. *plebeia.* 18, 31.
Fenestella sp. 4, 29, 32, 35, 37, 39.
Fenestella? 31.
Penniretepora gracilis (McCoy). 15.
Penniretepora sp. 35.
Rhabdomeson? 15.
Trepostomatous polyzoa indet. 4, 29.

BRACHIOPODA

Actinoconchus cf. *planosulcatus* (Phillips). 4.
Actinoconchus cf. *sulcatus* (Phillips). 1.
Antiquatonia aff. *costata* (J. de C. Sowerby). 4.
Antiquatonia muricata (Phillips). 12, 29–30.
Cf. *Antiquatonia muricata.* 16, 18.
Antiquatonia cf. *muricata.* 1, 17, 23, 29–30, 39.
Athyris sp. 1.
Athyris? 12, 27.
Avonia sp. 1.
Avonia? sp. nov. 17, 19.
Brachythyris sp. 15, 28.
Buxtonia sp. 14, 16, 19, 23–4, 29, 31, 33.
Buxtonia sp. nov. [coarse costae]. 23.
Buxtonia? sp. 23, 27, 29.
'*Camarotoechia*' *sp.* 1, 7, 12, 31, 33.
Chonetes sp. [s.l.] 12, 23, 29, 33.
Chonetipustula? 15.
Composita ambigua (J. Sowerby). 15, 19.
Crurithyris sp. 15.
Derbyia hindi I. Thomas. 32.
Derbyia cf. *hindi.* 23, 30, 39.
Derbyia sp. 4, 18–9, 24, 37–9.
Derbyia? 29, 33.
Dielasma hastatum (J. de C. Sowerby). 15.
Dielasma cf. *hastatum.* 18–9.
Dielasma cf. *sacculum* (J. de C. Sowerby). 33.
Dielasma sp. 1.
Echinoconchus cf. *punctatus* (J. Sowerby). 4.
Echinoconchus sp. 1, 12, 15.
Eomarginifera lobata (J. Sowerby). 27.
Eomarginifera cf. *lobata.* 7, 9, 12, 23.
Eomarginifera cf. *longispina* J. Sowerby. 1.
Eomarginifera setosa (Phillips). 27.
Eomarginifera cf. *setosa.* 1, 4, 6–7.
Eomarginifera sp. 4, 12, 24, 29, 32.
Gigantoproductus latissimus (J. Sowerby). 27.
Gigantoproductus cf. *latissimus.* 27.
Gigantoproductus sp. 5.

Lingula mytilloides J. Sowerby. 15, 29.
Lingula squamiformis Phillips. 29, 40.
Lingula sp. 6–7, 23, 26.
Martinia? 23.
Meekella? 19.
Megachonetes cf. *volvus* (McCoy). 38.
Orbiculoidea nitida (Phillips). 37.
Orbiculoidea cf. *nitida*. 29, 40.
Orbiculoidea sp. 35, 39.
Pleuropugnoides [*Camarotoechia*] cf. *pleurodon* (Phillips). 12, 27, 28.
Plicatifera thomasi (Paeckelmann). 1, 18, 19.
Plicochonetes cf. *buchianus* (de Koninck). 5.
Plicochonetes sp. 15.
Productus carbonarius de Koninck. 1, 14–5, 17–9.
Productus cf. *carbonarius*. 13, 15–6, 28, 35.
Productus cf. *concinnus* J. Sowerby. 27.
Productus indet. 2, 16, 29, 33, 39.
Punctospirifer sp. 4.
Pustula sp. 15.
Pustula? 15.
Reticularia? 15.
Rhynchonellid indet. 18, 25, 29.
Rugosochonetes laguessianus (de Koninck). 15.
Rugosochonetes cf. *laguessianus*. 4, 15, 36.
Rugosochonetes sp. 31–2, 38–9.
Schellwienella rotundata I. Thomas. 29.
Schellwienella aff. *rotundata*. 36.
Schellwienella cf. *rotundata*. 3, 23.
Schellwienella sp. 14, 19, 29, 36, 39.
Schellwienella? 8, 15, 17–9, 24–5, 35, 38.
Schizophoria resupinata (Martin). 4, 14–5, 18–9, 24, 29, 32.
Schizophoria cf. *resupinata*. 35.
Schizophoria sp. 25, 27, 39.
Sinuatella? 24.
Spirifer cf. *bisulcatus* J. de C. Sowerby. 4, 12, 29.
Spirifer cf. *duplicicosta* (Phillips). 28.
Spirifer cf. *striatus* (Martin). 19.
Spirifer sp. 15, 23.
Spirifer sp. nov. [*S. trigonalis* (Martin) group]. 4, 6–7, 9, 12, 15, 23.

GASTROPODA

Bellerophon sp. 2.
Bucanopsis cf. *decussata* (Fleming). 15, 29.
Bucanopsis cf. *exilis* (de Koninck). 26, 37–9.
Bucanopsis sp. 18, 37.
Bucanopsis? 35–6.
Bulimorpha cf. *flemingi* (Brown). 29.
Bulimorpha cf. *manni* (Brown). 29.
Donaldina cf. *elongata* (Fleming). 29.
Donaldina sp. 18–9, 39.
Euomphalus? 4.
Euphemites ardenensis (Weir). 15, 18–9.
Euphemites hindi (Weir). 35.
Euphemites aff. *multilira* (Weir). 26.
Euphemites cf. *multilira* (Weir). 15.
Euphemites urii (Fleming). 19.

Euphemites cf. *urii*. 18, 29, 37–9.
Euphemites sp. 11, 18, 23, 37, 39.
Glabrocingulum sp. 6.
Hypergonia quadricarinata (McCoy). 29.
Hypergonia cf. *quadricarinata*. 18.
Hypergonia sp. 35.
Hypergonia? 18.
'*Loxonema*' *oweni* (Brown). 29.
'*Loxonema*' *sp.* 15.
Meekospira? 29.
Mourlonia? 35, 37.
Naticopsis sp. 29.
Naticopsis? 1, 39.
Platyceras sp. nov. 15.
Ptychomphalus sp. 1.
Sphaerodoma? 19.

LAMELLIBRANCHIA

Aviculopecten cf. *knockonniensis* (McCoy). 2, 7, 18.
Aviculopecten cf. *murchisoni* (McCoy). 19.
Aviculopecten cf. *subconoideus* R. Etheridge jun. 29, 36.
Aviculopecten cf. *textus* de Koninck. 19.
Aviculopecten sp. 4, 15, 18, 23, 27–9, 35.
Aviculopecten sp. [coarsely plicate]. 18.
Aviculopecten sp. nov. [*A.* aff. *serratus* McCoy]. 15.
Aviculopecten? 37–8.
Cardiomorpha? 37.
Dunbarella sp. 29, 38.
Edmondia cf. *laminata* (Phillips). 29.
Edmondia cf. *primaeva* (Portlock). 29.
Edmondia cf. *senilis* (Phillips). 29.
Edmondia sulcata (Phillips). 20, 39.
Edmondia cf. *unioniformis* (Phillips). 19.
Edmondia sp. 19, 35.
Edmondia? 22.
Leiopteria cf. *thompsoni* (Portlock). 15, 28–9.
Leiopteria sp. 29.
Limatulina scotica Hind. 38.
Cf. *Limatulina scotica*. 37.
Limipecten dissimilis (Fleming). 29.
Limipecten cf. *dissimilis*. 14–5, 18–9.
Limipecten cf. *semicostatus* (Portlock). 37–8.
Myalina? 35.
? Nucula oblonga McCoy. 18.
'*Nucula*' *sp.* 37–8.
Nuculopsis gibbosa Fleming. 28–9.
Palaeolima cf. *simplex* (Phillips). 15, 18, 29.
Palaeoneilo laevirostris (Portlock). 15, 37.
Palaeoneilo aff. *laevirostris*. 35, 37–9.
Palaeoneilo cf. *laevirostris*. 2, 15, 18, 28, 35, 39.
Palaeoneilo sp. 29.
Cf. *Parallelodon angustus* Hind. 35.
Parallelodon cf. *fallax* (de Koninck). 19.
Parallelodon cf. *reticulatus* (McCoy). 35.
Parallelodon aff. *walciodorensis* (de Koninck). 19.
Parallelodon cf. *walciodorensis*. 18.

Parallelodon sp. 18–9, 29.
Polidevcia attenuata (Fleming). 11, 15, 19, 28.
Polidevcia cf. *attenuata.* 18, 37–8.
Polidevcia ? 35.
Posidonia corrugata (R. Etheridge jun.). 29.
Promytilus sp. 9, 29, 39.
Prothyris sp. 29.
'*Pseudamussium*' *sp.* 18.
Cf. *Pterinopectinella granosa* (J. de C. Sowerby). 15.
Sanguinolites aff. *clavatus* (R. Etheridge jun.). 29.
Sanguinolites cf. *clavatus.* 29.
Sanguinolites striatogranulosus Hind. 18.
Sanguinolites cf. *striatus* Hind. 19.
Sanguinolites aff. *variabilis* McCoy emend. Hind. 37, 39.
Sanguinolites cf. *variabilis.* 38.
Sanguinolites cf. *v-scriptus* Hind. 29.
Sanguinolites sp. 19.
Schizodus axiniformis (Portlock). 30, 37.
? *Schizodus axiniformis.* 18.
Schizodus cf. *axiniformis.* 18, 36.
Schizodus cf. *depressus* (Portlock). 18.
Schizodus cf. *orbicularis* (McCoy). 29, 35.
Schizodus sp. 2, 18, 30, 37, 38.
Sedgwickia ovata (Hind). 28.
Cf. *Sedgwickia ovata.* 18.
Sedgwickia cf. *ovata.* 19.
Sedgwickia sp. 29.
Solemya cf. *excisa* de Koninck. 19.
Streblochondria anisotum (Phillips). 15.
Streblochondria? cf. *anisotum.* 38.
Streblochondria sp. 15, 29.
Streblopteria laevigata (McCoy). 30.
Sulcatopinna flabelliformis (Martin). 18.
Wilkingia elliptica (Phillips). 5, 18–9, 36–7.

NAUTILOIDEA

'*Cyrtoceras*' *sp.* 38.
Epidomatoceras sp. 15.
Epistroboceras sp. 29.
Reticycloceras cf. *koninckianum* (d'Orbigny). 4, 27–8.
Solenocheilus ? 37.
Stroboceras sp. s.l. 18.
Tylonautilus nodiferus (Armstrong). 4, 18.
Tylonautilus cf. *nodiferus.* 19.
Tylonautilus cf. *nodiferus* [ribs slightly broader and ornament more spirally arranged than in typical specimens]. 18.
Tylonautilus sp. 18.
Coiled nautiloid indet. 15.
Orthocone nautiloids indet. 4, 6, 15, 18, 23, 27, 29, 37.

AMMONOIDEA

Anthracoceras glabrum Bisat. 18.

CRUSTACEA

Cytherella sp. 15.
Ostracods indet. 29, 38.

TRILOBITA

Weberides sp. 15, 29.
Trilobite indet. 35.

PISCES

Petalodont tooth [ident. by Prof. D. M. S. Watson]. 34.
Rhizodopsis sp. 13–4, 18, 28.
Fish fragments indet. 6.

Fossil Localities: Coal Measures

1. Brayton No. 5 Colliery dump [138 405], ½ mile S.W. of Aspatria station; D 2365–76.
2. Brayton Domain No. 3 Pit dump [162 416], Harriston; Hs 1355–8.
3. Brayton Domain No. 4 Pit dump [163 437], S.W. of Brayton station; Hs 1359–64.
4. Threapland Gill [1554 3945], N.W. of Threapland and N. of Thrushgill Quarries; D 2355–6.
5. Crabtree Beck [1606 3968], 600 yd N.E. of Threapland; TE 735.
6. Allhallows Colliery dump [201 424], Mealsgate; Hs 1339–52.
7. Newlands Row Cottages, dump [2134 4187] 150 yd E. of; Hs 4394–404.
8. River Waver [2403 4448], left bank, 120 yd above Shaking Bridge; Hs 3006–9.
9. River Waver [2416 4455], left bank, 200–300 yd above Shaking Bridge; Hs 3010–8.
10. Pow Gill Colliery dump [249 439], ¾ mile E.S.E. of Bolton Low Houses; Hs 3565–6.
11. Pow Gill [2534 4280], W. bank, 200 yd S.S.E. of Low Loughing Bridge; Hs. 3270–301.
12. Pow Gill [2530 4318], S.E. bank, 250–270 yd N.N.E. of Low Loughing Bridge; Hs 3255–69, TE 617.
13. Pow Gill [2536 4327], E. bank, 370 yd N.E. of Low Loughing Bridge; TE 618–24.
14. Pow Gill [2543 4339], W. bank, 500 yd S.E. of High Pow; Hs 3244–54, TE 605.
15. Pow Gill, tributary entering E. bank, 500 yd E. of High Pow, section [2549 4365] 20 yd above confluence; Hs 3240–3.
16. Pow Gill, tributary entering E. bank, 500 yd E. of High Pow, section [2552 4366] 50 yd above confluence; Hs 3216–39, TE 599–604.
17. Pow Gill [2545 4369], N. bank, at bend 380 yd E.S.E. of Low Pow; Hs 3212–5.
18. Pow Gill [2540 4371], E. bank, 350 yd E.S.E. of Low Pow; Hs 3185–211, TE 596–8.
19. Pow Gill [2523 4399], W. bank, 50 yd N.W. of Pow Gill Mill; Hs 3183–4.
20. Pow Gill [2520 4403], W. bank, 100 yd N.W. of Pow Gill Mill; Hs 3181–2.
21. Pow Gill [2520 4406], W. bank 150 yd N.W. of Pow Gill Mill; Hs 3164–80.
22. Pow Gill, tributary entering W. bank, 200 yd S. of Parson Bridge, section [2500 4426] 50–100 yd above confluence; Hs 3070–120, TE 606–16.
23. Pow Gill [2505 4428], W. bank, 250 yd S. of Parson Bridge; Hs 3121–32.
24. Pow Gill [2509 4432], N. bank, 200 yd S. by E. of Parson Bridge; Hs 3133–63.
25. Pow Gill [2506 4433], E. bank, 190–200 yd S. of Parson Bridge; Hs 3020–69, 4987–5000, Ht 1–50, TE 591–5.
26. Pow Gill [2506 4450], E. bank, just S. of Parson Bridge; Hs 3019.
27. Wiza Beck [3072 4486], left bank, 1000 yd S.S.W. of Causa Grange; He 928–43.

28. Chalk Beck [3232 4273], 150 yd above junction with Nine Gills, Hs 3900–9, 4622–34.
29. Chalk Beck [3242 4270], 30 yd above junction with Nine Gills; Hs 3910–36, 4635–80.
30. Chalk Beck [3273 4379], left and right banks, 850 yd E. 25° S. of Broadmoor; Hs 3960–81, 4681–730, FMT 211–21.
31. Chalk Beck [3277 4383], 900 yd E. 21° S. of Broadmoor; Hs 4731.
32. Chalk Beck [3283 4396], right bank, 900 yd E. 12° S. of Broadmoor; Hs 3982–93, 4732–45.
33. Chalk Beck [3289 4403], right bank, 320 yd S. 25° W. of Chalkbeck Bridge; Hs 3996–8, FMT 206.
34. Chalk Beck [3291 4407], left bank, 270 yd S. 25° W. of Chalkbeck Bridge; Hs 3994–5.
35. Chalk Beck [3344 4566], left bank, 400 yd S. 35° W. of Upper Greenquarries; Hs 4823–9.
36. Warnell Beck [3514 4187], 450 yd S. of Lonning Head; Hs 4355–91.
37. Busta Beck [3678 4277], 300 yd upstream from confluence with River Caldew; Hs 4343–54, Ht 51–86, FMT 205.
38. Roe Beck [3947 4157], left bank, 730 yd E. 26° S. of Cockleythwaite; Hs 4062–74, FMT 161–5.
39. Roe Beck, ditch on W. bank [3928 4209], 480 yd E. 30° N. of Cockleythwaite; FMT 144–8.
40. Roe Beck [3934 4210], right bank, 530 yd E. 25° N. of Cockleythwaite; Hs 4099–111, FMT 149–60.
41. Roe Beck [3854 4544], left bank, 700 yd E. 12° S. of Raughtonhead church; Ht 87–100, FMT 234.
42. Roe Beck [3863 4662], left bank, 40 yd N. of Flat Bank, Gatesgill; Hs 4830–72.
43. Brayton Domain Colliery, No. 3 Borehole [1723 4529], ½ mile S.E. of Langrigg; Ba 4189–91, from c. 1525 ft.
44. Crookdake Borehole [2065 4441], 300 yd S. 30° E. of Low Aketon; Bg 387–447, from 1399 ft 6 in to 1696 ft 0 in; Bg 470–1, from c. 2020 ft.
45. New Pit (1926) [2484 4400], 50 yd E. of school, Bolton New Houses; TE 374–84, from above Master Band.
46. Pow Gill [2538 4214], 70 yd S. of bridge at Powbank; ? Coal Measures; Hs 4959–86.

LIST OF FOSSILS: COAL MEASURES

The numbers which follow the fossil names refer to the localities listed above.

PLANTAE

FILICALES AND PTERIDOSPERMAE

Alethopteris decurrens (Artis). 7, 12, 38, 45.
Alethopteris lonchitica (Schlotheim). 12, 40, 45.
Aphlebia spinosa Lesquereux. 37.
Asterotheca lepidorachis (Brongniart). 37.
Cyclopteris sp. 37.
Dactylotheca plumosa (Artis). 38.
Eupecopteris spp. 37.
Mariopteris nervosa (Brongniart). 31, 40.
Neuropteris gigantea (Sternberg). 6, 8, 12, 20, 23, 38.
Neuropteris heterophylla Brongniart. 13, 33, 35, 38–9, 40, 42.
Neuropteris cf. *obliqua* (Brongniart). 45.
Neuropteris ovata Hoffman. 37.

Cf. *Neuropteris ovata*. 37.
Neuropteris rarinervis Bunbury. 37.
Neuropteris tenuifolia (Schlotheim). 10.
Neuropteris cf. *tenuifolia*. 9.
Neuropteris sp. 7, 9, 12, 23, 37.
Sphenopteris cf. *dilatata* Lindley and Hutton. 12.
Sphenopteris sp. 23.

LYCOPODIALES

Lepidodendron acutum (Presl). 5.
Lepidodendron lycopodioides Sternberg. 14.
Lepidodendron cf. *simile* Kidston. 45.
Lepidodendron sp. 9, 14, 18, 42.
Lycopod megaspores. 19.
Stigmaria ficoides (Sternberg). 1, 4.
Stigmaria minuta Göppert. 1.

EQUISITALES

Annularia galioides (Lindley and Hutton). 13.
Calamites suckowi Brongniart. 3, 12, 28, 34.
Calamites undulatus Sternberg. 6, 45.
Calamites sp. 8, 12, 14, 18, 38.

SPHENOPHYLALES

Sphenophyllum cuneifolium (Sternberg). 12–3, 23.

CORDAITALES

Cordaites sp. 40.

INCERTAE SEDIS

Pinnularia capillacea (Lindley and Hutton). 13.

ANIMALIA

PORIFERA

Hexactinellid sponge spicules. 30 (? S.M.B.).

ANNELIDA

Spirorbis sp. 2, 18, 29–30, 32, 36.

BRACHIOPODA

Cf. *Crurithyris carbonaria* (Hind.). 24 (B.M.B.).
Lingula mytilloides J. Sowerby. 24 (B.M.B.), 30 (?S.M.B.).
Orbiculoidea sp. 24 (B.M.B.).
Dictyoclostus craigmarkensis Muir-Wood. 24 (B.M.B.).

GASTROPODA

Bucanopsis sp. 24 (B.M.B.).
Donaldina cf. *ashtonensis* (Bolton). 24 (B.M.B.).
Euphemites? 24 (B.M.B.).

LAMELLIBRANCHIA

? Anthraconaia librata (Wright). 21.
Anthraconaia modiolaris (J. de C. Sowerby). 29.
? Anthraconaia modiolaris. 36.
Anthraconaia pruvosti (Chernyshev). 43 at 1525 ft, 44 at 1425 ft.

Anthraconaia cf. *pruvosti* [juv.]. 44 at 1596–7 ft.
Anthraconaia pulchella Broadhurst. 42.
Anthraconaia salteri? (Leitch). 1.
Anthraconauta phillipsii (Williamson). 44 at 1399½ ft, 1406 ft, 1412 ft and 1493–6 ft.
Anthraconauta phillipsii [juv.]. 44 at 1695–6 ft.
Anthraconauta phillipsii? 44 at 1596–7 ft.
Anthraconauta tenuis (Davies and Trueman). 44 at 1493–6 ft.
Anthraconauta tenuis [juv.]. 44 at 1695–6 ft.
Anthraconauta sp. [juv.]. 44 at 1487 and 1490 ft.
Anthraconauta? 44 at 1425 ft.
Anthracosia aff. *acutella* (Wright). 22.
Anthracosia cf. *acutella.* 25.
Anthracosia aquilina ? (J. de C. Sowerby). 6.
Anthracosia aff. *aquilina.* 18, 30.
Anthracosia atra (Trueman). 2, 25.
Anthracosia cf. *atra.* 21, 22.
Anthracosia cf. *beaniana* King. 18, 30.
Anthracosia 'carissima' (Wright). 30.
Anthracosia cf. *concinna* (Wright). 21.
Anthracosia aff. *disjuncta* Trueman and Weir. 30.
Cf. *Anthracosia nitida* (Davies and Trueman). 15.
Anthracosia cf. *nitida.* 17.
Anthracosia ovum Trueman and Weir. 1–3, 6, 15–6, 18, 30.
Anthracosia phrygiana (Wright). 6, 16, 18.
Anthracosia phrygiana? 7.
Anthracosia regularis (Trueman). 11, 14, 27, 36.
Anthracosia regularis [large]. 29.
Anthracosia cf. *retrotracta* (Wright). 18.
Anthracosia simulans Trueman and Weir. 21.
Anthracosia subrecta Trueman and Weir. 42.
Anthracosia sp. 19, 24.
Anthracosia sp. intermed. between *aquilina* and *phrygiana.* 7.
Anthracosia sp. nov. [large, elongate]. 16, 18.
Cf. *Anthracosphaerium cycloquadratum* (Wright). 11.
Anthracosphaerium turgidum (Brown). 18.
Anthracosphaerium turgidum ? 1.
Anthracosphaerium sp. 16.
Anthracosphaerium? 7.
Carbonicola aff. *bipennis* (Brown). 46.
Carbonicola cf. *bipennis.* 29.
Carbonicola cf. *cristagalli* Wright. 11, 28–9.
Carbonicola cf. *martini* Trueman and Weir. 46.
Carbonicola oslancis Wright. 11.
Carbonicola cf. *oslancis.* 27–8, 36.
? Carbonicola rhomboidalis Hind. 28.
Carbonicola torus? Eagar. 46.
Carbonicola venusta Davies and Trueman. 29, 36.
Dunbarella macgregori (Currie). 24 (B.M.B.).
Dunbarella sp. 24 (B.M.B.).
Naiadites angustus Trueman and Weir. 32.
Naiadites cf. *angustus.* 22.
Naiadites obliquus Dix and Trueman. 32, 45.
Naiadites productus (Brown). 22, 42.
Naiadites cf. *productus.* 32.
Naiadites quadratus (J. de C. Sowerby). 2, 6, 16.
Naiadites aff. *quadratus.* 18, 30.

Naiadites cf. *subtruncatus* (Brown). 11.
Naiadites sp. intermed. between *productus* and *quadratus.* 11, 16, 18, 29, 36, 38.
Naiadites sp. 25, 27.
Palaeolima cf. *simplex* (Phillips). 24 (B.M.B.).
Palaeolima? 24 (B.M.B.).
Pernopecten carboniferus (Hind). 24 (B.M.B.).
Pleurophorella? 24 (B.M.B.).
Posidonia sulcata (Hind). 24 (B.M.B.).
Posidonia sp. 24 (B.M.B.).
Schizodus cf. *antiquus* (Hind). 24 (B.M.B.).
Schizodus sp. 24 (B.M.B.).
Solemya cf. *primaeva* Phillips. 24 (B.M.B.).
Lamellibranchs indet. (possibly *Anthracosia*). 44 at 2019–20 ft.

NAUTILOIDEA

Huanghoceras costatum (Hind). 24 (B.M.B.).
Metacoceras cf. *perelegans* Girty. 24 (B.M.B.).
'*Orthoceras*' aff. *asciculare* Brown. 24 (B.M.B.).
'*Orthoceras*' cf. *conquestum* de Koninck. 24 (B.M.B.).
'*Orthoceras*' *sp.* 24 (B.M.B.).
Reticycloceras cf. *koninckianum* (d'Orbigny). 24 (B.M.B.).

AMMONOIDEA

Anthracoceras aegiranum H. Schmidt. 24 (B.M.B.).
Anthracoceras hindi Bisat [including juv.]. 24 (B.M.B.).
Anthracoceras cf. *hindi.* 24 (B.M.B.).
Goniatite, gen. et sp. nov. 24 (B.M.B.).
Politoceras politum (Shumard) [= *Homoceratoides jacksoni* Bisat]. 24 (B.M.B.).

CRUSTACEA

Carbonita humilis (Jones and Kirkby). 7, 11.
Carbonita pungens (Jones and Kirkby). 44 at 1399½ ft.
Carbonita salteriana (Jones). 44 at 1399½ ft and 1493–6 ft.
Carbonita wardiana (Jones and Kirkby). 44 at 1493–6 ft.
Carbonita sp., 22, 44 at 1425 ft and 1487 ft.
Cypridina? 24 (B.M.B.).
'*Estheria*'? [poorly preserved]. 41.
Euestheria simoni (Pruvost). 44 at 1487 ft and 1493–6 ft.
Euestheria ? 44 at 1695–6 ft.
Geisina arcuata (Bean). 11, 27–9, 36, 46.
Leaia bristolensis Raymond. 44 at 1629–30 ft.
Leaia cf. *bristolensis.* 41.

PISCES

Acanthodian spine. 44 at 1490 ft.
Listracanthus wardi A. S. Woodward. 24 (B.M.B.).
Megalichthys sp. 14.
Palaeoniscid scales indet. 9.
Platysomid indet. 22.
Rhabdoderma sp. 9, 24 (B.M.B.), 26.
Rhizodopsis sauroides (Williamson). 4.
Rhizodopsis sp. 9, 16, 22, 25, 28, 46.
Fish fragments. 22, 25–6, 28, 42, 46.

CONODONTS

Platformed conodonts. 24 (B.M.B.).

Appendix III

LIST OF
GEOLOGICAL SURVEY PHOTOGRAPHS

Copies of these photographs are deposited for reference in the library of the Geological Survey and Museum, South Kensington, London S.W.7., and of the Geological Survey Northern England Office, Ring Road Halton, Leeds 15. Prints and lantern slides may be supplied at a fixed tariff.

All numbers belong to Series A.

PLEISTOCENE AND RECENT

6586 **Common Moss.** An extensive tract of flat, peat-covered ground. Highlaws Delta in the distance. Viewpoint 1 mile N. of Westnewton.

6587 **Highlaws Delta.** The foreground is largely of boulder clay, with a well-developed drumlin in the middle distance. The flat top of the Highlaws Delta of sand and gravel forms the skyline. Viewpoint 1 mile N. of Westnewton.

NEW RED SANDSTONE

6588 **Quarry in St. Bees Sandstone.** The regularly dipping beds are capped by boulder clay. Left bank of Chalk Beck, near Barnetrigg.

6589 **Section of St. Bees Shales.** Chalk Beck, S.E. of Barnetrigg.

6590 **Gorge in false-bedded Penrith Sandstone.** Roe Beck near Highbridge.

6591 **Penrith Sandstone.** Close-up view of false-bedding. Roe Beck near Highbridge.

CARBONIFEROUS LIMESTONE SERIES

6593 **Vesicular basalt.** The basalt is one of the Cockermouth Lavas occurring between the Seventh Limestone and the Basal Conglomerate of the Carboniferous. Redmain, $2\frac{1}{4}$ miles N.N.E. of Cockermouth.

6594 **Cockermouth Lavas.** Lump of dark extraneous material in basalt lava. Redmain.

6595 **Cockermouth Lavas.** Vein of dark extraneous matter in basalt lava. Redmain.

6596 **Cockermouth Lavas.** Veinlets of dark extraneous material in a basalt lava. Redmain.

6597 **Clints Crags.** Characteristic outcrops of limestone of Carboniferous Limestone Series. One mile W. of Sunderland.

6598 **Limestone Escarpment and dip slopes.** Limestone in foreground is Sixth Limestone. The dip slope beyond is largely drift-covered. The Fourth Limestone forms much of the distant rising ground. Viewpoint 1 mile W. of Sunderland.

6599   *Saccammina* **Limestone.** Quarry 800 yd E. 30° N. of Uldale church.

6600   **Jew Limestone.** Viewpoint footbridge over Cald Beck 1 mile E. of Caldbeck.

6601   Gorge in **Jew Limestone** with Cald Beck in spate. Viewpoint footbridge 1 mile E. of Caldbeck.

6740   Thin bedded **Tumbler Beds** overlying the Main Posts of the **Great Limestone.** 300 yd W. of Parkhead N.E. of Caldbeck.

6741   Thin bedded **Tumbler Beds** overlying the Main Posts of the **Great Limestone.** 300 yd W. of Parkhead N.E. of Caldbeck.

6742   Rhythmic unit of **5 Yard Limestone.** ¾ mile E. 30° N. of church in Uldale.

BORROWDALE VOLCANIC SERIES

6603   **St. Johns Hill.** Ice-moulded hill of Borrowdale Lavas. 1¼ miles S.S.E. of Bothel.

6604   **Ice-worn crags of lava.** The lava is a porphyritic andesite of Eycott type. (See also A. 6605) 1¼ miles S.S.E. of Bothel.

6605   **Porphyritic lava** (Eycott Type). Close view showing large size of the crystals of feldspar. 1¼ miles S.S.E. of Bothel.

6609   **An agglomerate.** Binsey about 1 mile N.E. of Bewaldeth.

6610   **Crag of Andesite.** Binsey about 1 mile N.E. of Bewaldeth.

6611   **Crags of massive lava** of Eycott type. About ¾ mile N.N.W. of Hutton Roof.

6612   **Linewath Gorge.** Cut in Borrowdale Volcanic rocks. River Caldew about ¾ mile N.N.W. of Hutton Roof.

6613   **Dyke** in porphyritic lava of Eycott type. About ½ mile S.E. of top of Eycott Hill.

6737   **Weathered top of lava** showing auto-brecciation. 300 yd W. 15° N. of summit of Binsey.

6738   Weather-joint surface of lava showing **flow-banding.** At trig. station 1466 on summit of Binsey.

6739   **Slates** overlying and interbedded with lava. Passage beds between Skiddaw Slates and Borrowdale Volcanic Series. The interbedded slates are seen beneath the top post of lava, immediately above the hammer head. West of Over Water and 700 yd W.N.W. of Whitefield House.

6750   **Flow-breccia** in Eycott lava, showing lacy network of the matrix weathering out prominently from the 'fragments'. 700 yd E. 15° N. of Linewath.

6754   **Auto-injection** in basic dyke. An irregular series of cracks in a consolidated dyke has been filled with a later injection of a similar doleritic rock. 1400 yd W. 7° N. of bench mark 1124, Berrier, 2 miles E. of Mungrisdale.

6755   Weathered surface of **Eycott Lava.** 1400 yd W. 7° N. of bench mark 1124, Berrier, 2 miles E. of Mungrisdale.

6756   **Crags of Eycott Lava.** The dip is to the east-north-east (to the right). 1500 yd W. 14° S. of bench mark 1124, Berrier, 2 miles E. of Mungrisdale.

SKIDDAW SLATES

6626   **Columnar jointing** of Grits of Skiddaw Slates. Quarry on Watch Hill, 600 yd N.E. of Greenlands.

6627 **Watch Hill Grit.** Grits interbedded with shaly bands passing up into striped shales and siltstones with occasional thin bands of sandstone. Small quarry 300 yd W. by N. of Elva Hill.

6628 **Watch Hill Grit.** Note the repetition of thick to thinner posts of grit from below upwards indicating that the beds are not inverted. Small quarry 300 yd W. by N. of Elva Hill.

6629 Quarry in **Watch Hill Grit** and **'Diorite'.** The 'Diorite' (in the angle of the quarry) here fails to reach the normal surface of the ground. A shaly parting in the grits shows pseudo-false bedding due to movement. Elva Hill, 950 yd S. of Dunthwaite and $3\frac{1}{4}$ miles E.N.E. of Cockermouth.

6633 **Asymmetric folds.** The rocks affected are the thin-bedded sandstones interleaved with shales in the upper portion of the Watch Hill Grit. The folds are steeper to the S.E. than to the N.E. and pitch to the north-east. South of Hewthwaite.

6634 **Folding.** A photograph showing the type of small scale folding and overfolding characteristic of the flaggy beds of the Skiddaw Slates. Small quarry about $\frac{3}{4}$ mile S.S.W. of Bassenthwaite Lake station.

6635 **Small scale false-bedding** in flaggy sandstones. A near view of an outcrop of vertical beds in which the truncation of the original curved bedding planes may be seen. Crag 500 yd E. of Pleasant Hotel, Bassenthwaite station.

6658 The **River Ellen** near its source. Steeply dipping Skiddaw Slates in the foreground. $\frac{3}{4}$ mile E.S.E. of Stockdale.

6660 **Faulted Junction** of Skiddaw Slates and Borrowdale Volcanic Series. The Skiddaw Slates are seen on the left, and a tuff composed essentially of slate fragments on the right of the photograph. Stream section 600 yd E. 30° N. of outfall of stream from Over Water.

6662 **Slate Quarry,** Mungrisdale. General view of steeply dipping black slates.

6663 **Thrust** in Slate Quarry, Mungrisdale: A minor reversed fault has produced overturning on the thin bedded slates. Above the plane of the thrust a 2-ft dyke which follows the bedding is visible in the centre of the photograph.

6668 **Old Quarry.** Rough roofing slates have been obtained from this quarry. The rock is a flaggy, slightly cleaved, fine silty banded slate, altered to a spotted chiastolite-slate. It splits along the bedding.

6669 **Blencathra** from Bowscale Fell. The north end of the Helvellyn Range appears in the left distance.

6672 **Folding** in metamorphosed Skiddaw Slates (see A. 6673). River Caldew above Swineside, about $1\frac{3}{4}$ miles W. of Mosedale.

6673 **Folding** in metamorphosed Skiddaw Slates. The sharp folding of the hard cordierite-biotite-hornfels is earlier than the metamorphism. River Caldew above Swineside.

Carrock Fell complex

6743 **Banded Gabbro.** Alteration of feldspathic and ferromagnesian-rich bands in the southern belt of basic gabbro. 1020 yd W. 42° N. of bridge over River Caldew at Mosedale.

6744 **Pyroxene-rich patch** in variable basic gabbro. Rapid variations of
feldspathic and ferromagnesian-rich gabbros are common in the
southern belt of basic gabbro. 950 yd W. 43° N. of bridge over River
Caldew at Mosedale.

6745 **Feldspathic clot** in basic gabbro. Irregular clots or segregations of
light feldspathic material are of frequent occurrence in the variable
basic gabbro of the southern belt on Carrock Fell. 1200 yd W. 39° N.
of bridge over River Caldew at Mosedale.

6746 **Borrowdale lava inclusion** in gabbro. Fine-grained Borrowdale lava
enclosed in and veined by gabbro, the whole being penetrated by later,
narrow (white) strings of granophyric material. 1 mile W. of Mosedale.

6747 **Granophyric Veins** in basic gabbro. A pale granophyric vein locally
widening to include angular fragments of the invaded rock, a pyroxene-
rich basic gabbro. 1 mile W. of Mosedale.

MINOR INTRUSIONS and MINERAL VEINS

6640 **Close Quarry, Embleton.** The rock, a quartz-diorite, is quarried on a
large scale for roadstone.

6641 **Contact** between quartz-diorite of Close Quarry and hornfelsed Skiddaw
Slate. The contact between the under surface of the intrusion and the
Skiddaw Slate may be seen immediately to the left of the tunnel
entrance; it is inclined approximately towards the observer.

6642 **Joints in Quartz-Diorite** of Close Quarry, Embleton. The series of
well-developed major and minor joints which traverse the rock greatly
facilitate quarrying operations.

6643 **Close Quarry, Embleton.** A view of the upper and lower levels of the
quarry, showing major and minor joints.

6674 **Drygill Vein** (see also A. 6675). This strong mineralized quartz-vein
coincides with an important fault which brings Drygill Shales down
south (right) against lavas of the Borrowdale Volcanic Series (left).
N. side of N. branch of Drygills S.S.E. of High Pike.

6675 **Drygill Vein.** A strong quartz-vein carrying lead, a little copper, manganese etc. N. side of N. branch of Drygills, S.S.E. of High Pike.

6677 **Driggith-Sandbeds Vein.** Vein has been exposed by working (stoping)
to surface. Total width about 10 ft. ⅝ mile N.E. of High Pike Summit.

6678 **Driggith-Sandbeds Vein.** Collapsed shallow workings on this lead-vein.
⅝ mile N.E. of High Pike Summit.

GENERAL VIEWS

6592 View across **Derwent Valley** towards Wood Hall. The Seventh Limestone
of Wood Hall Park forms the left skyline.

6602 General View west from **Bothelcrags.** Borrowdale Volcanic Series in
the foreground; Cockermouth Lavas in the middle distance; limestones of the Carboniferous Limestone Series in the background.
1¼ miles S.S.E. of Bothel.

6606 **Camp Hill** and **Binsey** (left to right). These hills are made up of rocks
of the Borrowdale Volcanic Series which are faulted against Skiddaw
Slates occupying the lower ground. Viewpoint Bothelcrags 1¼ miles
S.S.E. of Bothel.

6607 **Binsey.** Lavas and tuffs of the Borrowdale Volcanic Series constitute the greater part of the hill. Viewpoint about 1⅜ miles N.N.E. of Bewaldeth.

6608 **Binsey** viewed from Bothelcrags. 1¼ miles S.S.E. of Bothel.

6616 Contrasting **Borrowdale and Carboniferous topography.** Craggy topography of Borrowdale Volcanic Series is succeeded by smooth regular scarps of the Carboniferous Limestone in the distance (north-east). Viewpoint Eycott Hill.

6618 General View of **Caldbeck Fells.** The older Palaeozoic rocks rise to form the high fells seen against the skyline. The general surface level is at about 2000 ft O.D., and the peaks rising slightly above it are, from left to right, Carrock Fell, High Pike and Knott. Viewpoint Parkhead, E.N.E. of Caldbeck.

6619 The **Caldbeck Fells.** View across valley of the Cald Beck. The hills in the middle distance are of Carboniferous Limestone. The fells behind are of older rocks; the igneous complex of Carrock Fell forms the twin-peaked mountain of Carrock Fell; Borrowdale Volcanic rocks lie to the right (west) as far as the peak, High Pike, and beyond. Viewpoint Lowthwaite Green, N.N.W. of Caldbeck.

6620 **Carrock Beck Valley** and **Carrock Fell.** Viewpoint, Driggith Mine, N.E. of High Pike summit.

6621 **Bowscale Tarn.** View showing corrie walls in Skiddaw Slates and morainic dam.

6622 Outlet of **Bowscale Tarn.** Showing morainic dam.

6623 The **Caldew Valley** from below Bowscale Tarn. The Carboniferous and Borrowdale rocks of Greystoke Park occupy the middle distance with the Pennines just visible on the far horizon.

6624 The broad peat-filled hollow of the **Caldew Valley** below Mosedale. Viewpoint above Bowscale Tarn.

6625 Fells above **Mungrisdale** and **Mosedale.** Showing abrupt termination of the high ground against the through hollow that lies on the watershed between the Greta and Caldew drainage areas. Viewpoint Lofshaw Hill, N. of Troutbeck station.

6630 **Elva Hill** and **Skiddaw.** On Elva Hill the nearest quarry is in diorite; the quarry in the middle distance is in diorite and grits of the Skiddaw Slates. On the skyline to the right is the Skiddaw massif.

6631 **Diorite intrusion** in Skiddaw Slates. Prominent feature formed by a small, sill-like intrusion of diorite in the Skiddaw Slates. Elva Plain, Setmurphy Common.

6632 Top of **Watch Hill.** The hummock on which the camera stands is of 'diorite', the farther one of grits. About 2 miles E.N.E. of Cockermouth.

6636 General View N.W. by N. from **Watch Hill.** The hills in the distance (Moota ⅓ from right) are of limestone; the partly wooded middle distance is of Cockermouth Lavas. Foreground, Skiddaw Slates.

6637 General View N.E. from the northern slope of **Watch Hill** near Hewthwaite Hall. Rounded hill (Binsey) of Borrowdale Volcanic Series. The ridge partly wooded in middle distance is of sandstones in Skiddaw Slates.

6638 View of **Skiddaw** from Watch Hill.

6639   The **Embleton Valley.** A general view taken from Sale Fell $\frac{3}{4}$ mile S.S.W. of Bassenthwaite Lake station, showing the steep character of the walls and the flat, drift-covered floor.

6644   The **Bassenthwaite** end of the Embleton Valley. Sale Fell and Wythop Fell (wooded) on the southern side; Skiddaw and Bassenthwaite Lake beyond. The valley is floored by Glacial and Recent deposits, while the fells beyond are of Skiddaw Slates. Viewpoint Close Quarry, Embleton.

6647   **Bassenthwaite Valley** from Sunderland Heads $\frac{1}{2}$ mile N.W. of Sunderland. Skiddaw on the left and the hills on the right are made up of Skiddaw Slates; the distant hills of Borrowdale Volcanic Series.

6648   **Bassenthwaite Valley.** View showing the steep western shore of Bassenthwaite Lake with "hanging valleys". The beginning of the Embleton Valley, with Wythop Fell and Sale Fell on the southern side, is on the extreme right. The peak in the distance is Grisedale Pike. Viewpoint 1 mile E. of Bewaldeth.

6649   **Skiddaw** and the foot of **Bassenthwaite Lake.** Ullock Pike on the flank of Skiddaw may be seen to the right of the photograph. Viewpoint $1\frac{1}{4}$ miles W.N.W. of Bassenthwaite Lake station.

6650   General View to N.E. of **Bassenthwaite Lake.** The Lake is in the middle distance, the hills from left to right are Binsey and Latrigg (both of Borrowdale Volcanic Series), Little Cockup, and the western slope of Great Cockup (both Skiddaw Slates). Viewpoint $\frac{3}{4}$ mile S.S.W. of Bassenthwaite Lake station.

6651   The **high fells** viewed from Sunderland Heads $\frac{1}{2}$ mile N.W. of Sunderland. The steep slope in the distance is the north side of Saddleback; the similar slope nearer the camera is at Dash. (Jacket Photograph.)

6652   The Skiddaw Slate country about **Dash.** Foreground of boulder clay. Middle distance from left to right: southern shoulder of Cockup; Great Calva with corrie; Dash Valley with 'step' therein, marked by waterfall; Broad End and Skiddaw capped by clouds. In the far distance is Saddleback. Viewpoint Binsey, about 1 mile N.E. of Bewaldeth.

6653   **Dash Beck Valley** and Dash Waterfall. The waterfall is flanked to the right by Dead Crags and to the left by Nettle Crags. Viewpoint near Brocklecrag.

6654   **Dash Beck Valley.** Description same as No. A 6655. Viewpoint near Brocklecrag.

6655   View of **Dash Beck Valley** looking south-east. Dash waterfalls are seen near the head of the valley with Dead Crags to the right and Nettle Crags to the left. Great Calva is seen in the distance behind the latter. Small mounds of boulder clay floor the lower slopes of the valley. Viewpoint about 1 mile S.E. of Orthwaite.

6656   Headwaters of **River Ellen.** An ice-eroded dry valley, seen in the centre of the photograph, truncates the watershed between the Ellen drainage and that of Burntod Gill, a tributary of Dash Beck. Viewpoint $\frac{1}{2}$ mile E. of Stockdale.

6657   View of headwaters of **River Ellen.** The valley of the River Ellen is seen in the middle distance, and the ice-eroded valley described in A. 6656 is seen between Great Cockup (right) and Meal Fell. The rocks in the foreground are tuffs and lavas of the Borrowdale Volcanic Series. Viewpoint ½ mile E. of Stockdale.

6659 **Over Water Reservoir** in valley of River Ellen. About 1 mile S.S.E. of Uldale.

6661 The **Glenderamackin Valley.** View from Mungrisdale. In the centre is the end-on view of the Tongue, a spur separating Bullfell Beck valley on the right from the main valley. The rocks are Skiddaw Slates.

6664 **Bannerdale Crags** and Glenderamackin Valley W. of Mungrisdale. The foreground is of boulder clay trenched by the Glenderamackin. Bannerdale Crags in the distance show typical effect of ice erosion with corrie formation, in Skiddaw Slates.

6665 **Bannerdale Crags** W. of Mungrisdale. The corrie-like head of Bannerdale Beck with Blencathra in the distance. The crags are formed of hornfelsed Skiddaw Slates dipping to the left (S.S.E.).

6666 **Bannerdale Crags** W. of Mungrisdale. In the middle distance the long low ridge is a moraine formed during the final stage of decay of the Bannerdale glacier.

6667 View down the **Bannerdale valley** W. of Mungrisdale. The low mound running half right from the camera is a moraine. The high ground in the centre of the view is the northern end of Souther Fell.

6670 The **Caldew Valley** and **Coomb.** Coomb in the centre is the eastern end of the spur between Grainsgill (right) and the Caldew (left). Metamorphosed Skiddaw Slate forms the river bed in the foreground. About ¾ mile W. of Mosedale.

6671 **Grainsgill** and the dumps of **Carrock Wolfram Mine.** Grainsgill Beck, about 2 miles W. of Mosedale.

6676 Head of **Drygill Beck.** Showing deep gully cut in the Upper Ordovician (Caradocian) Drygill Shales. About 500 yd S. of High Pike.

6748 View up head of **Caldew Valley.** The Skiddaw Granite occupies the valley bottom for two miles or more; Carrock complex forms the foreground; the whole of the remainder of the field of view is occupied by altered Skiddaw Slates of the granite aureole. Viewpoint ¼ mile W.S.W. of Carrock Fell.

6749 The **Mosedale depression.** Alluvial fans of the Caldew in the foreground and of the Glenderamackin beyond the wood in the left centre, with the peat flat of Bowscale Moss between them. Great and Little Mell Fells in the distance, with the Borrowdales of Eycott Hill on the left middle distance, and of High Street on the skyline. From hillside above Mosedale.

6751–2 Panoramic view of **Carrock Fell.** The eastern end viewed from east of the Mosedale depression. Viewpoint ½ mile W.S.W. of Hutton Roof.

6753 View up **Glenderamackin Valley.** From left to right are Souther Fell; Bannerdale Crag at the head of Bannerdale Beck (with the summit of Saddleback beyond); the rounded outline of Middle Tongue between Bannerdale and the Bullgill Beck Valley; and the shoulder of the eastern spur of Bowscale Fell on the right. Viewpoint 1 mile N.E. of Mungrisdale.

INDEX

Printed in England for Her Majesty's Stationery Office by Brown, Knight & Truscott Ltd., London and Tonbridge
Dd 696495 K14